Regnum vegetabile, a series of publications
for the use of plant taxonomists, volume 79

LINNAEUS AND THE LINNAEANS

P. Tanjé Sculp.

CAROLUS LINNÆUS

MEDIC. & BOTAN. PROF. UPSAL; HORTI. ACADEMICI PRÆFECT; ACAD. IMPERIAL:

MONSPELIENS: STOCKHOLM: UPSALÆ SOC; HUJUSQUE SECRETAR:

G. J. Wishoff Conr. Fil. Bibliopola Leidæ excudit.

Frans A. Stafleu

LINNAEUS
AND THE
LINNAEANS

The spreading of their ideas
in systematic botany, 1735–1789

1971
UTRECHT, NETHERLANDS
PUBLISHED BY A. OOSTHOEK'S UITGEVERSMAATSCHAPPIJ N.V.
FOR THE INTERNATIONAL ASSOCIATION FOR PLANT TAXONOMY

ISBN 90 6046 064 2

Distributed by: A. Oosthoek's Uitgeversmaatschappij N.V.,
Domstraat 5–13, Utrecht, Netherlands
and by: Stechert Hafner Service Agency, 866 Third Avenue,
New York, N.Y. 10022, U.S.A.

Preface

The literature on Carl Linnaeus, his life, ideas and works is second probably only to that on Charles Darwin in biology. The subject might be considered to have been nearly exhaustively covered. After 1945, however, there has been a marked revival of Linnaean studies of which many departed freely from the traditional views on Linnaeus of the nineteenth century and the first half of the twentieth. This revival of interest concerned in the first place Linnaeus's life and character, the shaping of his career and the technical aspects of his works in so far as relevant today to the natural sciences. In addition to this, however, there were also new attempts to assess Linnaeus's thinking and the background of his ideas.

On an air-trip somewhere over western Europe Ernst Mayr suggested to me, seven years ago, that there would still be room for an analysis of the background and development of Linnaeus's ideas in systematic biology. In trying to follow up this injunction I limited the period of my essay to that between 1735 and 1789. The first date is obvious; it is the year of the publication in Holland of Linnaeus's first works. The year 1789 is clearly a turning point not only in political and social history, but also, though perhaps more symbolically, in scientific thinking, especially in continental western Europe.

When trying to understand the spreading of Linnaeus's ideas and their impact on botany outside Sweden it is necessary to relate the events in the then so small world of science to those in human society and culture in general. The struggle between the hermeneutic and static view of the living world prevalent in the earlier part of the eighteenth century and the positivist, dynamic and romantic view which led to the birth of biology as a mature scientific discipline has for a long time fascinated me, especially because of the links between this intellectual process and the developments in society. This fascination may serve to justify the publication of this book at a time when a similar struggle is in full swing even though the other way around. The dynamic view of life and society was victorious on the wings of the Enlightenment. In the second half of the twentieth century the pendulum seems to swing back, primarily in the social sciences, but to a limited extent also in the realm of natural science.

The scope of this essay is limited: the analysis of Linnaeus's ideas in systematic botany is based mainly on the *Philosophia botanica* and on the much more concise introductions to some of the main descriptive works. For the spreading of the ideas I have limited myself to the western and north-western European countries without trying in any way to be exhaustive, but I have tried to include also the main reactions against Linnaeus and the influence of Linnaean thinking on the development of the ideas of his principal adversaries. The brief sketch of Linnaeus's life is given simply as background information, providing a setting for the picture of the development of his ideas. My main sources were Linnaeus's publications and his letters to colleagues, as well as those of his main contemporary followers and adversaries. No attempt has been made to evaluate Linnaeus's many and conspicuous achievements outside botany. I have touched only very lightly even upon his contributions to zoology, although of course much that is said of Linnaean botany holds equally well for his zoology.

I am indebted to many colleagues for directly or indirectly stimulating me to write this story. I have already mentioned Ernst Mayr and also want to pay tribute to the great influence of the man who might almost be regarded as the twentieth-century reincarnation of Linnaeus, William T. Stearn.

John Heller assisted me in many ways. He checked my interpretations of Linnaeus's Latin writings against the original texts and also translated for me various passages from other authors. His help and criticism in the evaluation of the at times unfamiliar and difficult statements in the *Philosophia botanica* have been invaluable.

I am grateful to Edmond Bonner and Frans Verdoorn for their effective help with the selection of illustrations and thank in particular the Utrecht Biohistorical Institute, the Utrecht University Library and the Conservatoire botanique at Genève for permission to reproduce material from their holdings. I am equally grateful to the directors and librarians of the

Preface

University of Utrecht, the Botanical Museum at Utrecht, the Rijksherbarium at Leiden, Teyler's Foundation at Haarlem, the Royal Botanic Gardens at Kew, the Conservatoire botanique de Genève, and the Hunt Botanical Library at Pittsburgh, Pa. for their liberal help with the literature and with archival material.

Mieke de Groot typed my difficult manuscript expertly and speedily, Mary Frances Southwell provided, as always, expert linguistic advice and excellent critical comments; Wil van Antwerpen kindly undertook the task of designing the lay-out, typography and general execution of this book, L. Bunge gave me general technical advice. To all four of them go my warmest thanks.

UTRECHT, 8 APRIL 1971

Contents

[IX]

List of illustrations

Part I
LINNAEUS

I

The Principal Character:
Carl Linnaeus

1. Introduction

The name of Linnaeus was for a long time almost synonymous with plant
classification. For nearly a century his main publications were found
useful by a great variety of plant systematists as the basis of their classifications. Linnaean schools of plant taxonomy developed in many countries, particularly in the Anglo–Saxon part of the world and, of course,
in Scandinavia. Linnaean Societies arose and disappeared, with the exception of one very conspicuous example. A much disputed figure during
most of his life, who gradually attained an extremely powerful position
in Swedish science in his last twenty-five years, Linnaeus became the subject of hero worship after his death to an extent previously unknown in
botany with the possible exception of Dioscorides. "Linnaeus was canonized and his life became an edifying piece of hagiology which was the
property of the whole nation" writes a recent Linnaean scholar (Lindroth
1966). Linnaeus became the symbol of rational classification but also of an
approach to nature which was challenged even during his lifetime. His
ideas appeared simplistic or antiquated at times, but his basic empiricism
and great mnemonic genius never failed to impress those who studied
his works. The literature on Linnaeus is immense, and for lack of an
up–to–date comprehensive and critical bibliography it is becoming increasingly inaccessible. Linnaeus's own literary and scientific output,
equally immense as will be clear from even a superficial scanning of
Soulsby's bibliography (1933), is, on the contrary, becoming more easily
accessible to botanists, because of the facsimile reprints of his main works
that are at present available. Linnaeus's position in botany makes itself
felt today in botanical nomenclature, which is based on his works, although
no longer to any great extent in modern systematic thought. However,

[3]

Linnaeus's taxonomic thinking, epitomizing as it did an age–old development, continued to influence taxonomy long after his death and well into the twentieth century.

Linnaean studies have taken a new turn in the course of the last twenty-five years. Simplistic approaches to this extremely complex and versatile personality, whether positive—the great majority—or negative—as exemplified by Sachs (1875)—are gradually giving way to a much more sophisticated attitude. Linnaeus's personality has been the subject of medico-psychological research, his pattern of thought has been exposed to clear philosophical and logical analysis, his taxonomic methods have found their place in the development of plant classification. The unqualified hero worship has disappeared and a more human understanding of this exceptionally gifted but difficult man is gradually evolving. Linnaeus's greatness has not suffered from this development; on the contrary, he emerges from this new phase of Linnaeology as one of the great builders of the natural sciences but his scope is human and his limitations are better understood.

The final biography of Linnaeus remains to be written. We have a long series of biographical studies of many sorts of which Stöver's book [1792] was one of the earliest. Stöver's biography was perhaps the first step along the road of the "Linnaean legend", building up Linnaeus as a Swedish national hero (see e.g. Franzén 1964). Fries's *Linné* of 1903 is our basic biography at the moment. It is best known outside Sweden in the abbreviated translation into English by Daydon Jackson (1923). The Fries–Jackson picture of Linnaeus is characterized by great detail and an impressive knowledge of sources. However, it is, as Lindroth (1966) has pointed out, the traditional romantic picture; it fails to do justice to the psychological complexity of Linnaeus's character, and it gives almost no impression of the basic features of Linnaeus's thought and scientific achievement. Knut Hagberg's *Carl Linnaeus* of 1939, more popular and much shorter, is the best known Linnaean biography. It shows the turning of the tide in Linnaean scholarship though it appeared before the mainstream of new Linnaeus studies which started after 1945.

Even though our knowledge of Linnaeus's life is probably more extensive in detail than that of any other botanist, we have no modern account of his life, character and achievements as an integrated whole; closest to this

[4]

comes at the moment Goerke's biography (1966)*. Only an exceptional scholar could undertake this, not only because of the unusual amount of published and unpublished material available, but also because it requires a profound understanding of the transitional stage between two phases of European culture which was the eighteenth century, a thorough knowledge of Swedish and Latin, an inordinate amount of detailed local knowledge on Sweden and Holland during Linnaeus's lifetime, and a great familiarity with the theoretical background of pre–twentieth–century biology.

2. *Youth*

The Sweden of 1707, the year of Linnaeus's birth, was still that of the expansionist Charles XII. Soon thereafter, however, the battle of Poltava (1709) virtually ended Charles' period of power, although he did not die until 1715 in Norway. Thus Linnaeus's lifetime encompassed Sweden's 'Era of Liberty,' which lasted until 1772. This era was characterized by a gradual economic development and an emphasis on early industrialization, strongly influenced by the ideas of the French Enlightenment. The early years of the 'Era,' however, were still very difficult for the war–impoverished country, with its primitive agronomy and weak intellectual superstructure. The Universities of Lund and Uppsala were understaffed and almost devoid of financial support.

Carl Linnaeus was born at Råshult in Småland on May 23, 1707, the son of the curate Nils Ingemarsson Linnaeus and his wife, Christina Brodersonia. The family moved to the more important Stenbrohult in 1708 upon Nils Linnaeus's appointment as pastor. The biographies of Linnaeus are sufficiently (or even overly) detailed on the events of his early boyhood, and a few words may suffice here to indicate that Småland was a region with very limited natural resources and that luxury was an unknown concept.

Linnaeus grew up in a thrifty atmosphere and in a family in which he enjoyed the interest of his father only. Relations with his mother (who was eighteen years old when he was born) were always strained, only in part because Linnaeus was not found to be sufficiently skillful at the

* When this paper went to press Wilfrid Blunt's, *The compleat Naturalist; a life of Carl Linnaeus*, had not yet been published.

Gymnasium of Växiö to be admitted to the one and only fashionable study of theology. Medicine was chosen instead, a profession not highly thought of in rural Småland.

3. Preparation

After an initial year as a medical student at Lund, where the medical faculty consisted of one professor, but where he made the stimulating acquaintance of the physician and amateur–botanist Kilian Stobaeus (1690–1742), Linnaeus went to Uppsala university in September 1728. He joined the Småland 'Nation,' a student corporation of which he would later (1742) become the respected 'Inspector.' The medical faculty was somewhat better endowed than that of Lund: there were two professors. Both were conspicuously inactive, at least in their public lectures: the practician Roberg and the theoretical physician Olof Rudbeck the Younger, who taught botany. Linnaeus soon discovered that self help was evidently expected and made good use of the somewhat neglected botanic garden and of the rich libraries of the University, of Rudbeck and of the 'Domprost' Olof Celsius. The botanic garden had been started in the previous century by Olof Rudbeck, Sr., but the number of species cultivated during Linnaeus's student years was small compared with the original collections. Linnaeus also found at Uppsala the herbarium of Joachim Burser and used it for his botanical training.

Linnaeus struck up a friendship with Petrus Artedi, a fellow medical student of whom he relates in one of his autobiographies that he was a noble competitor in the study and classification of the three kingdoms of nature.

An early manuscript by Linnaeus, *Praeludia sponsaliorum plantarum*, a somewhat poetic description of the 'love life' of plants, drew Rudbeck's attention. He appointed Linnaeus as 'docent' *ad interim* to 'demonstrate' plants in the botanic garden to the medical students. His lectures started in the spring of 1730 (May 4) and were based on manuscript texts entitled *Hortus uplandicus* and *Adonis uplandicus*, published in the nineteenth century (Soulsby nos. 234–243). It was also about this time that Linnaeus started on his *Fundamenta botanica* (Fredbärj 1965).*

* For this and other early Linnaean manuscripts see von Sydow 1963.

[6]

The official adjunct to Rudbeck, Nils Rosén, returned from the Netherlands in the autumn of 1731. Rosén had finished his medical training in the
Netherlands, the veritable centre of medical research in the Boerhaave
epoch, obtaining his doctor's degree at the small Gelderland University of
Harderwijk on 11 September 1730. His return marked the end of Linnaeus's
duties as demonstrator, a very unwelcome change. Some emotional
difficulties caused him to leave the house of Rudbeck, where he had stayed
for over a year. Undoubtedly at the suggestion of Rudbeck himself, an
old Lapland traveller whose collections had been destroyed by the great
Uppsala fire of 1702, Linnaeus's thoughts turned to a journey to Lapland.
Such a journey would enable him to discover an entirely new country and,
undoubtedly, many novelties in natural history. Linnaeus had already
realized that he could make no headway as a botanist if he remained at
Uppsala. The revival of the 'Era of Liberty' stimulated the general tendency
to explore the country and to assess its natural resources. The role of the
major Swedish scientific societies was primarily to make practical use of
scientific exploration for the benefit of the nation. Linnaeus submitted a
proposal for a Lapland journey to the Royal Scientific Society at Uppsala;
the society awarded him a travel grant, thereby literally exhausting its
treasury, and on May 5 Linnaeus started northward. The journey had a
profound influence on Linnaeus's scientific development. His pragmatic
approach, the matter–of–fact way in which he assembled information on a
country about which too many fantastic stories were still current, is
impressive. His horizons widened; independent research stimulated his
growth as a scientist. He realized the narrow provinciality of Uppsala
and began establishing contacts abroad. He continued his studies at Uppsala
in the winter of 1732–1733 but spent the next summer and winter at Falun
with his friend Claes Sohlberg, studying the flora, fauna and mineralogy
of Dalarna as well as its mining industry. Here he wrote the first sketches
of the *Systema lapidarum*, his *Iter ad Fodinas* (1733), which reveals human and
social concern for the miners, and his *Diaeta naturalis*. This tract was the
basis of his successful lectures on dietetics of later years (Fries 1903).

In the summer of 1734 he was back again in Dalarna for further research
and met Johannes Browallius, the private teacher of the Governor's
children, who advised him to finish his study abroad and to marry a rich
girl (fide Fries!).

It is not necessary to relate all the details, but Linnaeus followed the above counsel, if it was ever given in that form at all. He decided to do as many of his countrymen did at the time: to finish his studies in Holland. During Christmas time at Falun he met Sara Lisa Moraea, the daughter of the fairly well-to-do town physician Johannes Moraeus. The latter had also finished his studies abroad, in Leiden and Paris, taking his doctor's degree at Reims (Fredbärj 1963). A brief but apparently intense period of courting was followed by an agreement with Moraeus that Linnaeus would marry Sara Lisa upon his return from Holland with a degree, on condition that this should not be within the next three years. Sara Lisa was eighteen years old at the time.

In February 1735 Linnaeus left Stockholm for Holland, travelling by Helsingborg, Lübeck and Hamburg. The last stretch of the journey was by coaster from Hamburg over the Zuiderzee to Amsterdam, where he arrived in early June. Ample details about Linnaeus's years abroad are contained in Felix Bryk's *Linnaeus im Auslande* (1919).

4. Holland: Expansion and fulfilment

The years in Holland, 1735 to 1738, were decisive. Here Linnaeus's talent matured and his scientific horizon became that of the world of science of his time. Here he met his great contemporaries and experienced that most stimulating sensation of all in a scientist's life: communication with other scientists by word, letter and printed book. The young man arriving in Amsterdam in June 1735 had great expectations, carried with him the manuscripts of what would become his major works, but was after all only a student coming from a country whose scientific status had temporarily declined. He was a student with exceptional will-power and remarkable factual knowledge, but he was yet to be launched.

This launching was accomplished during the Dutch years by a group of scientists, of whom Herman Boerhaave, Jan Frederik Gronovius and Johannes Burman are the most outstanding, and by a magnificent patron of the sciences, a wealthy banker named George Clifford. When he left Holland in 1738 Linnaeus had fourteen printed works to show, some of which were manifest proof not only of great industry but of a remarkable capacity to create order in an immense multitude of facts. He left as a man of international repute, his publications far from undisputed but generally

[8]

acknowledged to be of fundamental importance for scientific botany. These crucial years have deservedly received more attention than the many years of his later life, because in this period his thoughts became crystallized. His later years brought an elaboration of what came to the fore in the Holland period, with the exception perhaps of his hybridization theory and the religious turn of mind. Even though the essence of Linnaean thought can best be studied from his 1751 *Philosophia botanica*, it should be stressed that basically this work was an elaboration of the principles laid down in the *Fundamenta botanica* and *Critica botanica* published in the Holland period. Much of this goes back even farther, to his early training in Sweden, but it was the Holland environment which provided the necessary basis for ultimate success.

On the day of his arrival, June 13, 1735 (n.s.), Linnaeus paid a visit to the renowned Amsterdam *Hortus botanicus*, then already on the site which it occupies today. The Amsterdam and Leiden gardens were centres for the receipt of new plants introduced mainly from the Cape of Good Hope but also from the Canary Islands, the West Indies and even, although in modest numbers, from Ceylon and the Indian peninsula. Dutch colonial and trade expansion was at its peak and Dutch ships sailed all over the world. The rising affluence of the Dutch 'Golden Age,' the seventeenth and the early eighteenth century, had created a group of wealthy merchants and bankers who became interested in promoting science and in growing exotic plants themselves. Boerhaave, in his *Index alter*, wrote: "practically no captain, whether of a merchant ship or a man–of–war, left our harbours without special instructions to collect everywhere seeds, roots, cuttings, and shrubs and bring them back to Holland."

The Leiden garden had been given its great impetus by Paulus Hermann in 1680; the Amsterdam garden had been created by Jan Commelin in 1682. Both gardens had grown conspicuously in the following decades and had attained world renown. Thousands of species from outside the Netherlands were in cultivation towards the end of the century. It is therefore understandable that the inquisitive Linnaeus directed his first steps on Holland soil to the famous Amsterdam botanic garden. The next day he presented himself to Johannes Burman and admired his library. Burman was understandably still unaware that he was dealing with an exceptional botanist and it was not until a few months later that the close contact between the two men developed. On June 15 Linnaeus visited the

[9]

aged Seba and his famous natural history cabinet, and on the next day he left for the small Gelderland town of Harderwijk.

The United Netherlands of 1735 was a confederation of seven semi-independent states, a situation not unlike that in the early history of the United States of America. Almost every state had a university of its own: Holland had Leiden, the oldest, established in 1572, where Boerhaave taught and where the well known botanist Jan Frederik Gronovius resided. Amsterdam had no university, but only an *Athenaeum* where it was impossible to obtain a doctor's degree; one could study medicine at Amsterdam but had to spend a final year in Leiden or Utrecht. Leiden had many foreign students but its fees were high and so were the scientific requirements. It was impossible to go there with a previously prepared thesis and obtain a degree; the university demanded a relatively long period of formal training on the spot.

The other six states were Utrecht, Zeeland, Gelderland, Overijssel, Groningen, and Friesland. All of them, except Zeeland, had a 'university,' even though none of them was even remotely a match for Leiden. At Utrecht botany was in the hands of the aged Serrurier and consequently practically non-existent (Linnaeus spent one day out of over a thousand days in Holland at this university); medicine was only modest. Gelderland had its Harderwijk university, small but with a reasonably active body of professors, among them Johan de Gorter. Harderwijk University enabled students from abroad to obtain a doctor's degree in a reasonably brief time, provided they passed a preliminary examination and were found to be sufficiently acquainted with the basic knowledge of the art. It is difficult to judge the quality of these examinations but it is certain that they were no mere formality. The main attraction of Harderwijk was that the fees were low and that no on-the-spot training was required. If the Harderwijk degree had been thought to be worthless at the time, people like Nils Rosén and Linnaeus, and many others as well, would not have felt satisfied in obtaining it. The degree was generally acknowledged as sufficient, although a Leiden degree would have rated higher.

Linnaeus's Harderwijk week went smoothly: he arrived on the seventeenth of June (at 3.00 a.m.) and presented himself at the University. The next day he passed the examination for medical candidate, and on the nineteenth he showed his previously written thesis to Johan de Gorter and obtained the fiat for printing. The next days were divided between hearing lectures, botanising and having the thesis printed at the local printing shop of H. J. Rampen. The formal 'promotion' took place on June 23, on the thesis entitled (Soulsby no. 1336): *Dissertatio medica in qua exhibetur hypothesis nova de Febrium intermittentium causa* (24 pages). Boerman (1957) has made it clear that this 'promotion' was not a mere formality, but that the candidate's knowledge and the quality of the thesis were duly tested.

On June 25 Linnaeus was back in Amsterdam again; on the 28th he visited Utrecht but left unimpressed, and somewhat later he presented himself at Leiden. Here he managed to meet Boerhaave and Gronovius and made a deep impression on both scientists. Linnaeus showed them his manuscript *Systema naturae*, and Gronovius was so impressed that he and his friend Isaac Lawson offered to finance its publication. The manuscript went to the publisher on July 11; publication took place between 9 and 13 December. Boerhaave and Gronovius recognized the exceptional qualifications of the young Swede and gave him just the support he needed. Boerhaave recommended him to Johannes Burman, who now invited the impecunious Linnaeus to stay with him in Amsterdam. Boerhaave furthermore advised one of his clients, the wealthy Amsterdam banker George Clifford [1681–1760], to employ Linnaeus as his house physician and to give him the opportunity to work at his country seat near Haarlem. Clifford had acquired the estate—de Hartecamp, at the foot of the dunes—in 1709 and had developed it into a naturalist's paradise. The gardens and the orangeries were richly stocked, thanks to Clifford's close connections with Burman and Boerhaave. He had a rich library and a well-kept, typically eighteenth-century 'natural history cabinet.' Clifford seems to have suffered from depressions, but it is not known whether Linnaeus was actually able to do anything about them. After an initial visit to the estate on August 13–14, Linnaeus was engaged by Clifford at a salary of Fl. 1000 a year to work at de Hartecamp. His main task was to catalogue the collections, the acquisition of new plants and the publication of his own manuscripts.

It is clear from what Fries (1903) and Heller (1968) relate that Linnaeus's first visit to Clifford's garden resulted in "love at first sight," best described perhaps in his dedication to the *Hortus cliffortianus* (fig. 1) (translation Heller):

"The fame of Your Garden, *illustrious* Clifford, was on the lips of a few men, but less constantly than it deserved to be, and I was persuaded that Your Garden was only a Tantalus or Hesperides, such as cover almost the whole of the intensely cultivated land of Holland; I hardly considered it worth visiting, but the actuality surpassed all expectation. Do you remember the day when You were asking a foreigner, who was walking through the Amsterdam Garden, about a proper warden for a Flora? On the spot you were inviting him to Your Garden, to visit Your Floras. [When I went,]

> Dumbstruck I gazed. It pierced my heartstrings through
> And still I gazed, and still my wonder grew.*

"I gazed at Your garden in the very centre of Holland bright with flowers, between Haarlem and Leiden, a charming spot between two thoroughfares, where boats, where carts pass by; my eyes were captivated by so many masterpieces of nature...

"Dumbstruck was I when I entered your Adonides, houses filled with so many and such varied shrubs as to bewitch a son of Boreas, ignorant of the strange world into which you had led him...

"Captivated as I was by these delights, stuck fast on these Siren–rocks, You bade me let down my sails, and You prevailed without much difficulty; I sat myself down in Your shade, I sported with Your Floras, Your *Muses* clapped their hands...

"In Your Paradise I have now completed two years of complete innocence forgetful of country, Friends, kin, forgetful of the future and of past misfortunes."

Linnaeus stayed at de Hartecamp from September 13, 1735 until October 1737, and then again in the spring and early summer of 1738 while recovering from a serious illness. He was registered in the *album studiosorum* at Leiden, 'honoris ergo,' and freely visited Amsterdam and Leiden during his Hartecamp period. The financial support for the publication of the *Systema* had helped him overcome the first difficulties in getting his manuscripts published. His *Fundamenta botanica* and *Bibliotheca botanica* (fig. 2), both dated 1736, were issued in September and October 1735 and were reviewed in Dec. 1735 in the *Göttingische Anzeigen von gelehrten Sachen*.

The *Systema naturae*, typographically a much more involved work, came off the press in December. The type-setting of the *Genera plantarum* started in 1736. Published in that year was the *Methodus*, a fly leaf, usually appended to the *Systema* of 1735, in which Linnaeus gives a key for the description of

---

* An adaptation of a couplet from Ovid, in which Paris confesses his wonder at his first sight of Helen's beauty...

HORTUS CLIFFORTIANUS

Plantas exhibens

QUAS

In Hortis tam VIVIS quam SICCIS,
HARTECAMPI in Hollandia,

COLUIT

VIR NOBILISSIMUS & GENEROSISSIMUS

GEORGIUS CLIFFORD

JURIS UTRIUSQUE DOCTOR,

Reductis Varietatibus ad Species,

Speciebus ad Genera,

Generibus ad Classes,

Adjectis Locis Plantarum natalibus
Differentiisque Specierum.

Cum *TABULIS ÆNEIS.*

AUCTORE

CAROLO LINNÆO,

Med. Doct. & Ac. Imp. N. C. Soc.

AMSTELÆDAMI. 1737.

Fig. 1. Title-page of the *Hortus cliffortianus* (1737). The vignette shows the view from the front of 'De Hartekamp' towards the garden and the 'overtuin', the garden on the other side of the Haarlem–Leiden road. The motto, *tantus amor florum* also appears on the title-page of the *Philosophia botanica* (1751). The book is dated 1737 but the first copies became available only in the course of the year 1738; they were privately distributed. *Reduced.*

CAROLI LINNÆI

Doctoris Medicinæ

BIBLIOTHECA
BOTANICA

recenfens

Libros plus mille

de plantis huc usque editos,

fecundum

Syftema Auctorum Naturale

in

CLASSES, ORDINES, GENERA & SPECIES

difpofitos,

additis

Editionis Loco, Tempore, Forma, Lingua &c.

cum explicatione

Fundamentorum Botanicorum pars 1ma.

AMSTELODAMI,
Apud SALOMONEM SCHOUTEN
1736.

Fig. 2. Title–page of the first edition of Linnaeus's *Bibliotheca botanica* (1736); corresponds with aphorisms 1–52, chapter I of the *Fundamenta botanica*. Even though dated 1736, the book came out in October 1735.

CAROLI LINNÆI, *SVECI,*
METHODUS

Juxta quam Phyſiologus accurate & feliciter concinnare poteſt
Hiſtoriam cujuſcunque Naturalis Subjecti, ſequentibus
hiſce Paragraphis comprehenſa.

I. NOMINA.

1. *Nomen Selectum* , genericum & ſpecificum Authoris cujuſdam , ſi quod tale , vel proprium.
2. *Synonyma* Syſtematicorum primariorum omnia.
3. . . . . Authorum , ſi poſſit, omnium Veterum & Recentiorum.
4. . . . Nomen vernaculum , latino etiam idiomate tranſlatum.
5. . . . . Gentium variarum nomina : Græca præcipue.
6. *Etymologia* Nominum genericorum omnium (1-5).

II. THEORIA.

7. *Claſſes* & *Ordines* ſecundum Syſtemata ſelecta omnia.
8. *Genera* ad quæ , â variis & diverſis Syſtematicis (7) relatum fuit Subjectum propoſitum.

III. GENUS.

9. *Character Naturalis* , omnes notas characteriſticas poſſibiles exhibens.
10. . . . *Eſſentialis* notam generi maxime propriam tradens.
11. . . . *Artificialis* , genera in Syſtematibus (7) conjuncta diſtinguens.
12. *Hallucinationes* Authorum circa genus (8) ex dictis (9).
13. *Genus Naturale* demonſtrabit. (9)
14. *Nomen Generis* (13) ſelectum (11) confirmabit , & cur alia rejiciat, indicet.

IV. SPECIES.

15. *Deſcriptio* perfectiſſima Subjecti tradatur , ſecundum omnes ejus partes externas.
16. *Species* generis propoſiti (13) omnes inventas recenſeat.
17. *Differentias* omnes inter ſpeciem propoſitam (1) & rotas (16) exhibeat (15).
18. . . . primarias inde retineat , reliquas rejiciat.
19. . . . ſpecificam Subjecti ſui componat , & rationem facti quoad omne vocabulum (1) reddat.
20. *Variationes* ſpeciei propoſitæ omnes apud Authores datas proponat.
21. . . . . has ſub naturali ſpecie redigat cum ratione facti (15).

V. ATTRIBUTA.

22. *Tempus* productionis , incrementi , vigoris , copulæ , partus , decrementi , interitus.
23. *Locus natalis.* Regio , provincia.
24. . . . Longitudo & latitudo Loci.
25. . . . Clima , Solum.
26. *Vitæ.* Diæta , mores , affectus.
27. *Corporis* Anatomia , præſertim curioſa ; & inſpectio Microſcopica.

VI. USUS

28. *Uſus œconomicus* actualis , poſſibilis , apud gentes varias.
29. . . . *Diæteticus* , cum effectu , in corpore humano.
30. . . . *Phyſicus* , cum agendi modo & principiis conſtitutivis.
31. . . . *Chemicus* ſecundum principia conſtitutiva , igne ſeparata.
32. . . . *Medicus* in quibus morbis præcipue & verè , demonſtratus ratione vel experientia.
33. . . . . . Officinalis ; quæ partes , præparata , compoſitiones.
34. . . . . exhibendi methodus optima , doſis , cautelæ.

VII. LITERARIA

35. *Inventor* cum loco & tempore.
36. *Hiſtoricæ Traditiones* de Subjecto variæ , jucundæ & gratæ.
37. *Superſtitioſa* vana rejicienda.
38. *Poetica* egregia illuſtrantia.

L U G D U N I   *B A T A V O R U M,*
Apud A N G E L U M   S Y L V I U M. MDCCXXXVI

Fig. 3. Linnaeus's method for a monographic description of objects of natural history.
Separately printed pamphlet (1736). See also K. P. Schmidt (1952) who gives a full translation. This broadside, a loose sheet, is usually bound with the first edition of the *Systema
naturae* (1735) and is included in the facsimile editions of this work of 1907 and 1964 (Engel
and Engel). The word *physiologus* in the title stands for natural scientist (biologists and
geologists).

'any' object of natural history (fig. 3). In the summer of that year Linnaeus visited England, where he met many outstanding naturalists, among them Sir Hans Sloane, Philip Miller and Johann Jakob Dillen. His first official honor came on October 3 of the same year, when he was elected member of the *Academia Naturae Curiosorum* (the 'Leopoldina'). The *Genera plantarum* appeared early in 1737, the *Flora lapponica* in April and the *Critica botanica* in July. The *Hortus cliffortianus* was printed in 1737, although distribution of copies did not start before 1738. The winter of 1737–1738 was spent at Leiden with Gronovius. During Easter–time in 1738 Linnaeus fell seriously ill and had to spend nearly two months recuperating at de Hartecamp.

The Dutch scientists, as well as Clifford, tried to keep Linnaeus in Holland. The chair at Utrecht would soon become vacant and there were several other possibilities. Linnaeus, however, wanted to return to Sweden. After all, the three years had gone by and Sara Lisa was still awaiting him. A visit to Paris was all he wanted to do: on May 7, 1738, he left Holland for France. His luggage contained fourteen printed books or pamphlets, the results of an incredible outburst of creative energy. Linnaeus had found his destiny: mature and established he left Holland, sure of a hearty welcome at Paris. He stayed for some weeks with Antoine and Bernard de Jussieu, botanized in the garden and went on field trips. He was elected foreign correspondent of the *Académie des Sciences*. Towards the end of June he left Paris for Le Havre where he took a ship to Sweden, landing at Helsingborg. The rest of the journey was by land: first to see his father at Stenbrohult, then to Falun to his fiancée, and finally to Stockholm, to start his career as a practsing physician, in September 1738.

5. Sweden: maturity and after

Linnaeus's international renown had roused only faint echoes in far–away Stockholm. The transition must have been difficult at first: Linnaeus is known to have quoted Juvenalis in this respect: "probitas laudatur et alget" (Berg 1965). Within a few months, however, Linnaeus had the good fortune to come into contact with Count Tessin, the leader of the ruling 'Hats' party. His praxis soon became a *praxis aurea*, but most important was his appointment to lecture on mineralogy and botany at the mining college, the 'Bergkollegium.' In October Linnaeus was elected member of the Science Society of Uppsala; early in 1739 he established, with other scientists, the Royal Swedish Academy of Sciences, and was chosen as its first president.

Linnaeus's Swedish star now rose rapidly. On May 3, 1739 he was appointed Physician to the Admiralty, also through Tessin and with the help of vice-admiral Ankarcrona. In June he married his 'monandrian lily', Sara Lisa, at Falun.

On June 8, 1739, Linnaeus wrote to Bernard de Jussieu to thank him for the hospitality enjoyed in Paris. Describing the events of the last year, he added: "I have succeeded in obtaining quickly the largest medical 'clientèle' of this town and I have also been appointed titular physician to the admiralty. I have just married the woman whom I wanted for years to marry and who, if I am permitted to speak this way between ourselves, is quite wealthy; I am therefore at last leading a quiet and satisfactory life."

Further changes were ahead: in 1740 Olaus Rudbeck died at Uppsala (on February 23) leaving a vacancy, filled by Rosén. In May Roberg withdrew from his professorship and Linnaeus was the most promising candidate for the post. The appointment came on May 5, 1741 shortly after the birth of Carl Jr. (January 20). A second edition of the *Systema naturae* had been published at Stockholm in May 1740.

Linnaeus's comment in a letter to Jussieu was (May 19, 1741): "Thank God I have been freed from my miserable [sic!] medical practice in Stockholm; I have at last the position which I wanted all the time..."

The summer of 1741 was spent on a journey to Öland and Gotland. After this Linnaeus moved to Uppsala to remain in that region (including Stockholm) until his death, except for some short trips to Western Gotland in 1746 and to Skåne in 1749. The last and longest phase of his life had begun: residence and professorship at Uppsala.

On the seventeenth of October 1741 Linnaeus delivered his inaugural address at Uppsala University on the necessity of travelling for a knowledge of one's country. Soon afterwards he exchanged his 'chair' for that of Nils Rosén and thereby assumed the teaching of botany.

Linnaeus's wordly career was now assured. Social and financial success continued unabated. There were many students; his books were printed and reprinted and spread all over the world. Children were born to him; he was made a knight of the Polar Star (1758) and even ennobled (1762), taking the name Carl von Linné; his financial resources were such that he

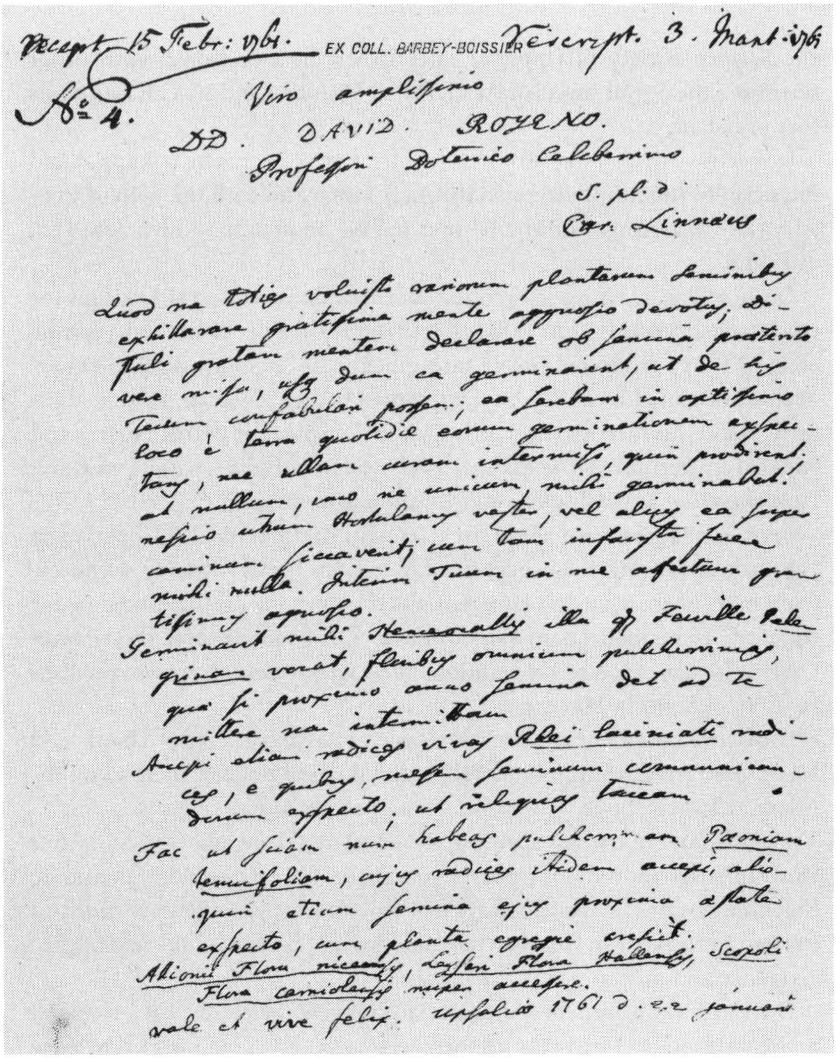

Recept. 15 Febr: 1761. EX COLL. BARBEY-BOISSIER Rescript. 3. Mart. 1761

No 4.

Viro amplissimo
DD. DAVID. ROYENO.
Professori Botanico Celeberrimo
S. pl. d.
Car. Linnaeus

Quod me toties voluisti variorum plantarum seminibus exhilarare gratissima mente agnosco devotus; distuli gratam mentem declarare ob semina praetenta vere missa, usque dum ea germinarent, ut de his Tecum confabulari possem; ea serebam in aptissimo loco e terra quotidie eorum germinationem expectans, nec ullam curam intermissi, quin prodirent; at nullum, vero ne unicum, mihi germinabat! nescio utrum Hortulanus vester, vel aliud ea semper caminum siccaverit; cum tam infausta fuere mihi nulla. Interim Tuum in me affectum gratissimus agnosco.

Germinant mihi Heracalli illa quae Feuille Pelegrinam vocat, floribus omnium pulcherrimis, quae si proximo anno semina det ad Te mittere non intermittam.

Accepi etiam radices vivas Rhei laciniati radices, e quibus, nescio seminum communicandum expecto, ut reliquis tecum.

Fac ut sciam num habeas pulcherrimam Paeoniam tenuifoliam, cujus radices itidem accepi, aliquam etiam semina ejus proxima aestate expecto, cum planta egregie crescit.

Allionii Flora nicaeensis, Leysseri Flora Hallensis, Scopoli Flora carniolensis nuper accepere.

vale et vive felix. Upsaliae 1761 d. 22 januarii

Fig. 4. Letter written by Carl Linnaeus to David van Royen at Leiden, dated 22 January 1761. The letter deals mainly with seed exchange and ends with an acknowledgement of receipt of several books among which Scopoli, *Flora carniolica* (1760) and F. W. von Leysser, *Flora halensis* 1761 [sic] [*Conservatoire botanique de Genève*]. *Reduced.*

could buy a home in the country, Hammarby (1762), faintly reminiscent of Clifford's residence. Scientific success was assured: the *Species plantarum* appeared in 1753, the *Systema naturae* reached a twelfth edition in 1767–1768. Linnaeus's pupils travelled all over the world and returned with rich collections. Theses were defended by the dozen.

In 1763 Linnaeus's health began to decline. He was excused from exercising his professional duties because of illness; his son Carl replaced him in part. Final failure of health started in 1772, accompanied by signs of increasing dementia. On January 10, 1778, Linnaeus died, 70 years old; he was buried in the Dom church of Uppsala on January 22. His mental condition had deteriorated earlier than his physical constitution. His autobiographies, letters and speeches all betray a loss of internal harmony and of self-assurance, a phenomenon indicative (according to Boerman) of a neurosis of the down-going lifeline. Profound changes in social and religious attitude took place, most clearly illustrated by the ever-recurring references to *Nemesis divina* (see Barr 1923), divine retaliation rather than justice, the concept of which preoccupied Linnaeus more and more; a strong tendency towards introversion developed.

Psychological studies of great men of the past are rare. In the case of Linnaeus such a study has been attempted by A. J. Boerman (1953, 1953a). The picture of a great man like Linnaeus tends to become blurred by irrelevant but very real unscientific influences. For Sweden—it has already been mentioned—Linnaeus assumed the rôle of a national hero. The picture of him in Swedish literature tended to become romantic and polished, one-sidely positive, that of a genius in an evil world, of a man of good faith surrounded by scoundrels. Of necessity most Linnaean studies were Swedish. Next came the British who tend to look upon Linnaeus as the French on Vincent van Gogh mainly because the great heritage of Linnaeus, his herbarium, manuscripts, library, but also his tradition, was so faithfully carried on by the British plant taxonomists of the late eighteenth and of the nineteenth century. Jackson's revised translation of Fries's biography of Linnaeus epitomizes this development. Modern scholarship, however, in Sweden (Lindroth, von Hofsten, Uggla, Sydow, Fredbärj, Selling), England (Cain, Stearn), France (Callot), Germany (Goerke), the United States (Svenson, Heller), and Holland (Engel, Boerman) alike operates in a world which is freer from taboos and myths than the nineteenth century and its aftermath.

Fig. 5. Carl Linnaeus. [Oil-painting 1774 by P. Krafft, now at the Swedish Academy of Sciences (Tullberg no. 107)]. *Reduced.*

[20]

On the other side there were unnecessarily acrimonious commentaries which showed a negative bias. Too much has been made of Linnaeus's egotism, vanity and pedantry; it has even been asserted that Linnaeus contributed not a single original thought to botany and that his importance was highly overrated.

Appreciation of character and of achievement were freely mixed. Boerman attempted to dissociate the two and to evaluate the former. It is not possible to reproduce his well-balanced arguments here to any extent, but a few of the main findings and conclusions may be cited with reference to the original publications for factual support. He rightly stresses that "the real significance of Linnaeus's achievements can only be understood if we have some insight into his instincts and inhibitions, his weaknesses and his strength."

Boerman's analysis was possible because of the existence of an extraordinary amount of documentary material in the form of diaries, autobiographies, letters, sketches by contemporaries, 'unconscious' remarks noted by others and similar data. The autobiographies were the least useful because they tend to be "too strongly coloured", containing, as they do, retrospective meditations of later years.

Linnaeus's sensitivity to definite impressions was striking. His diaries and travel books are characterised by an expressive form of extraordinarily strong sensual character, warm and rich descriptions, manifold recollections of previous experiences, a great directness and an easy mobility of the images formed in his mind. These characteristics make for an impressionistic prose which constitutes "classical examples of descriptive art in Swedish literature."

Linnaeus assimilated his impressions to a high degree: his spiritual property was large and he was always ready to add to it. Until late in life he retained his interest in new plants and animals. He relied strongly upon his impressions, except when these were in conflict with his religious beliefs. His judgment was often extremely subjective, the bias often based on irrelevant details. Boerman states that he has not been able to find in Linnaeus's correspondence a single unbiassed judgment on any person with whom he was acquainted.

Subjective judgment usually prevailed over the objective, even in the descriptions of natural objects. Linnaeus had a deep respect for concrete facts; he classified the facts with mastery, but he was often handicapped in the foundation of general rules by the limits set by religious or philosophical dogmas. Visual impressions were predominant in Linnaeus's world of imagination, sensual and emotional impressions played a lesser role. He memorized with ease long plant names, words and concepts, but had little talent for languages and arithmetic. It is significant that during his stay in Holland he never learned to speak Dutch and that there are hardly any Dutch words in his notes and correspondence. Latin and Swedish were his only languages, the former learned at a very early age.

Linnaeus had a pronounced artistic talent. He drew well himself and required of all descriptive scientists that they be able to draw. The decoration of Hammarby was exceptional for the period, and at Uppsala he was known as a connoisseur of paintings, but he had no ear for music.

Linnaeus was characteristically temperamental: a great willingness to react, a relatively weakly developed inhibition towards restraint. He threw himself with great energy into all tasks often working at high speed.

"His humour was on the whole expansive. He did not put his light under a bushel. He always wanted to teach and speak of his discoveries with others, and could not bear loneliness, e.g. when he stayed in Clifford's house." "However, after 1748 periods of depression occurred more and more frequently." Boerman gives ample proof that it is "impossible to see in Linnaeus a man of deep feeling." He had strong will-power and carried out his plans rapidly. In conversation he was apt to express his opinions on scientific matters with great frankness.

In his actions the tendency to assert himself was very pronounced, "and here in fact all forms of egotism manifest themselves; active egotism ... in the need of recognition and in the wish to excel; passive egotism with its cautiousness and calculation in the contacts with others..." "When he grew older, however, the dominance of these egotistic feelings gave way to his longing for spiritual submission in the light of his thoughts on the *Nemesis divina*, the divine retaliation" (see also Uggla 1968).

"Linnaeus's main characteristic was activity (will and brains); ...his mood vacillated between the craving for power and success and the admission of impotence and failure..."

All these conclusions, says Boerman, are quite plausible, but there remains nevertheless a certain arbitrariness. The situation differed in the various periods of his life, and the 'spiritual sublimation' of his later years certainly makes the picture even more complex.

[22]

Important for an understanding of Linnaeus's character are some firmly established facts from his boyhood.

The relations between Carl and his father were warm, but those with his mother were often strained. His decision to study medicine was a deep disappointment to her. Her attitude toward him changed only when she heard that he had been lecturing at Uppsala in 1732. Boerman sees this as an important reason why Linnaeus always attempted to obtain the admiration of those with whom he came into contact; furthermore, a certain tendency developed to prove that he was "an instrument in the hands of God," that his life had a metaphysical meaning. His craving for power turned in later years into a patriarchical attitude towards his pupils and an air of independence or indifference towards persons of higher standing.

Boerman's preliminary conclusion, in face of the great complexity of Linnaeus's character and of the time that separates him from us, is as follows (partly quoting Linnaeus himself):

"Linnaeus was a servant who doubled the talents that were entrusted to him."

"The enormous extent of the field in which he moved made it impossible to enter very deeply into the problems which it offered to his inspection; he was moreover too little philosophically disposed to do this. However, he stimulated his pupils to think logically and to see for themselves; by his own behaviour and by his vision of life he was to them an inspiring example, and this seems enough to secure him a place, when not among the very few of the first order, at least among the somewhat larger group of those who come next to them..."

2

Ideas and a theory of Botany

1. Background and principles

The eighteenth century witnessed an unprecedented increase in the number of new animals and plants that came to the attention of the naturalists. The nomenclatural and taxonomic systems proliferated, but the gap between their coverage and effectiveness on the one hand and the information explosion widened. More and more systems were developed, all based on simple characters, but they simply could not cope with the needs. The clumsy way of naming species by means of elaborate diagnostic phrases was certainly one of the major obstacles: the phrase names grew longer and longer. No two botanists used the same name for the same species, and the orderly genius of Linnaeus found a great task awaiting him. His aim was to set up an internationally acceptable taxonomic framework within which botanists could reach the same conclusions and by which their work would become comparable. The question is: what framework was chosen?

Linnaeus's training and background were scholastic; his whole approach is Aristotelian. At the gymnasium in Växiö he excelled in 'logic', a logic which was almost certainly the Aristotelian and Thomistic logic generally taught in secondary schools all over Europe.

The study of logic in accordance with Aristotelian–Thomistic principles was a common feature of eighteenth–century education. The principles imply a concept of nature which can be called essentialism. Karl Popper (1950, also e.g. in Hull 1965, Mayr 1969, Lehmann 1971) defines essentialism as: "the view held by Plato and many of his followers, that it is the task of pure knowledge or 'science' to discover and to describe the true nature of things, i.e. their hidden reality or essence..." These essences may be discovered by means of intellectual intuition; they have proper names and may be

[25]

described in words. The description of the essence of a thing is called the 'definition.'

It will be clear that the essence is abstract and that the things themselves are variations upon a theme. The theme may also be called 'type': typological thinking and essentialism are closely akin.

In creating order in one's environment, one classifies not the things but their essences. Aristotelian logic* deals precisely with this. A very brief outline (based on Cain 1958, which see for further details) is needed for the understanding of essentialist classification, and especially that of Linnaeus. After all, this essentialist classification was dominant from ancient times until well into the eighteenth century and its traces are even now noticeable in some taxonomic work. The main revolution against essentialism came from two sides: nominalism and empiricism, but the ultimate victory over essentialism in biology was achieved only after 1859, the year of publication of Darwin's *Origin of species*.

If A is a subject and B is a statement that can be made about A (a predicate), B stands to A in one of five relationships: Definition, Genus, Differentia, Property, Accident. These are defined as follows (by Cain):

The *definition* of a subject is a statement of what that subject must be in order to be just that and not something else; the statement of its essence. If the essence is changed, the subject is no longer the same.

The *genus* is that part of the definition which applies also to other subjects. (In the statement "man is a reasoning animal", animal is the genus).

The *differentia* is that part of the definition which cannot be said of the other elements (species) of the genus: it states the difference between a particular element (species) and all others in the genus.

A *property* is an attribute of the subject which follows from the essence as a consequence. A property is not part of the definition.

An *accident* is any other attribute of the subject which has no necessary connection with the essence. The accident may be absent or present.

In Aristotelian logic a genus is not just the sum of its species. The genus and the differentia together constitute the definition of the species, the statement of its essence. In Platonic terminology the species is one of the ways in which the idea of the genus (the general plan, the type) is realized.

---

* Aristotle's main criteria were mainly teleological and Linnaeus followed them faithfully, for instance in the classification of books as given in the *Bibliotheca botanica*. For this I can refer to the analysis of this work by Heller (1970).

The differentia states the particular way in which a species exists. The distinguishing of species within a genus is therefore called *logical division*: the differentia must be the variation upon the theme of the genus. This means that the differentiae must be cognate; in other words: there is one *fundamentum divisionis*.

Logical division is possible when we know the connection between the essence and its properties a priori, such as for instance in mathematics. When classifying triangles we know a priori that we are dealing with three straight lines, and our *fundamentum divisionis* may be based on this knowledge. We classify analysed entities.

In biology, however, we deal with unanalysed entities, and logical division is not a priori possible. We classify types and select characteristics by experience. Even so one can apply a–prioristic criteria to biological objects, for instance those based on general considerations such as the 'essence of life' or 'nature.' This attitude is characteristic of essentialist taxonomy, of which the Linnaean system was undoubtedly the most important and perhaps the final result.

It has often been said, correctly, that as far as ideas are concerned Linnaeus stood at the end of an era. His absolute criterion of the constancy of species, the dogma of special creation, was conspicuous and already somewhat old–fashioned in its original form. Later in life Linnaeus put forward an entirely different theory which involved some 6000 specially created prototypes and speciation by means of hybridization. The original dogma of the constancy of species, however, played only a minor role in his method; primary was his principle that biology is based on fixed genera. The botanist and the zoologist could in principle know all the genera; the master would know most of the species (256*) Knowledge was possible through definition of the taxa by means of their 'essential' characters.

The Tournefortian theme of the definition of genera is further elaborated by Linnaeus: all species with the same geometrical disposition of the parts of the flower belong to one genus (159). The criteria are number, shape, size and proportion; they determine the *essence* of the genus. The essence lies in the structure of the flower, a scholastic and an a priori concept which, however, found support in the high information content of the involved flower structure. As usual, it is difficult to say whether theory preceded or

* Numbers in parentheses are those of the aphorisms in the *Philosophia botanica* (1751).

followed practical experience, although the scholastic philosophy of Linnaeus is so outspoken that one is inclined to accept his reasoning at face value. Five obligatory ranks are recognized: class, order, genus, species and variety, in a close parallel to the five categories of scholastic philosophy, also applied in other sciences: genus summum, genus inter-medium, genus proximum, species and individuum (155).

The great merit of the sexual system was evidently that it provided a simple, easily comprehended structure for storage and retrieval of informa-tion. It standardized usage. In combination with the code designations for species afforded by the binomial system it provided a highly useful and simple framework which was indeed internationally acceptable and which led different people to the same result. It is clear that in the beginning the Linnaean nomenclatural revolution created some confusion, but the in-trinsic merits of the system soon overcame its disadvantages.

Although he admitted that it was provisional and not 'natural,' Linnaeus was nevertheless convinced that the sexual system had high taxonomic value, because it kept the natural genera intact and especially because he considered the flower characters as expressing the 'essence.' And what, after all, in scholastic thinking, was the difference between essence and nature?

For Linnaeus, species and genera were realities, created as such and existing in nature. Linnaeus's attitude here was strongly empirical, al-though with Thomistic overtones. With respect to classes and orders, however, his attitude was typically nominalist: they are the works of 'na-ture and art.' The more plants we know the more the gaps will be filled, and the boundaries between the orders and classes will disappear. These taxa have no objective reality, but are ideas of our own making. The Platon-ic principle of plenitude may have made its appearance in the higher eche-lons, but Linnaeus drew the line with the genera and species. The famous aphorism (77) of the *Philosophia botanica*, "nature makes no jumps" (inciden-tally: words crossed out in Linnaeus's own copy of the *Philosophia botanica*), and the statement that all plants show relationships on all sides like a country on a map of the world make this clear. Linnaeus's attitude towards the natural families is well known: he had an outline, he recognized their existence, but he was not convinced that their full recognition was within reach. He was perhaps not even convinced of the desirability of elaborating a natural system.

[28]

CAROLI LINNÆI SVECI

Doctoris Medicinæ

FUNDAMENTA
BOTANICA

quæ

Majorum Operum Prodromi inftar

THEORIAM

SCIENTIÆ BOTANICES

per

breves Aphorifmos

tradunt.

AMSTELODAMI,
Apud SALOMONEM SCHOUTEN.
1736.

Fig. 6. Title–page of Linnaeus's *Fundamenta botanica* (1736). Even though dated 1736, the book came out on September 14, 1735.

[29]

Creta inventa
1952

CAROLI LINNÆI

ARCHIATR. REG. MEDIC. ET BOTAN. PROFESS. UPSAL.
ACAD. IMPERIAL. MONSPEL. BEROL. TOLOS. UPSAL.
STOCKH. SOC. ET PARIS. CORRESP.

PHILOSOPHIA BOTANICA

IN QVA
EXPLICANTUR

FUNDAMENTA BOTANICA

CUM

DEFINITIONIBUS PARTIUM,
EXEMPLIS TERMINORUM,
OBSERVATIONIBUS RARIORUM,

ADJECTIS

FIGURIS ÆNEIS.

CUM PRIVILEGIO.

STOCKHOLMIÆ,
APUD GODOFR. KIESEWETTER
1751.
R.

Trans Vewth
1952

Fig. 7

Linnaeus published his main theoretical considerations in several places. A first sketch was prepared by him in the years before he went to Holland: the final manuscript (three manuscripts are known) of his *Fundamenta botanica* was one of the first to be sent to the printers in Amsterdam in the summer of 1735. Although dated 1736, copies were available as early as September 14, 1735, even befor the *Systema naturae* came off the press. Linnaeus himself noted in his copy "typis absolutus 1735: Sept. 3." The brochure of 36 pages is entitled: *Fundamenta botanica quae majorum operum prodromi instar theoriam scientiae botanices per breves aphorismos tradunt.* (fig. 6). The aphorisms number 365, as many as the days in the year; they are divided over 12 chapters. The *Fundamenta* contains the basic material worked out in much greater detail in the *Philosophia botanica*, which repeats the aphorisms of the *Fundamenta* almost verbatim but adds explanations, examples and critical notes. The first edition of the *Systema naturae* of 1735 also contains a number of statements of principle, agreeing, on the whole, with some of the *Fundamenta* (see Engel and Engel 1964). A reading of the *Systema*, the *Fundamenta* and the *Philosophia* reveals at first sight a strongly aprioristic approach. Ultimately, however, the use of arbitrary axioms in biological classification (to be clearly distinguished from the logical statements which are the axioms of a deductive science, such as mathematics) was gradually abandoned as the result of the growing conflict between experience and nature viewed *a priori*. Linnaeus too was sufficiently endowed with the makings of an inductive empirical scientist to finish his *Fundamenta* and his *Philosophia* with these significant words:

"In scientia naturali principia veritatis observationibus confirmari debent"

("In natural science the principles of truth ought to be confirmed by observation").

For a more detailed insight into his ideas and methods, it will be necessary to analyse the *Philosophia botanica* (1751). The book is well worth reading.

2. *The Philosophia botanica*

The *Philosophia botanica* (fig. 7), carrying the imprint 1751, was published in

Fig. 7. Title–page, *Philosophia botanica*, Stockholm, 1751. For the various issues see Soulsby [1934] and Guédes [1968]. The emblem (*tantus amor florum*) shows *Linnaea borealis*. [Copy of book at the *Biohistorical Institute, Utrecht*].

Stockholm in December 1750. Copies exist with title-pages giving the Stockholm printer (Kiesewetter) only; others have a Stockholm–Amsterdam imprint. For a detailed history of the publication of the book itself reference may be made to Dahlgren (1951); for the bibliography see e.g. Du Rietz (1966) and Guédes (1968).

In his preface Linnaeus points out that the *Philosophia* contains the elaboration, by means of examples, of the *Fundamenta*. Several of the chapters of the *Fundamenta* had been elaborated in the *Bibliotheca botanica* (1736), the *Classes plantarum*, the *Sponsalia plantarum*, the *Critica botanica* and the *Vires plantarum*. He presents his *Philosophia* only as a further sketch based on his botanical courses given at Uppsala, not as a final work.

The *Philosophia botanica* consists of the 365 aphorisms of the *Fundamenta* (only a few of them in a changed form or actually different) with the addition of extensive explanations, commentaries, references or other documentation printed in smaller type. It is obviously impossible to discuss here every aphorism, but it is important for an understanding of Linnaeus's thought to analyse a number of his aphorisms and elaborations, in the order presented by the author. This entails a certain measure of repetition, which, however, is necessary for a good understanding of this to some extent rather 'difficult' book, called by Von Hofsten (1922) "a comprehensive textbook without much reasoning." The *Philosophia botanica* is the key to Linnaeus and the epitome of the predominance of aristotelian–thomistic methodological thinking in taxonomic botany. The apodictic form of many of the statements is sometimes disturbing to the modern reader. However, this was all in the game: and a game it was to bring order out of chaos. Essentially, as far as he acted consciously, it was Linnaeus who created the order; the empirical blood ran thick, however, and the ultimate result of the classification, especially on the generic level and lower, was often influenced far more by empiricism than by essentialism. The biologists of the French Enlightenment were different: they were conscious of the fact, and formulated their theories accordingly, that they had to discover an order existing in nature. Their direct purpose was empirical even though they still showed many signs of essentialist and nominalist thinking. Linnaeus, however, nowhere indicates that he considers it his task to discover the order of nature itself. The Linnaean mind creates the order on the basis of the essence of things.

In the succeeding paragraphs I shall discuss Linnaeus's reasoning, follow-ing the numerical order of his *Philosophia botanica*. His chapters are as follows (the numbers are those of the aphorisms):

Introduction (1–4)
1. Bibliography (5–52)
2. The systems (53–77)
3. The plants (78–85)
4. The fructification (86–131)
5. Sex (132–150)

6. The Characters (151–209)

7. Nomenclature (210–255)
9. The differences (256–305)
9. The varieties (306–317)
10. The synonyms (318–324)
11. The natural history
    (adumbrationes) (325–335)
12. The properties (336–365)

The 'translations' given below are on the whole very free and are meant to express Linnaeus's ideas in contemporary idiom. A modern critical English translation of the *Philosophia* is not available. The *Elements of botany* by Hugh Rose dates from 1775. The most reliable translation into a modern language is F. A. Quesné's *Philosophie botanique de Charles Linné* (1788).

INTRODUCTION (1–4)

The introduction delimits the field of botany and contains the well-known statement "stones grow, plants grow and live, animals grow, live and feel." Like Ray in his *Methodus* (1682), Linnaeus repeats Jung's definition of a plant (*Isagoge*, 1678, c. 1): "The plant is a living body which does not feel, which is constantly fixed to a dwelling–place or abode where it can feed, grow and multiply itself." Another interesting and revealing statement quoted (4) (fig. 8) is that of Boerhaave:

"Botany is that part of the natural sciences by the help of which one obtains happily [sic] and easily a knowledge of plants and by which one remembers this knowledge." The rôle of botany in 'remembering' knowl-edge is emphasized: at that time classification (and botany as whole) heavily stressed the element of information retrieval. Botany is not defined as e.g. the science of obtaining insight into the history, structure and func-tioning of the world of plants, but primarily as a device to register and to remember, to store and to retrieve.

[33]

INTRODUCTIO.

1. OMNIA, quæ in Tellure occurrunt, *Elementorum* & *Naturalium* nomine veniunt.

Syst. nat. 6. Obs. in regna tria §. 6. 7.
Elementa simplicia sunt, *Naturalia* composita arte divina.
Physica tradit Elementorum proprietates.
Scientia Naturalis vero Naturalium.

2. NATURALIA (1) dividuntur in Regna Naturæ tria: *Lapideum, Vegetabile, Animale.*

Syst. nat. 6. p. 211. §. 14. 8. 9. Necessitas cognitionis.
Faun. suecic. præfat. 4. Actio primi hominis.
Act. stockh. 1740. p. 411. Usus.

3. LAPIDES (2) crescunt. VEGETABILIA (2) crescunt & vivunt (133). ANIMALIA (2) crescunt, vivunt, & sentiunt.

Syst. nat. 6. p. 211. §. 15. idem.
Syst. nat. 6. p. 219. §. 2. Lapides crescere.
Sponsal. plant. §. 1-14. Vegetabilia vivere.
Jung. isagog. c. 1. Planta est corpus vivens non sentiens, s. certo loco aut certæ sedi affixum, unde nutriri, augeri, denique se propagare potest.
Boerh. hist. 3. Planta est corpus organicum, alteri cuidam corpori cohærens per aliquam partem sui, per quam Nutrimenti & Incrementi & Vitæ materiam capit & trahit.
Ludwig. veget. 3. Corpora naturalia eadem semper Forma & Loco-motivitate prædita appellantur *Animalia;* eadem semper forma, sed loco-motivitate destituta *Vegetabilia; &* quæ diversam formam obtinent *Mineralia* dicuntur.
Obs. Petrificata & Crystalli figura conveniunt omnino in eadem specie. Locomotivitas in *Balano, Lernea;* uti in *Mimosa.*

4. BOTANICE est Scientia Naturalis, quæ *Vegetabilium* (3) cognitionem tradit.

Boerh. hist. 16. Botanica est Scientiæ naturalis pars, cujus ope felicissime & minimo negotio plantæ cognoscuntur & in memoria retinentur.
Ludwig. aphor. 1. Botanica est scientia vegetabilium, s. cognitio eorum, quæ per plantas & in plantis fiunt.

A   I. BIBLIO-

Fig. 8

I. BIBLIOGRAPHY (5–52)

The entries on botanical bibliography are a digest of Linnaeus's *Bibliotheca botanica*, of which the first edition appeared in Amsterdam in 1735 as an elaboration of the first chapter of the *Fundamenta*. Linnaeus used the first months of his stay in Holland (apart from taking a degree) mainly to bring this manuscript from Sweden up to date. A much enlarged new edition was published in 1751 almost concurrently with the *Philosophia botanica*. For a profound study of the *Bibliotheca botanica* and of the *Bibliotheca cliffortiana* I can refer to Heller's recent publications (1968, 1970) in *Taxon*.

The *Bibliotheca* is a concise history of botany in a dry, enumerative, but very efficient style. Linnaeus describes the development of botanical science by subdividing the botanical authors in various categories and by adding several statements on the main events in human affairs without which the growth of botany as a science cannot be understood. The often enlightening and amusing names for the various categories of botanists show not only a good knowledge of the literature, but also an awareness of the fact that botanical history is human history:

Phytologists (6) are all authors who can boast a commendable book on botany, whether they are botanists or amateurs (*botanophili*). A list is given of the most outstanding phytologists of all ages, beginning with Theophrastus, Pliny and Dioscorides, and then jumping to the fifteenth century: Gaza (the Italian Greek translator and commentator of Theophrastus, 1398–1478) and Hermolaus Barbarus. It is interesting to note here that Linnaeus at that time did not know the very important botanical writings of Albertus Magnus (1193–1280).

The sixteenth century list contains many well-known names: it starts off with Brunfels, Tragus and Cordus; in all there are 39 names. The names of Gesner and Cesalpino are capitalized. Without explaining this distinction, Linnaeus creates three categories of botanists: the really outstanding ones (names capitalized), the ordinary but true botanists (names in lower case roman) and the amateurs (names in italics). Most outstanding in later ages are Morison, Tournefort and Vaillant; Linnaeus prints his own name, uncharacteristically, in lower case.

The task of the true *botanists* (7) is two-fold: to understand botany from

Fig. 8. Philosophia botanica [1751], aphorisms 1–4, p. [1].

[35]

its true foundations and to know how to give an easily understood name to all plants. They are either *compilers* ('*collectores*') or *systematists* ('*methodici*').

The compilers are the fathers, commentators, delineators or illustrators (*ichniographi*), the describers or historians (*descriptores*), the monographers, the curiosi, the professors of botany (*adonides*), the authors of floras and the explorers.

The *fathers* (8) of botany of Linnaeus are not the same ones cited under that term by Sprengel and Sachs. They put forward Brunfels, Fuchs and Tragus as the—German—fathers of botany; Linnaeus calls them 'veteres.' Linnaeus—who, incidentally, was the first to use this somewhat misleading term—regards as the 'fathers' all writers without exception up to and including the fourteenth century, and uses the word very much as ecclesiastical historians do in 'fathers of the church.' Linnaeus repeatedly injects factual statements on the great political and cultural movements in the history of mankind: his chapter on the fathers starts off as follows:

> "The fathers laid down the first elements of botanical science.
> "Chronology ("Fata"): The *Greeks* followed the *Egyptians*, who followed the *Chaldaeans* [used by Linnaeus in the biblical sense of Babylonians.]
> "The *Romans* following the defeat of Pompey near Actium.*
> "The *Goths* pillage Rome in the fourth century, the *Lombards* in the fifth.
> "The *Arabs* enter Egypt in the sixth Century and Spain in the seventh.
> "In the eleventh century the peoples of Marocco [here Arab northwest Africa] obey the caliph."

This and similar entries later on show Linnaeus's inclination to look upon the history of his science in the context of the development of the human mind and of human society. His classical training is evident, and although he might have failed as a protestant minister, and might have been a rather apodictic historian, it would be a mistake to think of him as a natural scientist in spiritual and cultural isolation.

---

* J. Heller (1970) states that what Linnaeus means here is the defeat of Mithridates by Pompey, as he has it in his *praefatio* to the *Bibliotheca botanica* and corrected in mss. in his copy of the *Philosophia*. This event (63 b.C.) was not the battle of Actium (316 b.C.) "The phrase and the division are Tournefort's, who says (*Isagoge* p. 5, in *Institutiones* 1700) that the Romans, otherwise eager to learn, wrote nothing about plants until after the defeat of Mithridates." He quotes Pliny who relates how Mithridates was a great student of life. See also Haller, *Bibliotheca botanica* 1: 53.

The standard definitions, often quoted, appear for the Greek fathers:
    "Hippocrates, father of medicine...
    "Aristotle, first of the peripatetics...
    "Theophrastus, father of botany...."
and then, applicable to 'obscure' medieval writers:
    "who knew neither the natural history of plants, nor the art of making general descriptions..."
    "The *commentators* (10) elucidated the writings of the fathers."
    "In the middle of the fifteenth century, the Turks separated the Greek or Eastern empire from the West. The refugees brought Greek learning to Italy. Invention of bookprinting in 1440, and of gunpowder. Discovery of America in 1492."

The essence of the Italian renaissance caught in a few words: "The refugees brought Greek learning to Italy" (even though there were learned Greeks in Italy before the fall of Constantinople). The Greek Gaza, for instance, translated Theophrastus. The knowledge of Greek before the Italian renaissance, apart from the places in Southern Italy and Sicily where Greek was spoken, can be compared with that of modern Greek in Italy today. A much more intimate contact with the Greek classics was established by the Greek immigrants. As a first result we see a stream of translations and commentaries on the classic texts, spread by the new art of bookprinting. The relevance of gunpowder in this context is not clear until one realizes its rôle in colonial expansion. This colonial expansion itself was the direct cause of the great upsurge of botany in the sixteenth century: Linnaeus catches this by stating "America 1492."

    "The *illustrators* (ichniographi) depicted the plants by means of engravings."
    The importance of illustration by means of engravings, whether on wood or (later) on metal, did not escape Linnaeus. Naturalistic and empirical plant illustration developed rapidly in the course of the sixteenth century (Brunfels with Hans Weiditz, for instance) and was a major factor in spreading information about plants. Obviously one of the great disadvantages which faced the pre-Renaissance botanists was the difficulty of comparing species from different localities. There are three ways to solve this problem: illustration, growing plants in botanic gardens, and herbaria. The illustration, says Linnaeus, must be of natural size and show the parts in their proper places; it must also show even the most minute parts of the fructification.

[37]

The art of making herbaria developed from botanical illustration: pressed plants were originally used as material for the botanical artists. Without saying so in so many words, Linnaeus hints at this development by including in his aphorism II on ichniographers a paragraph on herbaria:

"A herbarium is better than any illustration; every botanist should make one." He adds technical instructions which are revealing: "The plants should be dried between sheets of paper and as quickly as possible, but hardly with a hot iron." The herbarium specimens must be as complete as possible; the fructification should receive extra care; they should be stuck on the paper by means of fish glue, not by means of paper strips; there should be only one specimen per sheet; the genus was to be written on the front side, but the species and the ecological and geographical details (*species et historica*) should go on the back side. Finally, a herbarium should be arranged methodically.

The '*describers*' are the authors who have given the *adumbrations* of the plants. Linnaeus's use of the term 'adumbrationes' requires an explanation. The usual translations, 'sketch,' 'outline' or 'silhouette,' are not applicable; what he meant was a description of what has long been called the 'natural history,' e.g. the ecology, geographical details, information on life cycle and similar incidental non–morphological information.

The term *monographers* is obviously used by Linnaeus in the same sense as ours. In his day, however, there were relatively few monographic treatments "dedicated exclusively to the study of a single plant" (plant in a general sense). Linnaeus quotes himself as the author of several monographic treatises (in his dissertations) and refers but to a small number of others such as Haller on *Allium*, Bradley on *Aloë*, Breyne on 'Ginseng', Kaempfer on *Thea*.

The *Curious* or the inquisitive (researchers) have dealt with rare plants. This is a somewhat odd category in which Linnaeus unites authors of regional floras (Ray for England, Gmelin for Siberia) and the authors of the inventories of the richest botanic gardens of his era, Leiden and Amsterdam.

The *Adonides* (15) are the professors of botany: they demonstrate the plants in the botanic gardens (winter–house: home of Adonis). In this paragraph Linnaeus picks up again the thread of his history of botany: the establishment of botanic gardens. The oldest garden mentioned is that of Padova '1540,' a date now known to be incorrect: it was 1545. The first University botanic garden was that of Pisa, set up by Luca Ghini in 1543 and 1544.

[38]

The last two categories of 'compilers,' the *floristic* botanists and the *travellers*, are again purely pragmatic: Linnaeus gives only a very fragmentary review of the literature on local floras and on botanical exploration.

The *systematists* (*methodici*, 18) who deal with the classification (*dispositio*) and naming of plants are either 'philosophers,' taxonomists (these are what Linnaeus calls *systematici*) or 'nomenclators.'

"The *philosophers* (19), made a science of botany by clear deduction from rational principles; they are orators, controversialists, physiologists or authors of textbooks (*institutores*). Linnaeus's definition of the philosophers is of great importance towards an understanding of his ideas on science. In the eighteenth century the word philosopher often meant (and it does so here) "natural philosopher" or, in modern terminology, a natural scientist who is concerned with theoretical aspects. The science of botany is made, says Linnaeus, *by deduction* from rational (read *a priori*) principles. It will be difficult to find in Linnaeus's writings a clearer and more direct statement showing his 'Aristotelian' approach. Deduction from a priori principles, not induction from empirical facts, is primary. The empirical element is mentioned, but in a pejorative way: "the botany of the classics was a purely empirical knowledge." This is only partly true: Aristotle and Theophrastus had many deductive elements in their teaching of the natural sciences, but what Linnaeus means is that classical botanists often did no more than register facts (e.g. Pliny, Dioscorides). For him the deductive method is an enormous step forward because pure science starts from reason. The philosophers, says Linnaeus, are to be called theoretical botanists; "we owe to them the canons and rules of botany." 'Canon' means here 'general rule or axiom' and has overtones of 'genuine and inspired,' known instinctively by a holistic, not an analytical, approach to the phenomena of life.

Of the philosophers, the *orators* (20) hardly count: they are mentioned because public lecturing was so important in academic life at Linnaeus's time. The *controversialists* (21) (called *eristici* by Linnaeus) are also of little importance, but are also mentioned in view of the importance of public disputation for eighteenth century scholars. One of the controversialists mentioned is Siegesbeck, the Petersburg botanist who so prudishly and so violently attacked the 'obscene' Linnaean sexual system. This entry on polemology, however, inspired Linnaeus to make some remarks on bloody wars sparked by plants: for instance, the Lebanon Cedar, which led Adrian to destroy Jerusalem.* Particularly penetrating is his remark on *Myristica*, the nutmeg, which caused one of the most violent episodes in the Dutch colonial expansion in the Moluccas: "*Myristica* Belgas in Indiis armavit."

Physiologists (22) were rare in the eighteenth century: Linnaeus counts himself among them because of his *Sponsalia plantarum*.

The *Authors of textbooks* (23) are those who laid down the rules and the principles. There are only three:

"*Jungius* [who gave an introduction to the study of plants in his] *Isagoge phytoscopia*"

"*We ourselves* in the present work" "*Nos* Fundamenta haec Botanica" [perhaps not modest, but true]

"*Ludwig* in his works *Regnum vegetabile* and *Aphorismi botanici*."

Linnaeus's debt to Jung is great and clearly acknowledged here. Jung established the bases of botanical terminology. His brochure was small and rare, but Ray knew it and made it the basis of his terminology in all his works. Linnaeus, perhaps through Ray, also used the *Isagoge* extensively, and he followed Ray in accepting Jung's morphological terminology.

---

* The note on *Abies* ("called *Cedrus*, incited Hadrian; as a result Jerusalem was destroyed") is badly confused, but in a curious way. In the first place, Hadrian did not destroy Jerusalem (that had been done by Titus 60 years before) but tried to rebuild it as a Roman colony and with a Roman temple on the site of the old Temple, thereby bringing on the most serious (132–34) of several Jewish revolts, which was ruthlessly suppressed, destroying rather the Jewish people in Palestine. On the other hand, we now know that Hadrian was in fact interested in the vast stands of trees on the Lebanon mountains, including no doubt the cedars. But Linnaeus did not and could not have known this. Modern historians infer from a large number of inscriptions found at various points on the now bare mountainsides that Hadrian had reserved certain tracts with "four kinds of trees" as public property, probably as a source of timber for the imperial navy, but the inscriptions were never published or interpreted until Renan's *Mission de Phénicie* (1864). Details and a map may be found in Hönigmann's article "Libanos" in the *Real-Encyclopädie der classischen Altertumswissenschaft* (13: 1. 1926), which also discusses the many previous expeditions sent to this region in quest of trees by Hellenistic monarchs and their predecessors in oriental kingdoms, all the way back to biblical times and beyond. Linnaeus probably coupled one of the biblical expeditions with a vague memory of Hadrian's war. Celsius has a long chapter (1: 14–105) on "Abies, vulgo Cedrus Libani" in his *Hierobotanicon* (1745–47), which Linnaeus certainly knew, but neither Celsius nor C. J. Trew in his later and classic monograph, *Cedrorum Libani historia* (1757, 1767), says anything about Hadrian. (John Heller.)

Linnaeus's *methodici* (18) ('philosophers,' taxonomists and nomenclators) are clearly what we now call *systematists*, that is those dealing with the biological structure and diversity of the living world. Plant classification, or taxonomy, is part of this. Linnaeus's use of the word *systematici* agrees fully with today's *taxonomists*. "The taxonomists (24) arrange the plants in taxa; they are either orthodox or heterodox." The first part of the aphorism is here very freely translated (*Systematici plantas in certas Phalanges disposuerunt*"); it is interesting to see that Linnaeus had a term for our 'taxon': 'phalanx,' originally a band of soldiers. The term never caught on because it was not until the end of the nineteenth century that theoretical botanists again felt the need for a general term to denote any kind of grouping of plants or animals. The term 'taxonomic group' was then coined, to be replaced unofficially in 1948, and officially by an International Congress in 1950, by the term *taxon*, promoted by H. J. Lam but originally proposed by Meyer in 1926, in his *Logik der Morphologie* (pp. 126–137). *Phalanx* had been forgotten by that time, except for incidental usage as a term for a subgeneric category.

The *fundamentum divisionis* for the taxonomists is their attitude towards the fructification. Those who arrange the plants on the basis of the fructification are *orthodox*; those who do this on the basis of any other criterion are *heterodox*.

The further categories of heterodox botanists are perhaps not important, but are too delightful and amusing to be skipped here: the alphabetics (by generic name), the rhizotomi ('root–cutters'), the phyllophiles (who arrange plants by the shape of the leaf), the physiognomists (by external appearance), the chroniclers (by flowering time), the topophiles (by habitat), the empiricists (by medicinal properties) and the pharmacists (who follow the order of the pharmacopoeias). It should be noted that there is no mention of botanists who based their classification on overall affinity. Linnaeus might have mentioned Magnol's *Prodromus* of 1689, but the significance of this work evidently escaped him; *a combination of characters* was in flat contradiction to the prime requirement of a single *fundamentum divisionis*!

The *orthodox taxonomists* (26) are described in more detail: after all, they were the only ones taken seriously by Linnaeus. They "establish their method on the true basis ("... *vero fundamento* ..."), that of the fructification; they are universal or partial."

"They describe and respect the natural genera, they arrange the genera on some part of the fructification, they assign a place in their system to the taxa which they have before them; then what is not there is self–evident." This statement shows again, implicitly, that for Linnaeus the fructification revealed the essence of the plants, because without qualification he accepts this as the 'true basis' for classification; the fructification is the major *fundamentum divisionis*. Cesalpino had stated in so many words that it was because propagation was primary and therefore 'essential' that he accepted the fructification as his basis for classification. Linnaeus does not specify or clarify, but states by axiom that 'true basis' is identical with 'fructification.' Elsewhere, however (no. 134), Linnaeus uses the Aristotelian *finis et essentia* for propagation. It might be argued that he did so on an empirical basis; however, in view of his ideas on the rational principles from which science is "deduced" [sic], this remains questionable. Linnaeus was by nature empirical, but in his argumentation and thought he gave priority to theoretical considerations.

It is revealing also to see that Linnaeus remarks that the orthodox taxonomists recognize natural genera: "genera observant naturalia." Logically this is circular reasoning since natural genera are defined as based on the fructification. The statement goes much deeper, however, because of Linnaeus's belief in the existence of a limited number of fixed genera. 'Natural' means here again: 'respecting the essence.' The practical side of this classification is stressed by the statement that it leaves room for what is still to be discovered. Such is the faith in the reliability and 'truth' of the basic principle that the essence is found in propagation, that the system ('method') is expected to have a high predictive value. This, however, was to be the strong point of the 'natural systems' of Adanson (1763) and his followers, and not quite that of the artificial systems.

The *universal* orthodox systematists (27) use the 'true method' (one is almost inclined to translate *genuina* here as 'natural' because this is undoubtedly what was meant) in distinguishing between the classes of plants, they are 'fructists,' 'corollists,' 'calicists' and 'sexualists.'

"The *fructists* (28) such as Cesalpino, Morison, Ray, Knaut, Hermann, Boerhaave base their classes on the fruit, the seed or the receptable." This is an oversimplification. Morison and Ray both based their systems on other characters as well; their classifications have strong empirical traits. The only real *fructists* are Cesalpino and Knaut, the most pur–sang Aristotelian logicians of the lot. Ray, Morison, and Boerhaave were primarily empirical scientists who used the principles of logical division but who never became its slaves. The two main *corollists*, Tournefort and Rivinus, are said to have based their systems exclusively on the corolla, which is, in general, true. What should have been emphasized as well, however, is that these two botanists were outspoken pragmatists who made it clear that they did not look for a universal method, but for a practical way to key out the plants.

Calicists are rare: Magnol in his posthumous *Novus character plantarum* of 1720, a rather disturbing step backward from his promising *Prodromus* of 1689, and Linnaeus himself in his *Classes plantarum* of 1738 (pp. 404–439).

The *sexualists* (?!) are those who based a system on the sex of plants: "ut *Ego*." "Like me (in Holland) 1735"; that is in the first instance in the *Systema naturae* of 1735 with its key, then Ehret's plate of 1736 (see Taxon 3: 175. 1954) and subsequently in all further publications. So far the sexualists had remained a monotypic taxon! The use of the word 'sexual' is actually misleading: the basis of the system is not the sexual function but something rather irrelevant for that function: the number of stamens and pistils.

The *partial* orthodox systematists (32) are the monographers who deal with a single group but in the correct way, that is, with the fructification as the basis of their treatment.

The 'nomenclators' (38) are the third group of systematists (next to the philosophers and the taxonomists): they are synonymists (such as C. Bauhin), critics (Linnaeus in his *Critica botanica*), etymologists, or lexicographers (Mentzel's *Index nominum plantarum multilinguis*).

The remaining botanical authors are the 'amateurs,' the 'botanophiles,' who made observations without direct relation to scientific botany. Examples are the anatomists (Malpighi and Grew), the gardeners (Philip Miller), the physicians, the astrologers, the 'chemists' (analysis of ashes, forerunners of our chemotaxonomists) and others of varying importance.

In a final paragraph (52), an appendix to this chapter on bibliography, Linnaeus mentions four additional categories: the economic botanists who dealt with the use of plants in the life of man, the biologists who wrote eulogies of various authors [this is the first use of the word biologist, though it was used in the sense of 'biographer'; the present sense stems from Lamarck]; "the theologists who wrote on the plants of the bible," such as *Celsius* [*Hierobotanicon*], and "the poets ... such as [Walafrid] Strabo and his *Hortulus* ..."

[43]

II. SYSTEMATA.

53. SYSTEMATICIS (24) Orthodoxis (26) nitor &
certitudo fcientiæ Botanices debetur.

Syft. nat. obf. veget. 3. idem.
Syft. nat. obf. veget. 4. Syftematici qui.

Cæfalpinus.	Rivinus.	Vaillantius.	Linnæus.
Morifonus.	Knautius.	Juffiæus.	Royenus.
Rajus.	Ruppius.	Scheuchzerus.	Gronovius.
Hermannus.	Ludvigius.	Dillenius.	Gmelinus.
Magnolius.	Tournefortius.	Michelius.	Guettardus.
Boerhavius.	Plumierus.	Hallerus.	Wachendorffius.
		Geinerus.	Gleditfchius.
		Burmannus.	Dalibard.

54. CÆSALPINUS (28) eft Fructifta & primus verus
Syftematicus, fecundum Corculi (86:6) & Rece-
ptaculi (86:7) fitum diftribuens.

Arbores corculo ex apice feminis. - - - 1.
　　　　　　　　e bafi feminis - - - 2.
Herbæ folitariis feminibus - - - - 3.
　　　　　　　baccis - - - - 4.
　　　　　　　capfulis - - - - 5.
Binis feminibus - - - - 6.
　　　capfulis - - - - 7.
Triplici principio fibrofæ - 8.
　　　　　　　　Bulbofæ - 9.
Quaternis feminibus - 10.
Pluribus feminib. *Anthemides* 11.
　　Cichorac. f. *Acanaceæ* 12.
flore *Communi* - 13.
folliculis - - 14.
flore fructuque *carentes* 15.

55. MORISONUS (28) eft Fructifta cum Phyfiogno-
mis (25) & Corolliftis (29) confpirans.

Lignofæ *Arbores* - - 1.
　　Frutices - - 2.
　　Suffrutices - - 3.

Herba-

Fig. 9

II. THE SYSTEMS (53–77)

In his second chapter Linnaeus reproduces in extenso some of the main systems* of his predecessors and some of his own. "The certitude of knowledge in botany and the splendour of that science are due to the orthodox taxonomists." Each of the aphorisms 54–77 deals with the system of a single author. The aphorisms themselves contain concise diagnostic descriptions of the authors and their systems, thus enabling Linnaeus to elaborate and to refine his apodictic statements on them in the *Bibliotheca*.

"Cesalpino (54)(fig. 9) is a fructist and the first true taxonomist; he based his system on the embryo and on the receptacle."

As in his *Classes plantarum* of 1738, Linnaeus makes the fundamental mistake of taking Cesalpino's books 2–16 as dealing with his main taxa. Bremekamp (1953) has shown that Cesalpino's system was much more refined, and in fact of higher quality than Linnaeus realized.

Aphorism 68 treats the sexual system: "I elaborated the sexual system in accordance with the number, proportions and insertion of the stamens with respect to the pistils." There follows a list of the names of the 24 classes.

The next aphorism, 69, introduces the term 'natural method': "Royen beautifully, Haller with erudition, Wachendorff with the help of Greek have tried to work out a natural method on the basis of the cotyledons, the calyx, the sex and other parts [sic: of the fructification!]." Linnaeus does not explicitly state what he means by 'natural method.' In his aphorism 77 he writes that the "fragments of the natural method must be sought with the greatest care." Then follow the often–quoted statements (fig. 10):

"This is the first and last desideratum among botanists.

"Nature makes no jumps.

"All taxa show relationships on all sides, like the countries on a map of the world."

* For Linnaeus 'System' is the application of logical division and the use of hierarchical categories in classification; the result of this process is what we now call *a* or *the* system; for Linnaeus this was a 'method'.

Fig. 9. Philosophia botanica [1751], aphorisms 53–54. Linnaeus renumbers the books 2–16 of Cesalpino, *De plantis libri XIV* to classes 1–15 which do not correspond with the classes of Cesalpino's actual system [Bremekamp 1953].

Linnaeus then adds his 'fragments,' which are essentially the same as those given in his *Classes plantarum* of 1738.

I shall discuss Linnaeus's sexual and natural systems in more detail in a separate chapter. It can be pointed out here that his 'fragments' are the tribute which Linnaeus paid to the principle of plenitude. He shows the characteristic ambivalence between a desire for practical logical classification and the intuitive realization that the multiplicity of forms of life is overwhelming and not compatible with artifical barriers, an ambivalence which we encounter all through the history of taxonomy. The word 'natural' still means the same thing: stating the essence on the basis of the characteristics derived from the fructification. This point should not be misunderstood. The natural groups are set up in agreement with groups easily recognized as homogeneous, such as grasses and umbellifers, groups easily grasped as units by the human mind without rational analysis. By analogy, there must exist many more such natural groups which one can detect by knowing all their component genera with their fructifications. The 'naturalness' of genera is beyond doubt for Linnaeus; a similar naturalness must exist for 'orders,' even though he may not be able to describe it.

The main reason why he cannot pursue this aim further is that for a natural method one must know all components; many, however, are still unknown. The final statement of the chapter is: "The plants which are as yet unknown make the natural method incomplete; knowledge about them will bring it to perfection, because in fact nature makes no jumps."

Linnaeus's 'map of the world' comparison is an image of the type of the *scala naturae* or of Donati's famous net. The world of living beings is a whole and there are no barriers. He realizes quite well that it is the task of the botanist to know that map of the world, but almost a priori doubts that he will succeed. This philosophical consideration may have strengthened the pragmatic side of the arch–classifier Linnaeus: the first task of taxonomy is for him to create order and to set up a system that will permit rapid identification. That system should be such that it could at once accommodate newcomers without the need for a group *vagae et etiamnum incertae sedis*. The sexual system met this requirement par excellence.

Fig. 10. Aphorism 77 (pp..) of the *Philosophia botanica* [1751], showing Linnaeus's statement on the natural system, including ordinal names. This aphorism also contains the famous *Natura non facit saltus*

[46]

73. MUSCOS (77: 65) stupenda industria detexit & absolvit DILLENIUS (36).

> Calyptrati.
> Calyptra destituti.

74. ALGAS (77: 66) DILLENIUS ex Textura, MICHELIUS secundum flores disposuit.

75. FUNGOS (77: 67) DILLENIUS (37) secundum Pileos, MICHELIUS (37) secundum fructificationes dispescuit.

> DILLENII divisio secundum Pileos, unde
>> Lamellosi,
>> Porosi,
>> Echinati.

76. LITHOPHYTA olim relicta *Plutoni*, MARSILIUS *Floræ* imperio subjecit, at PEYSONELLUS eadem *Faunæ* Regno restituit.

> *Amœn. acad. 80.* Ratio Peysonelli 1727. B. *Jussiæi* 1741.

77. METHODI NATURALIS Fragmenta studiose inquirenda sunt.

> Primum & ultimum hoc in Botanicis desideratum est.
> Natura non facit saltus.
> Plantæ omnes utrinque affinitatem monstrant, uti Territorium in Mappa geographica.
> Fragmenta, quæ ego proposii, hæc sunt:

1. PIPERITÆ.	Phœnix	Satyrium
Arum	Coix.	Serapias
Dracontium	3. SCITAMINA.	Herminium
Calla	Musa	Neottia
Acorus	Thalia	Ophrys
Saururus	Alpinia	Cypripedium
Pothos	Costus	Epidendrum
Piper	Canna	Limodorum
Phytolacca.	Maranta	Arethusa.
2. PALMÆ.	Amomum	5. ENSATÆ.
Corypha	Curcuma	Iris
Borassus	Kæmpferia.	Gladiolus
Coccus	4. ORCHIDEÆ.	Antholyza
Chamærops	Orchis	Ixia

Sisyrin-

Fig. 10

Implicit in Linnaeus's justification for the need of efficient classification, but nowhere stated to my knowledge, is the assumption that classifications enable the taxonomist to make inductive generalizations regarding living things. Both his sexual system and the fragments of a natural method were supposed to serve this purpose (see also Gilmour 1940, Hull 1969).

III. THE PLANTS (78–85)

The third chapter of the *Philosophia botanica* deals with the descriptive terminology of the vegetative parts of Spermatophyta, with the exception of the palms and the grasses. Linnaeus's precision in defining his concepts weakens here to some extent; the chapter is headed *Plantae*, but its very first aphorism (78) states: the *Vegetabilia* have seven families: the fungi, algae, musci, ferns, grasses, palms and plants. The rest of the chapter evidently applies mainly to Spermatophyta, but sometimes also to ferns or mosses. The use of the term *familia*, extremely rare in Linnaeus's writings, is remarkable. Linnaeus uses it for the main divisions of the plant kingdom as he sees them. It is not clear why he uses this term here. In the *Fundamenta* (1735) the aphorism is different:

"Vegetabilium *species* sunt: Lithophyta, Algae, Fungi, Musci, Filices, Gramina, Herbae cum arboribus."

This use of the word *species* agrees with its general use in classificatory logic, the genus being the *regnum vegetabile*, its species those seven groups.

The *Fundamenta* also gives a better explanation of the use of the word 'plant': (79) "Vegetabilium *partes* sunt *Planta* & *Fructificatio....*" Why Linnaeus dropped this more precise terminology is not clear; the word *plantae* in the title of the chapter clearly stands for the vegetative parts.

The use of the word 'family' for a category of a definite rank was first introduced by Magnol in his *Prodromus* of 1689, a book also mentioned in Linnaeus's *Bibliotheca botanica*. Magnol used it in our present sense for a group of genera (*ordo* in Linnaeus).

Aphorism 79 of the *Philosophia* abandons the difference between 'planta' and 'fructification' but states that there are three main parts of the plants "which the tyro must first distinguish": the root, the herb and the fructification. The explanatory part gives Linnaeus's concept of the structure of plants: "the *medulla* is covered by the *wood* (lignum) formed by the *bark*

[48]

(liber), covered by the *cortex* which itself is covered by the *epidermis.*" The fruit is produced by the *medulla* but cannot acquire new life without the intervention of the liquid essence of the stamens absorbed by the 'humor' of the pistil. "There is no new creation, but generation is continuous because the embryo of the seed is formed by the *medulla* of the root." (*Corculum seminis* is not always the embryo; it may also stand for part of the embryo: it is in fact a rather nebulous morphological term.)

The rest of the chapter gives a detailed descriptive terminology for the vegetative parts. Interesting is the use of the word 'herb,' explained more precisely in aphorism 81: "the herb is the part of the plant produced by the root, terminated by the fructification; it consists of the trunk, the leaves, the *fulcra* and the *hybernaculum.*" All terms are defined in great detail; the morphology of the leaves in particular is described in terms which are still in general use.

IV. THE FRUCTIFICATION (86–131)

The fructification is the basis of true Linnaean taxonomy; no wonder it receives special and detailed treatment in a separate chapter.

(86) "The fructification is a temporary part of the plant, dedicated to reproduction (*generatio*); it terminates the old, it begins the new: there are seven parts ...."

1. the calyx, *cortex* of the plant represented in the fructification,

2. the corolla, *liber* of the plant present in the flower,

3. the stamen, an inner part (*viscus*) for the preparation of the pollen,

4. the pistil, an inner part adhering to the fruit and meant to receive the pollen,

5. the pericarp, an inner part full of seeds which it releases when they are ripe,

6. the seed (*semen*) is a part which must separate itself from the plant: it is the beginning of a new being brought to life through the 'irrigation' by the pollen [sic *irrigatio*, not *irritatio* as in later editions!],

7. the receptacle, the basal part on which the six [other] parts of the fructification are inserted.

We shall later see that Linnaeus's rather arbitrary belief that the calyx is part of the *cortex*, the corolla of the *liber*, the stamens of the *xylem*, and the

88. Effentia FLORIS (87) in *Anthera* (86) & *Stigmate* (86) confiftit.

FRUCTUS (87) in *Semine* (86).

FRUCTIFICATIONIS (87) in *Flore* & *Fructu*.

VEGETABILIUM (78) in *Fructificatione* (87).

Character partium plantarum difficile eruitur, nifi affumantur duo prima *Pollinis* & *Seminis*.

1. POLLEN eft pulvis vegetabilium (§. 3.), appropriato liquore madefactus rumpendus, & fubftantiam fenfibus nudis imperfcrutabilem elaftice explodens.

2. SEMEN eft pars plantæ decidua, rudimento novæ plantæ fœta, & polline vivificata.

3. ANTHERA eft vas *Pollen* (1) producens & dimittens.

4. PERICARPIUM eft vafculum *Semina* (2) producens dimittensque.

5. FILAMENTUM eft pes *Antheræ* (3), quo vegetabili alligatur.

6. GERMEN eft *Pericarpii* (4) *Seminisve* 2) rudimentum immaturum, exiftens præcipue eodem tempore, quo Anthera (3) Pollen (1) dimittit.

7. STIGMA eft apex *Germinis* (6) roridus.

8. STYLUS eft pes *Stigmatis* (7), connectens illud cum *Germine* (6).

9. COROLLA & CALYX funt tegumenta *Staminum* (1.3.5) & *Piftillorum* (6.7.8, quorum hic ex *Epidermide* corticali, illa ex *Libro* orta eft.

10. RECEPTACULUM eft, quod connectit partes prædictas (5.6.9.

11. FLOS ex *Anthera* (3) & *Stigmate* (7) nafcitur, five tegumenta (9) adfint, five non.

12. FRUCTUS ex *Semine* (2), five Pericarpio (4) five non tectum, dignofcitur.

13. FRUCTIFICATIO omnis gaudet *Anthera* (3), *Stigmate* (7) & *Semine* (2).

14. VEGETABILE omne *Flore* (11) & *Fructu* (12) inftruitur; ut nulla fpecies his deftituta.

Seminis effentia confiftit in *Corculo* (§.86.) quod *Cotyledoni* adnectitur, & ab eodem involvitur, dein tunica propria arcte veftitur.

Corculi

Fig. 11

ovary of the *medulla*, has certain consequences for his theories of hybrid-ization. The reasons for this belief must be that the calyx is coarser and thicker, like the cortex, and the corolla more tender, like the *liber*. Under aphorism 90 Linnaeus says, however, that in nature there is no sharp distinction between calyx and corolla, as is evident, for instance, from *Daphne*.

The parts of the flower (87) are the calyx, the corolla, the stamen and the pistil; the fruit consists of the pericarp, the seed and the receptacle [sic]; the flower and the fruit together constitute the fructification.

This definition of the flower, which is the same as in the *Fundamenta* of 1735, is definitely an improvement over that given by previous authors. Linnaeus uses clear–cut terms, whereas authors like Jung and Ray (whom he quotes in the discussion) still talk about "the more delicate part of the plant" and Ludwig even uses very old terms like "a filamentose and mem-branous part of the plants, distinguished ... by its elegance ...." Previous authors had called the corolla and stamens the flower, and the calyx and pistil the fruit. Linnaeus remarks that the calyx must be a part of the flower even though it often accompanies the fruit, because in no case does the calyx develop only after flowering.

The Aristotelean overtones are strongest in aphorism 88 (fig. 11): because here are given the dictates that guide the taxonomist:
"The essence of the flower rests in the anther and the stigma,
of the fruit in the seed,
of the fructification in the flower and the fruit,
of the plants in the fructification."
The morphological complexity of the fructification is the empirical basis of Linnaeus's devotion to it. The character complex contains quite a few attributes which can be expressed in simple numbers, and numbers are ideal for logical division! However, even though it is possible to attribute Linnaeus's devotion to the fructification to subconscious empiricism, it was consciously a typical a priori choice based on his ideas on what constitutes the essence of vegetable life. The assumption that two plants agreeing in many respects in the structure of their flowers and fruits are closely related is an idea common to all phases of post–seventeenth–century

Fig. 11. Statement on the essence of the flower; aphorism no. 88 of the *Philosophia botanica* [1751].

taxonomy. In a way this assumption was also the basis for many speculations on evolutionary affinity. For Linnaeus it proved the 'naturalness' of his method.

Aphorisms 92 and 93, dealing with the structure of the fructification, are of the utmost importance for the understanding of Linnaean thought. The terminology is involved and obscure and requires an analysis. The crux of the matter is that the taxonomist notices the *differences*, and that these differences are the key to the essence from which all other properties can be deduced.

(92) "The botanist observes everywhere in all its parts the threefold structure of the fructification: the *most natural*, the *differential* and the *singular*, and he describes them accurately, using four *dimensions*: number, figure, proportion and situation." The four 'dimensions' are just so many columns of the art (*totidem artis columnae*).

This threefold 'structure of the fructification' can be understood only if it is realized that 'structure' stands here for the mutual relation of the parts of the fructification; this relation determines its 'character.' Leaving aside for the moment the less important 'singular' structure, this mutual relationship has two essentially different contingent aspects: 'natural' and 'differential.' The 'natural' structure is what we should now call the description, the differential structure is the diagnosis. For Linnaeus there is no doubt which of the two expresses the 'essence': this is the differential structure. The 'natural structure' certainly also contains the statements on the essence, but they are hidden between statements on properties deducible from the definition.

Aphorism 93 elaborates this theme even further: "The most natural structure of the fructification is taken from the plurality of the objects which present themselves: number, figure, proportion and situation."

The additional remarks accompanying this aphorism are among the most revealing of the *Philosophia botanica*. They show that Linnaeus was convinced that a complete description was anti–taxonomic and even misleading; the true 'character' contains a statement of the diagnostic details only. The main aim is to state the timeless essentials; the rest is irrelevant because it is supposed to follow from the essence as a logical consequence. Definition prevails over description, taxonomy over systematics, logical division on aprioristic principles over a biological approach.

[52]

"All fructifications differ and in this respect they all agree."

The most natural structure becomes familiar with experience and is not further observed by the genuine botanist; however, the band of sciolists [*idiotae*] and strangers in the world of botany* describe it at great length and by this they show only their ignorance which they praise in their perversity."

"An excellent Agrostologist [probably Scheuchzer] seems not to have hit the mark in this respect though otherwise he was truly great."

"I give here as an example a barbarically constructed description ('character'): Calyx green, straight, short, divided in five parts ...." The description goes on for 18 lines and ends with the italicized words: "*Who would say that this is Linum.*" This final exclamation seems somewhat peculiar to a modern botanist, because there seems to be nothing wrong with the description which applies undoubtedly to *Linum*, or rather to the Linaceae. For Linnaeus, however, it was absurd to go to all this length to define Linum.

The four subsequent aphorisms describe the most natural number (calyx and corolla have the same number of segments), *figura* (calyx, corolla, stamens, pistil; calyx permanent, corolla and stamens deciduous), proportion (calyx smaller than corolla ...) and situation (a superior ovary ...).

The *differential structure* of the fructification (98), however, is taken from the parts which differ often in different plants. "This must be the basis of the genera and of their definitions (*characteres*). The more natural a class is, the less evident is the differential structure. Every singular structure is different, but not every different structure is singular."

The differential structure is reflected by the diagnosis or definition, here also called *character* by Linnaeus. Aphorisms 99–104 explain the extensive general floral terminology which we encounter in Linnaeus's writings. Here lies the core of the Linnaean method of classification by definition and precise terminology.

The 'singular' fructification (105), or rather the special fructification, is a special case of the differential structure. "It derives from the particular structure which one finds in a small number of genera." This category enables Linnaeus to develop his highly skilful special floral terminology

* *peregrinatores* are strictly speaking travellers, but Linnaeus obviously refers to the use of *peregrinor* as 'to be a stranger.'

[53]

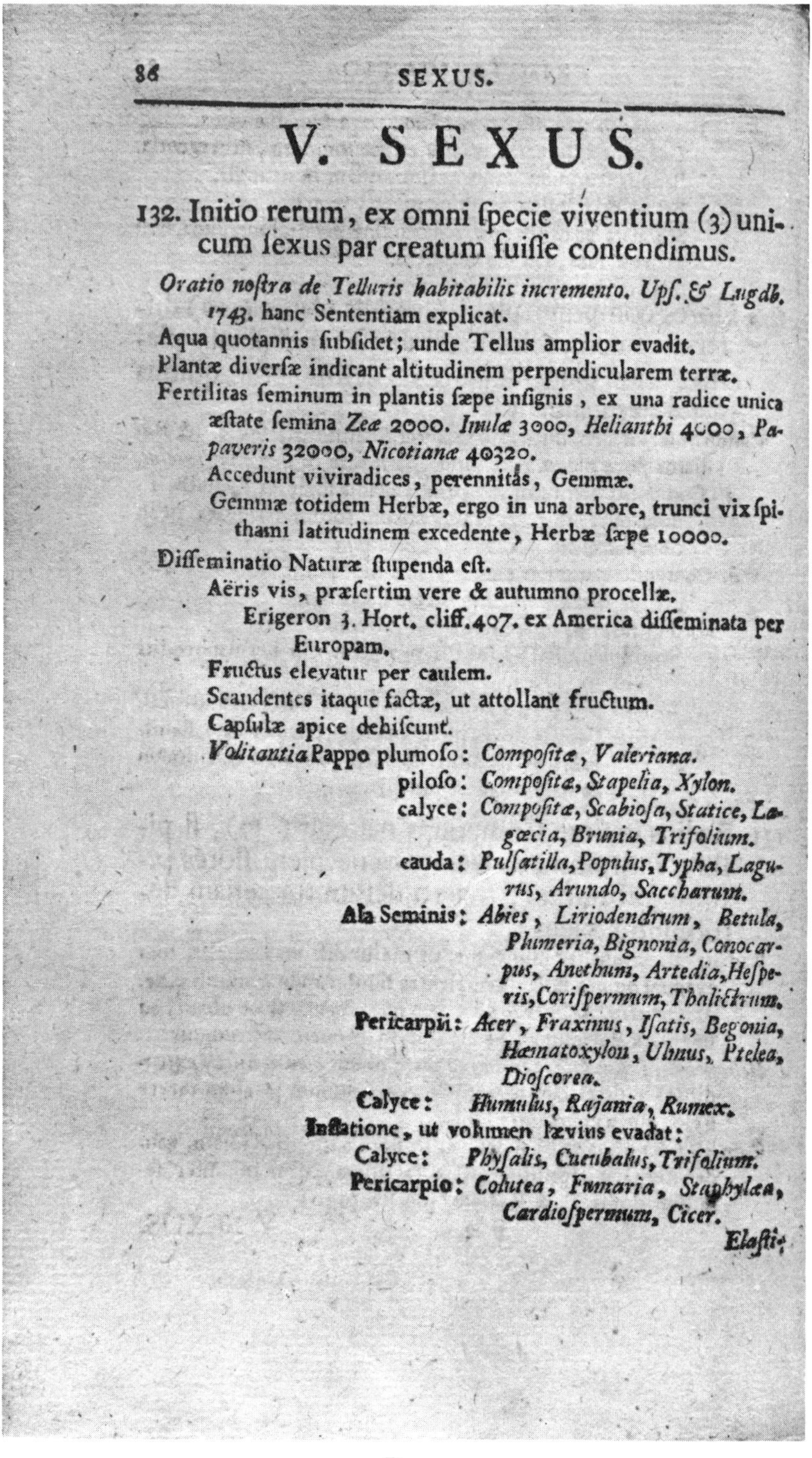

V. SEXUS.

132. Initio rerum, ex omni fpecie viventium (3) unicum fexus par creatum fuiffe contendimus.

*Oratio noftra de Telluris habitabilis incremento. Upf. & Lugdb.
1743.* hanc Sententiam explicat.

Aqua quotannis fubfidet; unde Tellus amplior evadit.

Plantæ diverfæ indicant altitudinem perpendicularem terræ.

Fertilitas feminum in plantis fæpe infignis , ex una radice unica
æftate femina *Zeæ* 2000. *Inulæ* 3000, *Helianthi* 4000 , *Pa-
paveris* 32000, *Nicotianæ* 40320.

Accedunt viviradices, perennitas, Gemmæ.

Gemmæ totidem Herbæ, ergo in una arbore, trunci vix fpi-
thami latitudinem excedente , Herbæ fæpe 10000.

Diffeminatio Naturæ ftupenda eft.

Aëris vis, præfertim vere & autumno procellæ.

Erigeron 3. Hort. cliff.407. ex America diffeminata per
Europam.

Fructus elevatur per caulem.

Scandentes itaque factæ, ut attollant fructum.

Capfulæ apice debifcunt.

Volitantia Pappo plumofo: *Compofitæ , Valeriana.*

pilofo: *Compofitæ, Stapelia, Xylon.*

calyce: *Compofitæ, Scabiofa, Statice, La-
gæcia, Brunia, Trifolium.*

cauda: *Pulfatilla, Populus, Typha, Lagu-
rus, Arundo, Saccharum.*

Ala Seminis: *Abies , Liriodendrum , Betula,
Plumeria, Bignonia, Conocar-
pus, Anethum, Artedia, Hefpe-
ris, Corifpermum, Thalictrum.*

Pericarpii: *Acer , Fraxinus, Ifatis, Begonia,
Hæmatoxylon, Ulmus, Ptelea,
Diofcorea.*

Calyce: *Humulus, Rajania, Rumex.*

Inflatione, ut volumen lævius evadat:

Calyce: *Phyfalis, Cucubalus, Trifolium.*

Pericarpio: *Colutea , Fumaria , Staphylæa,
Cardiofpermum, Cicer.*

Elafti-

Fig. 12

in the aphorisms 106–131. Both the general and the special floral terminology of Linnaeus have had a tremendous influence on descriptive and diagnostic plant taxonomy (see Stearn 1966). Most of the terms were perhaps not new, but Linnaeus stabilized their usage.

v. SEX (112–150)

The chapter on sex [fig. 12] is the least taxonomic and the most biological of the *Philosophia* (and *Fundamenta*). Whereas the other chapters deal with plant classification in all its aspects, we find in the fifth chapter a digest of the early manuscript *Praeludia sponsaliorum plantarum* (not to be confused with the 1746 dissertation *Sponsalia plantarum*, which is a further commentary on chapter 5 of the *Fundamenta*). In view of the importance attached by Linnaeus to sex as the primary essence of vegetable life on which the definition must be based, however, the chapter occupies a logical place in the book. The biological details are in many ways out of date and the subject matter is often highly specialized, but many of the thoughts are very characteristic of Linnaeus. A brief and necessarily incomplete digest may therefore be given here.

(132) "We hold that in the beginning there were created a single sexual pair of every species of living beings."
"The water retreats further every year, hence the growth of the land."
"Diverse plants indicate the 'perpendicular altitude' of the earth."
'Perpendicular altitude' stands for the thickness of the crust of the earth. This is the only place in the *Philosophia* and one of the very few in any of his writings where Linnaeus makes a reference, and then only obliquely, to fossils. The existence of fossil plants and animals was known to him but never influenced his thinking to any extent. However, he did raise elsewhere the question of the time lapse indicated by the fossils. Nathorst (1908) points at Linnaeus's vague but real presentiment as to the length of geological time, for instance in the following quotations and translations from the *Systema naturae* and the *Museum tessinianum*:

Fig. 12. Although headed *Sexus*, the first aphorism of this chapter of the *Philosophia botanica* deals with reproduction and dispersal rather than with the actual sexual processes.

[55]

"My mind reels when, on this height, I look down on the long ages that have flowed by like waves in the sound and have left traces of the ancient world, traces so nearly obscured that they can only whisper now that everything else has been silenced." And:

"Of what use are the great numbers of petrifactions, of different species, shape and form which are dug up by the naturalists? Perhaps the collection of such specimens is sheer vanity and inquisitiveness. I do not presume to say; but we find in our mountains the rarest animals, shells, mussels, and corals embalmed in stone, as it were, living specimens of which are now being sought in vain throughout Europe. These stones alone whisper in the midst of general silence."

"The infinite number of fossils of strange and unknown animals buried in the rock strata beneath the highest mountains, animals that no man of our age has beheld, are the only evidence of the inhabitants of our ancient earth at a period too remote for any historian to trace."

Buffon, and in his wake Adanson, went one step further. Buffon realized, because of the fossils, that living beings have a history in time. Linnaeus, however, (it has been said before) thought in timeless essentials. The fossils worried him though, as is evident from the above citations.

Aphorism 133 cites the evidence that both plants and animals *live*. The well known statement *Omne vivum ex ovo* applies also to plants (134). The fact that the seeds of plants are 'eggs' is shown by their 'End' (and Essence, in Aristotelian theology); this 'End' is the production of offspring conforming to the parents. Futhermore, reason and experience tell us that plants spring from eggs: the cotyledons confirm this (135). The cotyledons are the seed-lobes, filled with milk; they nourish the *plumula* as long as it has no roots: a function similar to that of the placenta or cotyledon of the animals (136). The fact that heredity does not spring from the egg alone, nor from the seminal liquid alone, but that it proceeds from both together is proved by hybrid animals, reason [sic] and anatomy (137). The examples for reason are: "hereditary deficiences, dogs, chickens." An egg must be fertilized before it can germinate (138).

The flower precedes the fruit as generation precedes delivery (141). The subsequent aphorisms contain a detailed description of the structure of the anthers and the stigma and a discussion of the actual proof that pollen fertilizes the pistil. The analogy between the floral parts and the animal genitalia is given, and some of the more subsidiary parts are sometimes presented in the light of striking analogies: the calyx is the nuptial bed (*thalamus*), the corolla the curtains (*aulaeum*) ... "the calyx might be regarded as the *labia majora* or the foreskin; one could regard the corolla as the *labia minora* (146).

"The earth is the belly of the plants; the *vasa chylifera* are the roots, the bones the stem, the lungs the leaves, the heart the heat; this is why the ancients called the plant an inverted animal." (147)

"Those who want to penetrate further into the mystery of the sex of plants should consult the 'Sponsalia plantarum'." (150). In this instance, in the *Philosophia* of 1751, Linnaeus refers back to his 1746 dissertation.

VI. CHARACTERES (151–209)

The *character* as understood by Linnaeus is the definition of a plant, expressing its essence. For our purposes we can best use the word 'diagnosis' for it. It definitely does not denote 'characteristic,' a single feature; for this Linnaeus uses the term *nota* (pl. *notae*). In his chapter entitled *characteres* Linnaeus discussess the basis of classification, the nature of the categories, the existence of certain character complexes, in short the theoretical foundation of descriptive botany. It is therefore one of the most important parts of the *Philosophia botanica*.

(151) "Botany has a double basis: classification (*dispositio*) and nomenclature (*denominatio*)." This statement is characteristic: it shows again Linnaeus's approach from the outside: classification and nomenclature are basic, no further botanical research is possible without them (fig. 13).
"The names of plants ought to be stable [*certa*], consequently they should be given to stable genera."
"Classification is the basis for nomenclature."
"Botanical science hinges upon these two points: within a year, at first sight, without teacher, without figures or descriptions, all plants are learned and constantly remembered: he who knows how to do this is a botanist, no one else is."
The role of memory in Linnaeus's concept of botanical science is very important. Since there are (or should be) stable genera, these should be remembered by the botanist; the device to remember them is classification.

[57]

Classification will succeed in this way only if it is free from all irrelevant descriptive details and restricted to essentials. This extremely narrow view of nature is understandable only through Linnaeus's Aristotelian approach. Classification is a frame of reference which must be at the disposal of each botanist by memory; further research is useless without it because the scientist will then lose sight of the 'essence.' The strong brake put upon the development of science by essentialism becomes clear. However, Linnaeus himself did not confine his empirical approach to nature within these narrow limits. This becomes clear when he introduces the concept of 'practical classification' in his next aphorism (152):

"Classification shows the divisions or the affinities of the plants; it is either *theorethical*, instituting the classes, orders and genera, or *practical*, establishing the species and the varieties."

"The classification of plants on the basis of the fructification is an invention of recent authorities."

"Practical classification is for those who know nothing about a system."

"Theory leads to system. Cesalpino, Morison, Tournefort and others elaborated it."

A strict translation of *dispositio vegetabilium divisiones s. conjunctiones docet* is 'arrangement teaches the divisions or conjunctions of plants' (cf. Cain 1958 p. 151). However, I prefer to use for Linnaeus's *dispositio* our word 'classification' because this is actually what he is talking about. Whether *docet* in this context means 'teaches' or 'shows' is a matter of taste. 'Conjunctions' is a somewhat difficult word in taxonomy; 'affinities' comes closer, because affinity is 'structural relationship,' and this is what Linnaeus means here. The conjunction is that which unites; division is its opposite. The use of these words shows again that Linnaeus applies here the principles of logical classification and division. The statements made in classification are 'per genus et differentiam,' by that which unites and by that which divides.

(153) "Plant classification is either *synoptic* or *systematic* and is usually called method."

Linnaeus's use of the word *methodus* here can be translated as method, provided it is realized that it comes close to our 'taxonomy.' The word

Fig. 13. The beginning of the chapter on 'characters' of the *Philosophia botanica* [1751]. Statement that botany has a double basis: classification (*dispositio*) and nomenclature (*denominatio*).

VI. CHARACTERES.

151. FUNDAMENTUM Botanices (4) duplex est: *Dispositio & Denominatio.*

Syst. nat. veget. 2. Fundamentum Botanices consistit in Plantarum Divisione & Denominatione Systematica: Generica & Specifica.

Class. plant. 4. Nomina plantarum debent esse certa, adeoque imposita certis Generibus.

Dispositio est Denominationis fundamentum.

Scientia Botanices his cardinibus nititur; Sic plantæ omnes uno anno, primo intuitu, absque præceptore, sine iconibus aut descriptionibus, constanti memoria addiscuntur. Ergo, qui hoc novit, Botanicus est, alius non.

152. DISPOSITIO (151) Vegetabilium divisiones s. conjunctiones docet; estque vel *Theoretica*, quæ Classe, Ordines, Genera; vel *Practica*, quæ Species & Varietates instituit.

Dispositio plantarum, ex fundamento fructificationis, recentiorum inventum est.

Practica ab eo potest tractari, qui de Systemate nihil intelligit.

Theoretica curam Systematis gerit; hanc *Cæsalpinus*, *Morisonus*, *Tournefortius* & alii excoluere.

153. Dispositio Vegetabilium (152) vel *Synoptice* vel *Systematice* absolvitur, & vulgo *Methodus* audit.

Synoptica divisio seculo XVI & XVII maxime in usu fuit.

Systematica vero seculo XVIII præcipue exculta fuit, incepta a Tournefortio & Rivino.

Methodici summi methodo *mathematica*, in scientia naturali, a simplicioribus ad composita adscendunt, adeoque incepere ab Algis, Muscis, Fungis, uti *Rajus*, *Boerhaavius* &c.

Naturalis instinctus docet nosse primum proxima & ultimo minutissima, e. gr. Homines, *Quadrupedia*, *Aves*, *Pisces*, *Insecta*, *Acaros*, vel primum *majores* plantas, ultimo minimos Muscos.

Natura ipsa sociat & conjungit *Lapides* & *Plantas*, *Plantas* & *Animalia*; hoc faciendo non connectit perfectissimas

G   Plan-

Fig. 13

methodicus is best rendered as taxonomist. Later use by French authors is different; Adanson, for instance, restricts the use of the word 'method' to the natural system; all artificial arrangements are 'systems' on the analogy of the use of that word in classificatory logic.

Linnaeus also discusses in this aphorism (153) the starting point of taxonomy: should we start with the higher plants and the higher animals, or with the simplest organisms?

"Famous taxonomists (*methodici*), adapting the method of mathematics to natural science, go up from the simple to the involved; they start therefore with the algae, the mosses, the fungi; as did Ray and Boerhaave."

"A natural instinct tells us to know first the objects which are closest to us, and the smallest ones last, for example: man, quadrupeds, birds, fishes, insects, mites; or first the *larger* plants and last the *tiny* mosses.

"Nature associates and unites stones and plants and animals; in doing this she does not connect the most perfect plants with the most imperfect animals, but she combines the imperfect animals with the imperfect plants ..."

The naturalists of the early eighteenth century often show a tendency to make man the standard of all things. Especially in animal taxonomy, we encounter classifications on the basis of the distance between man and the respective animals. Strongly empirical naturalists, such as Ray and Adanson, would not do so, but those whose approach was on an a priori, essentialist basis all start from man. This concept of man as the model of the universe did not stand the test of time: when Linnaeus wrote his *Philosophia* it was already out of date. The consequence of such an attitude is, as Daudin (1926, p. 110) has clearly pointed out, that the differences between organisms are not described in the form of a comparison of increased complexity or progress, but "in the form of a degradation, of a series of reductions of which formula and reason should be found by starting from that summum of organization." This anthropocentric view had a strong basis in the Christian philosophy of man as the image of God. God being the ultimate essence, it can be understood that essentialist thinking in natural history went downwards, from "ideal" to "low"; it was essentially static and timeless, because nobody would dream of stating that the lower forms had come about by degradation of the higher ones. This set of concepts was therefore one of the greatest barriers to the introduction of the time element in the life sciences: Linnaeus classified but was not a biologist in his taxonomy. His biological research was mainly restricted to that on sex.

(154) "*Synoptic* classification (*Synopsis*) gives arbitrary divisions which are either too long or too short, too numerous or too few; in general it should not be adopted by botanists."

"A *synopsis* is an arbitrary dichotomy which, like a road, leads toward botany but does not fix the boundary paths."

"A synoptic key to the classes is in accord with the art, to avoid confusing things which should be distinguished."

"Various taxonomists have followed this road [of synoptic classification]: Ray, Knaut, and others."

Linnaeus's sympathy does not rest with the synoptic approach. Such a synopsis, a more or less exhaustive description, does not differentiate between primary essentials and secondary properties: no description, but a diagnosis, is required. The trouble is that Linnaeus is so firmly convinced that one knows beforehand which are the essentials: the rejection of the synoptic method is based upon this conviction.

The opposite, for Linnaeus commendable, method of plant classification is *systematic*:

(155) "System breaks the classes up into five appropriate categories ['system has five categories (levels) of classes' is actually what is meant, class being used here in a general sense]: Classes [special sense], orders, genera, species and varieties."

"Examples taken from other sciences make this clear: Geography: Kingdom, province, territory, parish, village, Military: Regiment, company, platoon, squad, soldier, Philosophy: Genus summum, genus intermedium, genus proximum, species, individuum, Botany: Classis, ordo, genus, species, varietas."

The philosophical terms are those in use in classificatory logic; logical division (taking a genus and distinguishing species within it) and logical classification (bringing the species together in genera) are the opposite operations of classificatory logic. In logical division the 'genus summum' is the principal category, the other terms denote divisions of a lower rank. Cain (1959, p. 150) has pointed out that Linnaeus's parallel is not quite correct: logical division deals with universals, never with the individual. At the lowest rank in the classificatory hierarchy are the species infimae, not the individuals. Apart from this the examples are enlightening:

[61]

the five main ranks of taxonomic categories are class, order, genus, species and variety, in close parallel to the *genus summum*, the *genera intermedia* and the *species infima* which in Linnaeus's day were part of the philosophical terminology learned at school.

In a commentary on these categories Linnaeus states: "Botany owes the limits of those families to Tournefort," using 'familia' for category at any level (rank). Tournefort was indeed one of the first to use the categories class, ordo and genus in such a way that the taxa within these ranks were actually equivalent.

Linnaeus is of the opinion that a synoptic classification proceeds by strict dichotomy, whereas in a systematic classification division may be by any number, hence the following, at first sight somewhat surprising explanation of how the systematic treatment, with only five levels, provides a greater number of slots for classification than the synoptic:

"Synoptic: a 2; b 4; c 8; d 16; e 32,

Systematic: a 10; b 100; c 1000; d 10.000; e 100.000."

(156) "System is Ariadne's clew for botany without which all [the kingdom of plants] is chaos."

One of the most frequently quoted aphorisms. There is no doubt that Linnaeus's orderly mind herewith grasped the first need of botany of his time: there should be an internationally acceptable device which would enable all botanists to reach the same conclusions with respect to the same animals or plants, making their work, in general, comparable. The symbol is very telling: "System (that device) is Ariadne's clew": an extraneous element brought into the maze; the classification is not based on the maze itself. Again: the difference between the artificial and the natural, the anthropocentric and the empirical approach. However, when the object is merely storage and retrieval of information, this is irrelevant; important here is that 'system' (in Linnaeus's sense the hierarchy of categories used to classify, not the system in today's sense of the word, i.e. the result of classification) enables quick identification:

"Take for instance an unknown plant from the Indies, a 'botanophile' will look through descriptions [the word is actually used!], illustrations, all indexes, but he will not find its name except by pure chance; a taxonomist, however, will soon establish the genus, whether the old one or the new."

"The system indicates even the plants that have been omitted; this is something which an enumeration in a catalogue will never achieve."

Here and elsewhere Linnaeus uses the argument that a diagnostic and consistent system will accommodate all taxa and immediately identify the newcomers. The rather pitiful kind of synoptic treatment described by him certainly does not fulfil this requirement; however, this is more a question of quality than of principle.

(157) "We count as many species as there were forms created in the beginning." [fig. 14].

This famous aphorism is spelled out even more clearly in the next part (cited as of "Class. plant. 5"):

"There are as many species as the infinite being created diverse forms in the beginning, which, following the laws of generation, produced many others, but always similar to them: therefore there are as many species as we have different structures before us today."

"Evidence against the occurrence of new species is offered by continuous generation, propagation, daily observations, the cotyledones."

This dogma of special creation was old-fashioned even when Linnaeus formulated it for the first time in his *Fundamenta* of 1736, let alone in 1751. Later in life he formulated an entirely different theory which involved several thousands of specially created prototypes and which allowed for speciation by hybridization (see below).

Even though special creation was a conspicuous feature of Linnaeus's thinking, the fixity of genera was really primary in his method. The constancy of species is an illustration of Linnaeus's adherence to religious principles, but he could easily modify this later without modifying his method because it is the genus around which Linnaean taxonomy revolves.

The examples illustrating this aphorism are numerous but not very convincing. Linnaeus knew of Marchant's discovery of a mutation in *Mercurialis* and had himself been temporarily shaken in his belief by the discovery of the *Peloria* (1744, see also Linnell 1953). By 1751, however, faith had almost reasserted itself. In that year he also published his *Plantae hybridae*. In later years Linnaeus's doubts were revived: he was for instance deeply interested in Duchesne's simple-leaved strawberry (*Fraisier de Versailles*) (Hylander 1945).

(158) "There are as many varieties as there are plants produced by the seed of the same species."

In a way this is an excellent statement of the essential meaning of biological variation, but it is clearly only a coincidence. Linnaeus drew the wrong conclusion from the phenomenon of variation: he considered it absolutely unimportant. In his opinion varieties are all what is now called phenotypic: "a variety is a plant changed by an accidental cause due to climate, soil, heat, winds, and it returns to its original state when the soil [etc.] is changed."

"Varieties can be excluded from the kingdom of plants, except that
"The commercial plant growers prize the showy and crisp plants,
"The gardeners esteem the double-flowered and colourful ones,
"The physicians esteem those which are savory and fragrant."

The next aphorism (159) contains the really fundamental assumption of Linnaean thought and method: the naturalness and the fixity of genera. We shall encounter this in several places, e.g. in (209): "botany is based on fixed genera ..."

The constancy of species, accepted axiomatically, does not necessarily entail a fixity of genera. We have already seen that Linnaeus has a nominalist attitude towards classes and orders: "They are the work of science and art." We may then ask: why not also the genera? Basically the answer lies with Linnaeus's conviction that genera are natural: all species with the same geometrical disposition of the parts of the flower and fruit belong to one genus. It is unimportant how many species may have to be united in a genus: all those with the same 'construction' (cf. Daudin 1926, p. 35–36) must be united in one genus. Linnaeus formalized here a development which had started out with the use of *genus* for any comprehensive group but had been narrowed to denote a more or less fixed rank in a hierarchy of categories. The first to delimit the genera of plants is often said to have been Tournefort. This is certainly the case with respect to the uniform treatment of generic descriptions. The stabilization of the use of the term 'genus,' however, is found in varying degree with many authors, of whom Magnol and Ray are conspicuous examples.

The 'theoretical' classification, that is that of genera, orders and classes, as opposed to the 'practical' classification of species and varieties is evidently of superior importance for Linnaeus. Still in many respects his attitude towards the genus is different from that towards orders and classes. The

Fig. 14. The statement on the constancy of species in aphorism 157 of the *Philosophia botanica* [1751].

Veri fyftematici Auctores f. Inventores probe a Compilatoribus diftinguendi.

Syftema etiam omiffas indicat per fe plantas, quod nunquam Catalogi enumeratio.

157. SPECIES (155) tot numeramus, quot diverfæ formæ in principio funt creatæ

Claff. plantar. 5. Species tot funt, quot diverfas formas ab initio produxit Infinitum Ens; quæ formæ, fecundum generationis inditas leges, produxere plures, at fibi femper fimiles. Ergo fpecies tot funt, quot diverfæ formæ f. ftructuræ hodienum occurrunt.

Oratio de *Telluris habitabilis incremento.* Upf. & Leyd. edita, confequentias plurimas fuper hóc argumentum edocuit.

Radix extenditur in herbam inque infinitum, usque dum apice rumpantur integumenta in fl rem, formantque femen contiguum, ultimum terminum vegetationis; Hoc femen cadit, prognafcitur, & in diverfo loco quafi plantam continuat; hinc fimillimam fobolem producit, uti Arbor ramum, Ramus gemmam, Gemma herbam; ergo Continuatio eft Generatio plantarum.

Novas Species dari in vegetabilibus negat generatio continuata, propagatio, obfervationes quotidianæ, Cotyledones

Dubium movere *Marchant. act. parif.* 1719; Ego in *Peloria* 1744; *Gmelinus* in *orat. inaugur.* 1749. vide *Amænit. acad.* 71.

Nymphoides T. Herba *Nymphææ*, fructificatio *Menyanthis.*
Datifca, mas *Cannabis*;   femina *Refeda.*
Tragopogon Hort. upf. 3. quafi ex patre *Lapfana.*
Hyofcyamus Hort. upf. 2, - - - - *Phyfalide.*
Poterium Hort. upf. 2. - - - - - *Agrimonia.*
Saxifraga Fl. fuec. 358. - - - - *Parnaffia.*
Dracocephalum Hort. upf. 6. - - - *Nepeta.*
Primulæ fp. alpina - - - - - *Cortufa.*
Carduus Hort. upf. I. degenerans in *Carduum Pyrenaicum.*
Mefembryanthema numerofa ad *Caput Bonæ Spei.*
Gerania africana, conformia flore, ad *Cap. bon. fpei.*
Cacti omnes in fola *America.*
Aloë numerofiffimæ in *Africa.*
Varietates fingulares numerofæ. *Tournef. corollar.*
Verbena virginica nobis obfervata.

         Delphi-

Fig. 14

genus is 'natural' and 'fixed,' provided one uses the correct criteria (configuration of the fructification). This is hardly the case with the higher categories, which are much more dependent upon 'art' than upon 'nature.'

Aphorism 159 can be read as follows:

"We admit as many genera as there are different [rather: groups of] natural species of which the fructification has the same structure." "*Cesalpino*: If the genera are confused, everything is confused by necessity."

"*Class. plant. 6.* Revelation, discovery and observation confirm that all genera and species are natural."

"*Syst. nat. veg. 14.* Every genus is natural and created as such in the beginning; genera should neither be divided nor united because of the fancy of one's will, or in favour of one's theory."

"Examples are provided by the *Ranunculi*, the *Aconitia*, ... the *Hibisci*, *Passiflorae*, and endless others, especially a posteriori."

A series of remarkable statements. Even though the establishment of the genera is said to be 'theoretical,' they are at the same time said to have been created as such. The naturalness of genera and species is evidently synonymous with their special creation. 'Revelation' is cited as confirming this fact, in addition to 'discovery and observation.' Which is primary? In theory, undoubtedly revelation; however, the mind of the keen observer Linnaeus was perhaps more open for 'discovery and observation' and for the purely practical need for stability in taxonomy and nomenclature. Cesalpino's dictum about the 'confusion of genera' occurs in many places in Linnaeus's works. The practical systematist realized the dire need for a constancy of genera and species. Revelation could possibly be of some help here.

(160) "A class is an agreement of several genera in the parts of their fructifications in accordance with the principles of nature and art."

A nominalistic and practical definition: the class is a convenience. However, there are also natural classes:

"The fact that there are natural classes, created as such, is proved frequently: Umbellifers, Labiatae, Cruciferae, Leguminosae, Compositae, Grasses, etc."

"The artificial classes will take the place of natural ones until the latter have all been discovered. This will take place on the basis of the discovery of many new genera; the delimitation of the classes will then be difficult."

"When imitating nature one must guard against losing the clew of Ariadne, as did Morison and Ray."

Linnaeus stresses the fact that many genera are still to be discovered. The ones he knows now are distinct and 'natural'; he evidently does not expect this picture to change when all genera are known.

As Cain has pointed out, there is always the theoretical possibility that when our knowledge of the genera is complete we shall find that there are no gaps. In fact the principle of plenitude requires this, and in other places Linnaeus himself speaks of the taxa as neighbouring countries on a map of the world. The principle of plenitude, by itself timeless, has received an entirely different meaning through the theory of evolution. To Linnaeus, the idea that genera might be arbitrary because they are phylogenetically connected could not occur. An ambivalent attitude, however, cannot be denied.

Even more geared towards practical purposes is the definition of *ordo*: (161) "An order is a subdivision of classes needed to avoid the possibility of having more genera to be distinguished at one and the same time than the mind can easily follow."

"An order is a subdivision of the classes; for it is easier to distinguish ten than a hundred."

A summing up of the position is given in aphorism 162: "The *species* and the *genus* are always the work of nature [i.e. specially created]; the *variety* mostly that of circumstance [Linnaeus says 'of cultivation', of the way it grows]; the *class* and the *order* are the work of nature and art."

"The species are extremely constant (*constantissimae*) because their reproduction constitutes a real continuation."

"One becomes convinced of the naturalness of the genera through observation of various plants: ... the *Aconita* ...."

"Gardening proves that varieties are the work of cultivation ..."

"The natural orders [referring to no. 77, fragments of the natural method] show that most of the classes and orders are natural."

Revelation has been dropped: a plain empirical attitude is at the basis of these statements.

The next aphorism (163), on the 'habitus' of plants, occupies twelve pages. 'Habitus' is the sum of all characteristics *not* derived from the fructification.

Linnaeus stresses that Bauhin and the classical botanists were sometimes

[67]

extremely successful in establishing the affinities of plants on the basis of these characteristics. He admits that the systematists sometimes divided what they would have brought together, correctly, if they had let themselves be guided by the 'habitus.' He repeats: "The natural method is the ultimate aim of botany." "The fructification, a recent invention, has opened a road towards this natural method, but so far it has not yet been used widely enough to discover all classes ...."

From the previous aphorism (162) it is clear that Linnaeus believes also in specially created natural classes and that these, as is the case with genera and species, can best be found by using the characteristics derived from the flower and fruit. Sometimes, however, other characteristics point in the same direction; they may provide a shortcut to the 'natural method.'

We should not forget, however, that notwithstanding the remarks on 'affinity,' Linnaeus's idea of a 'natural method' is not that of later times, because it is not based on *overall* affinities. The natural method in the Linnaean sense distinguishes and recognizes the specially created (and therefore called 'natural') species, genera and classes. The way to recognize these entities is that of logical division: the determination of the essences. In view of the fact that 'natural' stands for 'special creation' in 'natural' taxa and for 'essence' in 'natural method,' it is not possible to say that Linnaeus's' idea of a natural system is that of later usage. The results of the two approaches—that of Linnaeus by means of 'essences' and that of Adanson and others by means of 'overall affinity'—are comparable in many ways because so much of the involved structure of the fructification which determines the essence plays a role in this overall affinity. These more or less comparable results, however, should not obscure their fundamental philosophical differences. The most important of these differences is that the approach by way of overall affinity opened the road for the introduction of the time element, for a biological approach, ultimately responsible for the growth of the idea of evolution. The essentialist approach, however, was dogmatic and antibiological; it barred the way towards evolutionary biology. Several commentators, such as Sachs (1875), have made too much of the comparable results, and have paid too little attention to the background thought. Linnaeus stimulated botany by his pragmatic order, but his arguments contained little 'biology.'

The greater part of aphorism 163 treats the descriptive terminology of various character complexes other than the fructification. The treatment of the *placentatio* deserves mention. *Placentatio* is here the 'disposition' of the cotyledons upon germination. There are four classes: acotyledones, monocotyledones, dicotyledones and polycotyledones (Gymnosperms). No further conclusions are drawn.

(164) The primary (and most commendable) classification of plants is based solely on the fructification. Previous authors had an incomplete knowledge of the parts of the fructification, found it insufficient as a basis of classification and consequently neglected it; but Linnaeus, convinced of the contrary, made much use of it. All genera which are not based exclusively on the fructification are therefore fictitious. This statement shows again the essentialist character of Linnaeus's ideas on natural genera.

In support of his thesis Linnaeus cites a great many 'fictitious' genera and indicates in what natural genera they belong. It is not surprising that the majority of them are now indeed recognized as independent genera. He also cites instances of genera of similar *habitus* but different fructification, such as *Malus* and *Pyrus*, *Cerasus* and *Prunus*, etc. Many of these are now, ironically enough, generally considered congeneric.

After the true fashion of the exercises in Aristotelian logic, Linnaeus also presents the inversions of his theses:

(165) "Whatever plants agree in the structure of their fructification must not, other things being equal, be divided in theoretical classification.

"This supreme discovery in botany belongs to Gesner; Cesalpino introduced it, Morison revived it and Tournefort worked it out."

The second paragraph is an oversimplification. Gesner certainly did not base his theory exclusively on the fructification, Cesalpino did, Morison certainly not, and Tournefort only on the grounds of purely pragmatic considerations.

(166) The opposite: "Whatever plants, on the basis of correct observations, are seen to differ in the parts of their fructifications, must not be united."

(167) "Each characteristic must be taken from the number, figure, proportion and situation of all the different parts of the fructification," in agreement with aphorism 92, in which these four 'dimensions' were first mentioned. Linnaeus uses the term *nota* or *nota characteristica* for what is at present called character or characteristic. The Linnaean 'character' is the definition, the statement of the essence, the 'diagnostic description.'

In his chapter on the descriptive terminology of the fructification Lin-

[69]

naeus describes no fewer than 38 independent characteristics which can be used in taxonomy. Each of those can be described in number, figure, situation and proportion. The number of combinations is therefore, always according to Linnaeus, $38 \times 38 \times 4$, that is, 5776. Consequently, the fructification is sufficient to describe at least 5776 genera "which [may] never exist." It was "therefore wrong to admit as characteristics habitus, colour, height, cotyledons, etc., with certain exceptions."

A somewhat shaky aphorism: it is not necessary to discuss the advantages of using the fructification if the essence of a taxon must be deduced from it; furthermore it is not clear at first sight why, if using the fructification is simply convenient, one should not use other characteristics as well. The next aphorism (168) makes allowance for the exceptions:

"One must consult the habitus secretly, under the table (so to speak) in order to avoid the formation of incorrect genera."

"Experience ['experientia' is *not* experiment here], a guide in everything, often allows us to guess at first sight the families [sic] of plants on the basis of their external appearance."

"Examples confirm the rule..."

"Very often a trained botanist distinguishes at first sight plants from Africa, Asia, America and the Alps, though he himself could not easily say by what character he does so. Why are those from Africa sinister, dry and sombre, why those from Asia superb and exalted, those from America gay and brilliant, those from the Alps tight and hardened?" Linnaeus's imagination, not overly developed, here seems to run away with him.

One must make a very circumspect use of the habitus, to avoid including it among the true characteristics and delimiting the genera too narrowly. But examples are given in which *characteres habituales*, though not sufficient in themselves, do in fact characterize an order.

(169) "Characteristics which establish a genus in one case, are not necessarily of the same importance in another genus."

(170) "One rarely finds a genus in which there is not some aberrant part of the fructification."

"Many fictitious genera have been founded because species differed in some part of the fructification..."

"If one does not observe this rule one will witness the introduction of as many genera as there are species..."

Aphorisms (168), (169) and (170) show a practical approach. Evidently the

[70]

use of the *habitus* is admissible because it provides a good check on the circumscription of the 'natural' genus. In the aphorisms which follow it is said that the variation may differ in the different parts and that, if the flowers are the same, a genus should not be split off solely because of the fruit. The value of a characteristic may be different in different genera.

Linnaeus worked therefore to some extent with correlation of characteristics, with character–complexes, as did the later adherents of the natural system. Here again we find a practical convergence with more modern systematics, even though Linnaeus's basic principles were entirely different. Cain (1926, p. 159) quotes a letter from Linnaeus filius to Abraham Baeck, dated 21 April 1778, which confirms this interpretation of Linnaeus's actual practice (translated by Cain). Latin words, here in parenthesis, are supplied in the letter to explain the Swedish words:

"My father's secret art of determining (delimiting) genera in such a way that species should not become genera? This was no other than his practice in knowing a plant from its external appearance (externa facie). Therefore he often deviated from his own principles in such a way that variation as to the number of parts (numero partium) did not disturb him, if only the character of the genus (character generis) could be preserved. Foreigners don't do so, but as soon as a plant has a different splitting (cleavage) of the corolla and calyx, or if the number of stamens and pistils (numerus staminum et pistillorum) varies, they make a new genus. This is what Aublet, Forster and others have done. If possible he (Linnaeus) tried to build the character genericus on the cleavage of the fruit, so that all species that constitute a genus should have the same shape of their fruit."

This is clearly a departure from strict logical division, a departure in favour of an approach based on overall affinity. There is conflict between the clear, sharp and practical rules of logical division and the overwhelming profusion of nature. Nature, in its fullness and complexity, does not always admit an 'entweder oder,' a 'tertium non datur.' The conflict is an old one and can be stated in admittedly too simplistic terminology as that of Aristotelian versus Platonic, logic versus plenitude.

The outcome of this conflict varies with each author. Linnaeus, notwithstanding his strong aprioris, partly on a religious basis, was too good an observer to be fully their slave. In practice he often worked as an empirical systematist, hence his success in recognizing natural groups.

[71]

In a previous aphorism (105) Linnaeus had pointed out the existence of what he calls 'singular' (special) fructifications: those showing highly specialized characteristics occurring in relatively few taxa. Aphorism 171 states that some special characteristic will be found in almost every genus. If such a very special characteristic is not present in all species of a genus (172) one has to be careful not to compose several different genera. A highly specialized characteristic is of great taxonomic importance: the two little horns on the anthers of *Erica* distinguish this genus from the otherwise very similar *Andromeda*.

(174) "The more constantly a feature of the fructification appears among several species, the more certain is its value as a generic character..."

"The corolla of *Cassia* is constant, not the pod..."

(175) "In some genera one part of the fructification is most constant, in others another, but none is entirely constant."

(176) "If the flowers are in agreement although the fruits differ, other things being equal, one must unite the genera."

These aphorisms also illustrate the tendency of Linnaeus to take into account the overall affinity as shown by co-variation of characteristics and to beware of attributing too much importance to single exceptions. He discusses details and examples in the aphorisms 177–185.

The Definition. The remaining part (186–209) of this chapter on what Linnaeus calls the 'character' contains a detailed methodological discussion of the nature of the definition (diagnostic description) and of the way to establish it. In order to avoid confusion I use here the word 'definition' where Linnaeus uses 'character,' except in no. 186. We have seen that the definition is a statement of the essence, or a 'diagnostic description', in more modern terms:

(186) "The 'character' is the definition of the genus, it is threefold: the *facticious*, the *essential* and the *natural*."

"The *'generic character'* is the same as the *definition of the genus.*"

"The habitual character, based on the habitus of the plant, is the one used by the ancients; after the discovery of the fructification, however, it has become obsolete for the description of genera."

(187) "The essential definition attributes to the genus to which it applies a characteristic which is very particularly restricted to it, and which is 'special' (cf. no. 105)."

"The essential definition distinguishes, by means of a unique idea, each genus from its neighbours in the same natural order."

"The shorter a definition, the better."

"It is simple to learn the plants by their essential definition."

(188) "The facticious definition distinguishes a genus only from the other genera in an artificial order."

(189) "The natural definition lists all possible generic characters; and so it includes the essential and the factitious definitions...."

"I was the first who wrote down ('composed') these definitions."

"The natural definition unites all other possible definitions, it is useful for any system, it lays the basis for new ones, it remains unaltered notwithstanding the discovery of an infinity of new genera."

(190) "The factitious definition is a temporary substitute, the essential is the best but hardly possible in every case; the natural definition is very difficult to establish, but once established it is the basis of all systems, the infallible guardian of all genera, applicable to every system that is possible and true."

"I have given the natural definitions in my 'Genera plantarum'..."

The last statement, though printed only in small type, contains the real explanation for this variety of definitions. A definition geared to a single artificial system is evidently useless for more general purposes. It is facticious. Linnaeus's 'essential definition' is more involved. In principle, species, genera and families are specially created, and therefore natural entities. We can know them only through their 'essences,' that is, the features which make them what they are and without which they would be different phenomena altogether. The knowledge of the 'essence' of the 'natural' taxa, however, is not easily gathered: the profusion of life is too great. Sheer experience teaches us that theoretically we may be convinced of the existence of the essence, but in practice we often have difficulty in grasping it. The botanist must therefore bring together in his definition all characteristics (of the fructification, sic!) which distinguish the genus from others. Later, when we know all the genera, some of those characteristics will prove to constitute the essential definition. At this state of our knowledge, however, this is impossible.

This is what Linnaeus calls his *character naturalis*. It is true that it permits the setting up of any artificial system based upon the whole or part of the fructification; it is true also that it is the 'infallible guardian of all the genera,' because Linnaeus himself had laid down the requirement that

[73]

genera are to be based solely on the characteristics of the fructification.

The term *character naturalis* has often been misunderstood. In principle, it has nothing whatsoever to do with a natural system, or with an expression of natural affinities. On the contrary, it is a definition uniting all the admissible characteristics of a 'natural,' i.e. specially created, taxon, a taxon distinct by its nature, by the way it was 'born' (created).

The natural definition, however, unites in fact a great many characteristics of high information content. As a result, many of Linnaeus's genera are 'natural' in any sense! It should be pointed out, however, that it was not really Linnaeus who produced for the first time consistently composed definitions (diagnoses) and therefore comparable descriptions of genera. The honor for this goes to the pragmatic empiricist Tournefort.

The use of the words 'nature' and 'natural' by Linnaeus is always bound up in some way with the uniqueness of the relevant item through creation: they have no bearing on relations or affinities between taxa.

Linnaeus stresses correctly that one of the main services rendered by the natural definitions is to distinguish clearly and rapidly between the new and the old. If one builds a system only on facticious or essential definitions, one is in trouble as soon as one deals with a new genus. A system must allow for recognition and placement of all new genera. This is possible only if the system has as its basis comprehensive diagnoses of the genera, clearly and at all times delimiting the one from the other in a uniform way. It is mainly for these reasons that Linnaeus states in the next aphorism (191):

"The natural definition ought to be memorised by every botanist."

"The natural definition is the basis of the genera; without it one cannot wisely judge any of them: it is and will remain therefore the absolute basis of the knowledge of plants."

One of Linnaeus's main points is that a botanist can and must know all genera, and must memorize their 'definitions.' The natural definitions given in the various editions of the *Genera plantarum* are intended to facilitate this.

It is not a simple task to give good natural definitions of genera (192). One must have a profound knowledge of the constituent species and one must use all parts of the fructification. Even those characteristics which cannot be seen by the naked eye but only with a 'microscope' ('which, however, should be used sparingly') must be used, because without a knowledge of the fructification no certainty is possible regarding the genus. No generic definition is infallible (193) until it has been checked against all species of the genus. In this respect it is interesting to quote (from Svenson's translation, 1953) part of the preface to the *Genera plantarum* of 1737:

"Genera are as many as there are common attributes next (in rank) to those of distinct species, such as were created in the beginning: this is confirmed by revelation, experiment, and observation. Hence *all genera and species are natural*. We must attentively and assiduously by observation inquire into the limits of genera. These limits may be difficult to determine, but *confusion in genera means confusion in everything*. Natural genera being assumed, there are two requirements for maintaining them sound: that only true species and no others be placed in the genus; that each true genus be circumscribed by limits and terms which we call the *generic character*. No authority except dissection in the herbarium should be acknowledged."

Aphorisms 194–201 of the *Philosophia* give practical advice on the drafting of generic definitions and the use of the proper terminology.

The insistence on the 'natural definition' is in fact aimed at stability in taxonomy. If there is general agreement on the circumscription of the genera, it will be much simpler to memorize them. A new system will then not automatically entail a change in generic definitions. The higher categories are always less definite and open to dispute; the species are too numerous to be remembered. True stability will therefore be achieved by agreement on the genera, not only in taxonomy but also in nomenclature.

The rules for the generic definition hold also for classes (204), although one can be somewhat less strict. The statement "The genus of the genera is the order, but the genus of the orders is the class" is a strict application of the principles and terminology of classificatory logic. A move in the direction of nominalism is:

(205) "The class is more arbitrary than the genus and the order more than the one or the other." This statement shows that Linnaeus still had a very artificial system in mind, in which the orders especially were rather arbitrary. There are of course 'natural classes' such as the Orchids and the Malvaceae, and here one has to be careful not to take the natural class for a single huge genus. However: "the more natural the classes are, the more valuable they are, other things being equal" (206), and it is the main task of the botanist to find and describe them.

Three main obstacles had stood in the way of progress towards a natural method:

"The contempt for the 'habitus,' ever since the doctrine of the fructifica-

[75]

tion came into force, and especially the failure to use the aestivation."

"The absence of foreign genera as yet undiscovered."

"The affinity of genera to more than one natural group."

It is remarkable to see Linnaeus plead here for the use of characters not derived from the fructification. His discovery that aestivation of buds has a high taxonomic value (discussed in aphorism 163 no. VI) certainly lent support to this clear recognition of the need for and possibilities of a 'natural system' in the Linnaean sense.

Classes and orders should not be too large (207) because they will then be less useful. The orders should always bring closely related genera together without exception. The arrangement of the genera within an order should always be in conformity with their 'natural' affinities: for instance (example cited by Linnaeus) the *Tetrandria monogynia* unite the natural orders of the *Rubiaceae (Stellatae)*, *Onagraceae (Calycanthema)* and *Aggregatae* (this is not really a natural group in the modern sense). In the *Genera plantarum* and *Species plantarum* we find that the genera are indeed often arranged in accordance with the order given in Linnaeus's *Fragmenta*. The order of the genera inside the classes of the sexual system is, of course, not at all arbitrary but in agreement with an arrangement which is based on overall affinity of the characters of the fructification.

I do not know whether any analysis has ever been made of the way in which Linnaeus arranged his genera within the classes of his sexual system. The example of the *Tetrandria monogynia* is very striking; a further comparison between the order in which Linnaeus lists the genera in his 'natural orders' and in the orders of his sexual system is even more revealing. The sexual system accommodates of course all genera, many of which are not found listed in the *Fragmenta* because their place is still obscure. It is evident, however, that Linnaeus used a considerable amount of information on character complexes in the arrangement of the genera in the sexual system.

This chapter on the 'generic definition' closes with a final statement that *botany rests on fixed genera* and with lists of the new genera described by various authors. This list shows more clearly than any other that Linnaeus made good use of the Tournefortian genera; still, Linnaeus's own contribution is not forgotten:

"I have examined all these genera according to the principles of the art, I have reformed the definitions and I have, so to speak, erected a new building."

VII–X. NOMENCLATURE (210–324)

In the *Critica botanica* Linnaeus worked out the rules of nomenclature as given in the *Fundamenta botanica*. These are the aphorisms 210–324 of the *Philosophia botanica*, comprising chapters VII (*nomina*), VIII (*differentia*), IX (*variationes*), and X (*synonymia*) in both these works as well as in the *Philosophia botanica*. These four chapters, as well as their further elaboration (especially for specific names) are dealt with in my next chapters. First a few paragraphs on the remaining chapters of the *Philosophia*.

The first part of the *Philosophia*, chapters I–VI, discussed above, contains the hard core of Linnaean thought, as well as his descriptive terminology. Chapters VIII–X deal with the nomenclature, chapters XI–XII with the natural history and properties of plants.

XI–XII. THE NATURAL HISTORY OF PLANTS ('ADUMBRATIONES') AND THEIR PROPERTIES (325–365)

The Linnaean use of the word *adumbrationes* is somewhat broader than 'natural history,' but his chapter with this heading deals essentially with the descriptions, illustrations, habitats and life cycle. In addition Linnaeus counts as adumbrations (325) the whole complex of nomenclature and definitions.

Aphorisms 326–331 deal with the *description*. A description, in the Linnaean sense, is the combination of the natural definition of a plant [i.e. the description of its fructification] with the summing up of the characteristics of all other parts. When drawing up such a description one should not limit oneself (as accepted usage had done) to the root, the stem, the leaves and the fructification, but one should also examine duly the petioles, peduncles, stipules, bracts, glands, hairs, buds, aestivation and all that is 'habitus' (326). The description can be kept brief by using the adequate terminology (327) and should follow the order in which the parts are developed in the life cycle (328). A number of practical guide lines are given to insure that the descriptions will be of the appropriate length, clearly worded in systematically arranged paragraphs and provided with measures based on the palm of the hand.

The *illustrations* must be of natural size [easier said than done] and show

[77]

the natural position of the parts. "A painter, an engraver and a botanist (332) are all equally necessary to produce a good illustration; if one of them goes wrong, the illustration will be wrong in some respect. Hence botanists who have practiced the arts of painting and engraving along with botany have left us the most outstanding illustrations."

The paragraphs on *habitat* and *life cycle* are very detailed and provide descriptive terminology, often surprisingly original.

Stearn (1955, 1966) has repeatedly drawn attention to the importance of Linnaeus's contributions to descriptive botanical terminology. Linnaeus was a master of the art of *stipulative definition*, the process of deliberately and arbitrarily choosing a term for a certain concept. "Linnaeus's mission being to record in an ordinary manner the works of the Creator, he had to do so with precision, clarity and conciseness—with precision, because of his respect for facts and because to do otherwise would be misinterpreting the Creator's work; with clarity, because he wished to be widely under-stood; with conciseness because otherwise he would never have got through so massive a task, nor have achieved publication." (Stearn 1955).

In his *Fundamenta* and his *Philosophia* Linnaeus laid the foundation for what is today called 'botanical Latin.' This terminological reform cannot be pursued any further here, but it may be said to have contributed heavily to the success of Linnaeus's ideas and methods.

The twelfth chapter of the *Philosophia*, on properties (*vires*), also lists many details, but is hardly of interest for the pursuit of Linnaean thought. The chapter ends the main part of the book (there are some appendices* with the words (also cited above):

"In the science of nature observation ought to confirm the principles of truth."

Linnaeus could not have expressed more concisely his basic dilemma: there are a priori principles of truth, and as such they need no confirma-tion. In natural history, however, empiricism had taught him that these 'principles of truth' are not so easily grasped a priori and that they are subject to the tests of unbiassed observation. A priori logical pragmatism interacts with the appreciation of the infinite diversity of nature.

---

* These include ten plates with captions illustrating descriptive terminology and separate lists of aphorisms for or on the pupil, the herbarium, botanical excursions, the garden, the botanist, and the 'metamorphosis of plants.'

[78]

3

Linnaean nomenclature and collections

1. Philosophia and Critica

The binary names of species are most conspicuous in Linnaean nomenclature. Thanks to the introduction of what he called the 'trivial names,' the single specific epithets, Linnaeus's thought and books dominated the world of taxonomy for nearly a century. The binary names were code designations, like the generic names themselves, and this is exactly the reason why they were so successful. Their introduction, however, was to a certain extent accidental, and it constituted a conspicuous departure from the almost sacred Aristotelian–scholastic process of definition *per genus et differentiam*. It may now seem difficult to understand why a uninomial code designation was acceptable for a genus and not for a species. We have seen that, according to Linnaeus, all genera can be known; they are basic and for that reason they have a 'name.' The species could be defined only with respect to the genus. The step from differential definition (phrase–name) to code designation (trivial name) was difficult for psychological reasons. This had not always been the case: in pre–Cesalpinian botany this was no problem, but then of course the principles of logical division were not yet applied so strictly.

The accidental nature of the introduction of the 'trivial names' is responsible for the circumstance that they play no rôle in the *Fundamenta botanica* or in the *Critica botanica*, the elaboration of the nomenclatural chapters of the *Fundamenta*. The *Philosophia* of 1751 contains a brief but important reference to them.

Because of the dominant rôle of the genus in Linnaean taxonomy, the nomenclature of the genera is treated in all three works in the first instance and in great detail. Linnaeus's ideas on nomenclature (except then for the trivial names) are elaborated most clearly in the *Critica botanica* of 1737, an

[79]

English translation of which is generally available (Hort 1938). For our purpose, the tracing of Linnaean thought and method, we follow mainly the more concise and mature *Philosophia botanica*. When discussing the Linnaean generic reform (see below p. 91), however, we shall follow the *Critica*.

Aphorisms 210–255 of the *Philosophia* deal with 'nomina' (chapter VII), mostly generic names; numbers 252–255 deal with names of orders and classes. The next chapter (VIII) is entitled 'differentia' and comprises aphorisms 256–305 dealing mainly with the specific names (phrase names) but also with the specific characters. Aphorisms 306–317 (chapter IX) treat the varieties and 318–324 (chapter X) the synonyms. These four chapters constitute the Linnaean rules of botanical nomenclature, with some additional material on differentiating characteristics.

As in the previous chapter, I give more or less free versions of the aphorisms and comments. In some cases, not always so labelled, my quotations are from Hort's translation of the *Critica*.

VII. THE NAMES (210–255)

210. "Nomenclature, the other foundation of botany, should provide the names as soon as the classification is made." "If the names are unknown knowledge of the things also perishes." "For a single genus, a single name." (fig. 15).

211. "Only the orthodox botanists can assign true names to plants," orthodox botanists being the taxonomists who use the fructification as the basis of their classification. "The botanists know the distinct genera and the names previously accepted."

This last remark is fundamental: the true botanist knows his genera, their names and synonyms. This, for Linnaeus, is the basis of all botany. "Idiotae imposuere nomina absurda" is the follow–up to this remark; a translation seems superfluous.

In the *Critica* Linnaeus gives his definition of a botanist (211): "by a botanist I mean one who understands how to observe the genera of nature."

Names are of two kinds: those that are *muta*, tacit or implicit like those of classes and orders, and those that are *sonora*, explicit and in use, such as

Fig. 15. Basic statements on nomenclature; aphorisms 210–212 of the *Philosophia botanica* [1751].

VII. NOMINA.

210. DENOMINATIO alterum (151) Botanices fundamentum, facta dispositione (152), nomina primum imponat.

Nomina si nescis, perit & cognitio rerum.

Unicum ubi genus, unicum erit nomen. §. 215.

Veterum nomina plerumque præstantissima; Recentiorum pejora fuere.

Critica Botanica Denominationem genericam, specificam & variantem rationibus & exemplis proposuit; hinc de ea in præsenti paucis.

211. Nomina vera plantis imponere *Botanicis* (7) *genuinis* (26) tantum in potestate est.

Botanicus novit genera distincta, & nomina antea recepta.

Idiotæ imposuere nomina absurda.

RELIGIOSA.

Pater Noster	Cyperus	Christi *oculus* Aster
Bonus Henricus	Chenopodium.	*Palma* Orchis
Noli me tangere	Impatiens	*Spina* Rhamnus
Morsus Diaboli	Scabiosa.	*Lancea* Lycopus
Filius ante Patrem	Tussilago	Mariæ *calceus* Cypripedium
Herba Fumana	Cistus	*Chlamys* Alchemilla
Mater herbarum	Artemisia	*Stragula* Galium
Surge & ambula	Gentiana	Veneris *labrum* Dipsacus
Fuga Dæmonum	Hypericum	*Umbilicus* Cotyledon
		Calceus Cypripedium
		Pecten Scandix
	Jovis *Barba*	Sempervivum.

NON SYSTEMATICI BOTANICI.

Bontiania Pt.
Breyniana Pt.
Ruyschiana Pt.
Drakena Cluf. Dorstenia.

212. Nomina omnia sunt in ipsa vegetabilis enunciatione vel *Muta*, ut Classis (160,) & Ordinis (161); vel *Sonora*, ut Genericum (159), Specificum (157) & varians (158).

Nomen omne plantarum constabit nomine Generico & Specifico;
Nomen

Fig. 15

those of genera and/species. This is again the age–old tendency of the human mind to create order in its environment by means of a comprehensive and a differential category: genus and species. Nobody ever felt the need to include names of higher taxa in the names of species. In the *Critica* Linnaeus states that this is not necessary since these higher taxa are "easily retained in the memory, in which the genera are marshalled as in a phalanx." Again the emphasis on memory!

The generic name then is basic. All plants belonging to one genus should be designated by the same generic name (213), all plants belonging to a different genus by a different name (214); one genus one name (215), or (216): "in one and the same genus the generic name will be constantly the same."

The commentary in the *Critica* with respect to this last aphorism is of special importance: it reveals Linnaeus's conviction that stability in nomenclature could be achieved only with a system of stable genera (and generic names) independent of the system used for their classification. One should not argue about the genera, but find their true 'natural' limits. One may argue about the systems in which the genera are arranged, but a change in a system is on no account a reason to change a name.

This was sensible advice; the botanical world was craving for stability and Linnaeus could provide it. Stable genera required stable circumscriptions and neat definitions. These he supplied in his *Genera plantarum*, mainly by elaborating the Tournefortian (essentially pragmatic) circumscriptions.

It is a pity that Linnaeus felt that he had to start with a nomenclatural reform. His rules for coining generic names were so strict that he rejected many of the well-established older ones, a practice which did not particularly endear him to his contemporaries. Even Tournefort's names were not exempt from this *Generalbereinigung*, although Linnaeus would very often abide by his taxonomy.

No specific name should be composed before the generic name is given (219); the specific name without the generic designation is like a bell without a clapper. The same metaphor will later be used for the trivial name in combination with the generic one.

One of Linnaeus's hobby horses was his aversion to what he called primitive generic names, i.e. names having no meaning other than that assigned to them arbitrarily at the moment of their first application to a genus. All barbarous names are like primitives "because they are taken from languages which are not understood by the erudite" (20). This is amusing because

Linnaeus was a poor linguist: he spoke only Swedish and Latin. In his three years in Holland he never learned the language. The definition of 'erudite' as 'speaking Latin' had a scholastic flavor: Latin was the esoteric language, it united the initiated but was not a medium for common usage. Plant names, to be given by true botanists, belonged in that esoteric world. Hence the strictures upon non-classical usage, hence the rigorous application of formalistic rules of nomenclature. On the other hand, we must admit that for a new beginning this was a good attitude. Linnaeus would have been the last to be surprised had he known that in the nineteenth century his works would be proclaimed the basis of botanical nomenclature, brushing away the past.

Several of the aphorisms deal with this cleaning up of Latinity. Hybrid names formed of Latin and Greek components, names composed of a fragment of one and a full second generic name, names ending in *–oides*, names ending in *–ella*, *–ellus*, etc., pseudohomonyms, names of which the root is neither Greek nor Latin, names taken from anatomy, pathology, art, names which contain inner contradictions, names identical with names of classes and orders, etc. etc., all are to be rejected. Generic names should also not commemorate persons "quite unconnected with botany or at least with natural science," as is still stated in our present Code. (Rec. 20A). Names commemorating true botanists, however, should be "religiously conserved." (238)

In his *Critica* Linnaeus elaborates this theme. He mentions one important argument used by those who oppose such names derived from personal names: the argument that the generic name should be indicative of an essential characteristic of the genus. Implicitly, Linnaeus answers by pointing out the arbitrary or code character of all names: not one in fifty contains any essential character of the genus. "What has Anglia (England) to do with an angel (*angelo*) ..."? (Linnaeus possibly never heard the story of the dark, wild Irish, capturing and enslaving the golden-haired and blue-eyed Englishmen, obviously children of the sky, calling them angels ...).

Even so: "it is commonly believed that the name of a plant which is derived from that of a botanist shows no connection between the two ..."; there are, however, definite associations such as (*Critica botanica*):

"*Linnaea* was named by the celebrated Gronovius and is a plant of Lapland, lowly, insignificant, disregarded, flowering but for a brief space— after Linnaeus who resembles it."

[83]

Could Linnaeus be serious here? His sense of humour was not very well developed, even when we consider that humour differs with the ages.

Granted the use of such 'personal names,' however, those generic names indicating the 'essential character' or the general habitus of the plant are the best (240):

"the habitus indicates resemblance, the resemblance sparks the idea, the idea gives birth to the name."

The remaining part of the chapter gives some more recommendations on the formation of generic names, several of which are still to be found in our International Code of Botanical Nomenclature, and on that of names of classes and orders.

VIII. THE DIFFERENTIAE (256–305)

The chapter on differentiae in the three books (*Fundamenta*, *Critica* and *Philosophia*, nos. 256–305) deals with the specific names in the Linnaean sense, the diagnostic phrases distinguishing the species, as well as with the characteristics which denote specific differences.

(256) "A plant is completely named when it is furnished with a generic and a specific name."

"The pupil knows the classes, the candidate all the genera, the master a great many species. The more species a botanist knows, the greater his excellence."

"If the genus is not stated there is no certainty with respect to the species."

"The specific 'differentia' states the characters by which a species differs from the other species of the same genus."

The paragraph on the candidate (read: botanist) knowing all the genera and the master most of the species shows again the emphasis on memory which is so characteristic of Linnaeus and which explains so much of his economy in words and insistence on 'essence.'

To stress that a species cannot be known without knowing its genus is of

Fig. 16. Binary nomenclature (*Nomina trivialia*) mentioned almost casually in aphorism 257 of the *Philosophia botanica* [1751].

[84]

VIII. DIFFERENTIÆ.

256. Perfecte nominata est planta nomine *generico* & *specifico* (212) instructa.

Botanices Tyro novit Classes, *Candidatus* omnia Genera, *Magister* plurimas species.

Quo plures Botanicus noverit species, eo etiam præstantior est.

Cognitione specierum innititur omnis solida eruditio Physica, Oeconomica, Medica; immo omnis vera cognitio humana.

Speciei notitia consistit in nota essentiali, qua sola ab omnibus congeneribus distinguitur.

Sine notitia Generis nulla certitudo speciei.

> *Cæsalpinus:* Ignorato genere nulla descriptio, quamvis accurate tradita, certam demonstrat, sed plerumque fallit.

Differentia specifica continet notas, quibus species a congeneribus differt.

Nomen specificum autem continet Differentiæ notas essentiales.

Notæ in nomine specifico sint

non *lubricæ incertæ* aut *falsæ* §. 259 - 274. 281. 283.
sed *firmæ, certæ, mechanicæ* §. 275 - 280. 257. 287.
quæ *caute, caste, judiciose* §. 284 - 305.

257. Nomen specificum *legitimum* plantam ab *omnibus* congeneribus (159) distinguat; *Triviale* autem nomen legibus etiamnum caret.

Fundamentum est hic canon nominum specificorum, quo neglecto, lubrica erunt omnia.

Nomina specifica omnia, quæ plantam a congeneribus non distinguunt, falsa sunt.

Nomina specifica omnia, quæ plantam ab aliis, quam congeneribus distinguunt, falsa sunt.

Nomen specificum est itaque Differentia essentialis.

NOMINA TRIVIALIA forte admitti possunt modo, quo in *Pane suecico* usus sum; constarent hæc

Vocabulo unico;
Vocabulo libere undequaque desumto.

Ratione hac præcipue evicti, quod differentia sæpe longa evadit, ut non ubique commode usurpetur, & dein mutationi obnoxia, novis detectis speciebus, est. e. gr.

PYRO-

Fig. 16

course truly Aristotelian-scholastic. In modern biology it would be more appropriate—though not very practical—if the species were taken as the basic unit and as a unit per se, named with a single term. The age–old traditional background of thinking in genera and species, however, is such a fundamental part of our taxonomy that it would be undesirable now to bring about such a profound change.

(257) "The *legitimate* specific name distinguishes a plant from all others in the genus; the rules for *trivial* names have not yet been drawn up."

This is one of the places where the *Philosophia* has a revised text: the old aphorism of the *Fundamenta* (256) reads "the specific name distinguishes the plant from all others in the genus." The specific name is now the *legitimate* one, and the *trivial* name is mentioned (fig. 16). The comments which follow are worth quoting in full (the part on the trivial names is the translation by Heller 1964, p. 54):

"This principle is fundamental for specific names; if it is neglected, everything will be in a state of flux" (actually: ... *lubrica erunt omnia*).

"All specific names which do not distinguish a plant from the others in its genus, are wrong."

"All specific names which distinguish a plant from other plants but not from the others in its genus are wrong."

"The specific name is therefore the essential difference." [sic.]

"Trivial names may perhaps be admitted after the fashion which I have followed in *Pan suecicus*; they should consist of *a single word, a word freely taken from any source.*

"The argument which we have found especially convincing is that a specific differentia often turns out to be so long that it cannot be used easily on every occasion, and furthermore is subject to change on the discovery of new species, e.g.

> *Pyrola irregula*[ris]   "Pyrola staminibus adscendentibus,
>   pistillo declinato *Fl. Suec.* 330.
>
> *Pyrola Halleriana* ...."

"But in the present work we set trivial names aside, being concerned only with the differentia."

We shall follow the example of the *Philosophia botanica* and treat the history of the trivial names separately. For the moment it is sufficient to conclude that they played a minor rôle in Linnaeus's thinking until he realized how successful the device had been. It was of little importance to Linnaeus the theoretician, but it suited Linnaeus the practical systematist.

(258) "The specific name identifies at first sight the plant to which it refers because it states the *differentia* which is imprinted on the plant itself."

The 'natural character' of the species is the *description*, but the 'essential character' is the *differentia*.

Linnaeus's method is here in principle the same as with the genera: it is most important to know the 'essence' of the species, but this essence is here expressed by the specific *name*. The statement of the essence is necessary to memorize the taxa, but it remains unclear why this could not be done by using a code designation for the term indicating the species as well as for that of the genus. The difficulty of memorizing long 'specific names' in large genera was one of the major factors which made Linnaeus introduce his trivial names. He looks upon his strict definition of the specific name as the statement of the essence (in modern terms: the diagnosis) as an invention of his own:

"I was the first to make essential specific names; before me there was no differentia of any merit."

The statement is somewhat surprising: Ray and Tournefort, to mention only the two most conspicuous examples, had done exactly the same. The only explanation for this statement of his own superiority lies in Linnaeus's conviction that he had deliberately eliminated descriptive but non-essential elements from the phrase–names, making them entirely diagnostic, whereas those of his predecessors usually contained purely descriptive elements as well. Some of his more astute contemporaries, he says, have followed this example, among them Guettard, Royen, Gronovius, and—often—Haller, Gmelin and Burman. This is really only a half-truth, but it shows how much importance Linnaeus attributed to the 'specific names': in this form they were his invention, in full agreement with his scholastic method.

Linnaeus had explained this reform of specific names as early as 1737 in his *Critica botanica* (aphorisms 256–305) and in the fourth paragraph of his preface to the *Hortus cliffortianus*. In the latter book he writes (translation Heller 1968):

"Specific names I have put down in every case, newly drafted, since the old ones can hardly be accepted in any case; ..."

[87]

"I have not gone so far as to think that all my specific names are so outstanding that other names, much shorter, less ambiguous, and more appropriate, cannot at some time be devised, but I was obliged rather to try a doubtful remedy on Botany than none at all, since only in this way is there any hope for her health."

"No true student of botany should shudder at new names for plants; if an Empiric [sic!], he should not suffer himself to be held back by the too often absurd statements of the ancients, but neither should he regard these differentiae as just wantonly increased names, when he is aware that these names are not burdens on the memory, but are the essential characters of the species, so linking together names and plants that, if this or a similar diagnosis is removed, no definite idea of the species remains."

Linnaeus could not have better expressed the rôle he attributed to the *differentiae* or diagnoses; they link together names and plants in an objective way, just as the type-specimen does today. From this it will be clear that when taxonomic botanists agreed in 1930 to introduce the type–method for linking names and plants, thereby abandoning the method of circumscription, what they actually abandoned was Linnaeus's essentialism.

In view of this important rôle of the diagnostic phrase names, aphorisms 259–282 deal with the requirements of their "true formation."

One of the main prescriptions is that diagnostic details cannot be obtained from variable parts of plants (259). Nobody in his senses has ever taken the animal races differing only in colour or size or some accidental feature, e.g. of cows and dogs, as species. By describing varieties as species, however, many botanists disregarded the laws of generation! Nature's law is that of continuous generation and this makes the species, not man. The reason why many of his predecessors sinned against this law of nature (species are natural entities delimited by continuous generation) is that they did not really recognize what was essential.

The skill of the botanist lies in knowing which characters indicate that the relevant taxon is a species. In the animals mentioned one knows by experience that the races interbreed: in plants one has to deduce this from the characters. 'Patrons of varieties' who described varieties as species were, according to Linnaeus, for instance Boerhaave and Tournefort. "This introduction of varieties has dishonored botany more than anything else; the synonymy was becoming so confused that science would have been destroyed without a prompt remedy." This prompt remedy was the correct

[88]

recognition of specific characters; aphorisms 259–282 provide guidance. Colour, fragrance, taste, use, sex, pubescence, ecological characters are all of no use. One can expect good specific characters only from the roots, the stems, the leaves, possible tendrils, etc., the inflorescence and the fructification, and this always, as in the genera, through "number, figure, situation and proportion." These four criteria are always usable: in the living plant, in the herbarium and in the illustration.

Linnaeus's statement under aphorism 259 on the true nature of species should be noted: it is "the law of nature to which the Creator has entrusted the generation of species, not to man." Species are objects, created as such, and recognizable by man through a knowledge of their essence, but by no means creations of the human mind. It has been said before: the only field in which Linnaean thought was truly biological was in that of sex and generation. He formulates here, in his own language, a biological species concept. It does not occur to him, however, to test this concept by biological means; on the contrary, the species can be known on the basis of secondary phenomena, all purely descriptive, equally well obtainable from "the living plant, the herbarium and the illustration." He also mentions, under aphorism 283, the possibility of distinguishing between varieties and species by means of cultivation under different conditions: this will bring out what is accidental in variation.

The remaining aphorisms of the chapter on the 'differentia,' nos. 284–305, contain instructions with respect to the formation of the names: the specific name must always be associated with (and follow) the generic name: after all, a specific name without a generic one "is like a bell without a clapper." It must be as short as possible:

"One should never use more than twelve words in the differentia, just as generic names should not consist of more than twelve letters." (291).

"One cannot give a specific name to a species which is the only one in the genus." (293)

This aphorism is again fully in accordance with the principles of logical division: there is no division in a monospecific genus, and there is therefore no need for a specific name. A perusal of the *Species plantarum* shows that Linnaeus was consistent in this respect. The fact that he did give trivial names to species of monotypic genera shows even more how important a deviation binary nomenclature was from logical division: the practical systematist was victorious over the scholastic theoretician.

[89]

The rules given for the formation of the specific names are sometimes very precise and apt. It is difficult not to forget that they apply to the *nomina specifica* and not to the *nomina trivialia*. Linnaeus never formulated rules for the formation of what we now call specific epithets. Many of the precepts for the phrase names, however, hold equally well for the trivial names, and in choosing the latter Linnaeus often—although not always— let himself be guided by them.

IX. THE VARIETIES (306–317)

If there is one subject on which Linnaean thinking was archaic, it was on varieties. The 310th aphorism: "Varietates levissimas non curat Botanicus" is the essence of typological thinking on the basis of fixed species. The biological importance of variation did not occur to Linnaeus: the varieties are objects for the 'anthophiles,' the flower-lovers:

"The beautiful flowers of the Tulip, the Hyacinth, the Pulsatilla, the Ranunculus, the Violet and the Primula are the object of their study; they have given to their secret varieties names which take one's breath away; they practice a floral science all their own, grasped only by their devotees; no botanist in his senses will enlist in their camp ..."

So much for the cultivars, many of which (several of the examples such as *Gemma hollandiae* and *Sponsa amstelodami* prove it) he got to know during his years with Clifford, amidst the early bulb-growers. "Varieties are plants changed by some accidental cause ..." (158) The botanist deals with them simply because public utility requires it.

"The order of the Fungi is still shamefully a true chaos: here the botanists do not yet know how to distinguish the species from the varieties."

In the *Critica botanica* Linnaeus became eloquent (Hort's translation, p. 196):

"All the species recognized by Botanists came forth from the Almighty Creator's Hand, and the number of these is now and always will be exactly the same, while every day new and different florist's species arise from the true species recognized by botanists, and when they have arisen they eventually revert to the original forms."

"Accordingly Nature has assigned to the former fixed limits beyond which they cannot go, while the latter display without end the infinite sport of Nature."

In the preface to the *Hortus cliffortianus*, Linnaeus' distaste for 'varieties' is expressed even more pointedly (translation Heller 1968):

"... botany has been burdened and overborne by the system of varieties for long enough, especially in the recent period, to such an extent that very few, if any, agree as to what constitutes a species, or what a variety; and so the number of species has been lamentably enlarged! I wish the system of varieties were entirely excluded from Botany and turned over entirely to the Anthophiles, since it causes nothing but ambiguities, errors, dead weight and vanity ..."

Linnaeus never faltered in his belief that the species had fixed limits: the varieties were sports, unworthy of the attention of the philosopher.

The tenth chapter of the *Fundamenta* and *Philosophia* deals with the synonyms. It contains details on bibliographic citation, choice, etc., but contains little of theoretical interest.

2. *The generic reform*

Linnaeus's ideas on genera have been explained above. Stability of generic taxonomy and nomenclature was one of his first aims, and the way he went about achieving it aroused the criticism of many of his contemporaries. Yet, this generic reform is one of his most important achievements: his genera and their nomenclature stand at the beginning of the victory of Linnaean taxonomy. It is necessary therefore to look at this reform in greater detail, with special reference to the theoretical chapters on generic names in the *Critica botanica* and to the main practical work on the subject: the *Genera plantarum*.

Tournefort had achieved a certain measure of stability in taxonomy on the generic level, drawing partly on the work done by Ray and Rivinus. His genus concept was not the old scholastic one (any comprehensive category) but that of today: an assemblage of species. His genera are taxa of comparable rank and are described with consistency and precision. In 1737, the year of the publication of the *Critica* and of the first edition of the *Genera*, Tournefortian nomenclature was reasonably firmly established and followed. Tournefort had, in fact, two types of genera. His primary genera were based on characters derived exclusively from the fructification. For Tournefort this was a practical proposition which worked quite well in general. In several instances, however, he had 'secondary' genera which were not only based on characters of the fructification but which differed from their nearest relatives by characters derived from other parts of the plant. *Pinus, Abies* and *Larix* differ in vegetative characteristics but are different genera with Tournefort; another example is offered by *Quinque-folium* and *Pentaphylloides*. Linnaeus's first objection to the Tournefortian generic structure was of a taxonomic nature and on an apriori basis. Natural genera are based on characteristics derived from the fructification; if species do not differ in the fructification they belong to the same genus. We have seen that Linnaeus was firmly of the opinion that such genera were the only natural—created—genera. The first part of his generic reform consisted of the lumping of genera which differed only in vegetative characteristics. He combined *Pinus, Abies* and *Larix* into *Pinus; Quinquefolium* and *Pentaphylloides* into *Potentilla*. *Allium, Cepa* and *Porrum*, still retained as different genera in the first edition of the *Genera plantarum*, were later combined into *Allium*. Linnaeus' activity was of course not directed solely at Tournefort. In his 216th aphorism (see *Fund. bot., Crit. bot.* and *Phil. bot.*) he states: "In one and the same genus the generic name will be constantly the same." Basically this is the axiom that genera are fixed and therefore cannot be changed under different systems. In the *Critica* Linnaeus gives many examples of this taxonomic process of lumping: *Viola aquatica* Rj. [Ray], *Myriophyllum* Rv. [Rivinus], *Stratiotes* V. [Vaillant], and *Hottonia* B. [Boerhaave] become *Hottonia*; even clearer perhaps is the treatment of *Radiola* D. [Dillen], *Linoides* Rp [Ruppius], and *Chamaelinum* V. [Vaillant] which all become *Linum*. This essentially taxonomic reform rested on the apriori assumption that there were fixed genera, that these had been created as such and that they could be recognized on the basis of the fructification. Critics of Linnaeus would later point out, not at all inappropriately, that several of his genera declared 'natural' on these grounds were definitely artificial, but then these critics had an entirely different criterion: that of overall affinity.

Even in 1737 many taxonomists were more or less resigned to the fact that there are different generic concepts and consequently splitters and lumpers. What everybody resented, however, then as now, was a change of names not accompanied by a taxonomic reform but solely on the basis of formal rules. Hence the great reaction against the second part of the Linnaean generic reform: the nomenclatural revolution.

A revolution it was, because in the past generic names had been coined quite arbitrarily. The then prevailing custom is neatly summed up in the present article 20 of the International Code of Botanical Nomenclature: "The name of a genus ... may be taken from any source whatever, and may even be composed in an absolutely arbitrary manner." The present Code, however, is slightly less permissive than pre–1737 custom: the name must consist of one word and it must be "a substantive in the singular number, or a word treated as such."

It is against this, in his opinion, too general permissiveness that Linnaeus revolted. Genera were such an important concept that their names should be treated in earnest, free from arbitrariness. As a result he proposed a number of rules for the formation of generic names which entailed a great many changes. Some of these rules are still accepted today (such as the rejection of biverbal generic names and of the use of technical terms as names of genera), but the great majority is no longer in force, although in part still recommended practice (Recommendation 20A). Linnaeus was as good as his word: in his *Systema naturae* and *Genera plantarum* he brought all his rules into practice.

The rules are contained in the *Fundamenta* but are worked out in greater detail in the *Critica*. We mention them here (quotations are from Hort's translation) because they are an essential—and the most controversial—part of the Linnaean reform, a part which was doomed to be only partially successful. The order of the rules is that of Linnaeus.

(211) "It is only real botanists who have the power of assigning true names to plants." Only true botanists understand what genera are: they alone can judge what is an appropriate name. Many of the names given by the ancients (the 'commentators') are "absurd, foolish and ridiculous" and must be replaced by others:

Bonus henricus becomes *Chenopodium*

But even more recent authors had coined such foolish names: *Clusius* for example is—very unjustly—regarded as a non-botanist and his *Drakena* has to become *Dorstenia*.

Names with a religious significance are out:

Pecten veneris becomes *Scandix*
Oculus christi becomes *Aster*

(220) "No sane person introduces 'primitives' as generic names."

"By primitives,' as is well known, are meant words which have no root, no derivation, no significance."

"... if we would not be considered utter barbarians, let us not (especially in an age so alert as ours) invent names which cannot be derived from some root or another."

Linnaeus admits that primitives do not in themselves cause any confusion and has some praise even for Paracelsus' *Nostoc*. It is clear that with this aphorism all arbitrarily formed generic names are or can be rejected, among them many non-Latin ones of which the derivation is not clear at first sight.

(221) "Generic names formed from two complete and distinct words are to be banished from the commonwealth of botany."

This provision still stands: not *Auricula ursi* but *Auricula*, not *Umbilicus veneris* but *Umbilicus*. In many instances Linnaeus gives an entirely different name: *Bella donna* becomes *Atropa*, *Calamus aromaticus* becomes *Acorus*.

In later years Linnaeus, practical as ever, would still make use of these rejected generic names: they often became specific epithets (*nomina trivialia*): *Acorus calamus*, *Amaryllis belladonna*, *Thlaspi* [later *Capsella*] *bursa-pastoris*.

(222) "Generic names compounded of two entire Latin words are scarcely to be tolerated."

Latin words do not compound as easily as Greek: "moreover the masters of eloquence could easily find arguments with which to attack botanists, if they should advance too far on this path."

Virg-aurea becomes *Solidago*, but *Saxi-fraga* is retained. This is a mere recommendation, mainly for the future; Linnaeus rejected few names solely on these grounds.

(223) "Hybrid generic names, namely those made from a Greek compounded with a Latin word, and the like are not to be recognized."

The present Code still recommends (but does not rule) "not to make names by combining words from different languages." Apart from the names ending in *–oides*, rejected separately, there are relatively few examples *Cardam-indum* Tournefort (becomes *Tropaeolum*).

(224) "Generic names compounded of two words, one a part of another

[94]

name of a genus of plants, and the other an entire word, are unworthy of botanists."

This rule was responsible for the rejection of a great many names. To Linnaeus a name like *Cytiso–genista* was misleading because it was neither the one nor the other (he names it *Ulex*) and in conflict with the independent 'natural' character of genera. "If there were such a thing as metamorphosis of plants, so that from one species could arise another belonging to a different genus (even as the Ancients dreamed that wheat could become barley and barley become oats), such names would no doubt be excellent and admirably suited to such plants."

The reasons for the rejection of these names go deep: for Linnaeus the constancy of species (wheat could *not* become barley) was a recent acquisition of science and a great step forward beyond the crude beliefs of *generatio spontanea* and mystic transformations. He did not want to have these shadows of the past reflected in his modern system. Out went *Lauro–Cerasus (Padus)*, *Arisarum (Arum)*, *Capnorchis (Fumaria)*, *Melo–Pepo (Cucurbita)* and many other well–established names.

(225) "A generic name to which one or two syllables are prefixed, to make it denote an entirely different genus from that which it denoted before, is not to be admitted."

The reasons for this are the same as for the previous rule: "... I beseech you to have distinct genera, distinct ideas, distinct names. If you introduce confusion in names, ideas are confounded, and so are genera ..."

Needless to say that names beginning with *Pseudo–* are absolutely outlawed. By itself Linnaeus's idea to have distinct names for distinct genera is correct. He looks upon the names as a code–designation only in a very special way: if they contain elements which might give rise to non–taxonomic associations, they are not acceptable. They must still obey certain positive formal rules as well, and as a result his concept of names is not really clear. Basically he is convinced that the names should express the essence, or represent the essence, by being completely independent. In addition the names should never disagree with the rules of Latin or Greek; again an association with the past.

A great many names were rejected on these grounds, giving rise to wrong associations: e.g. *Chamaebuxus (Polygala)*, *Monorchis (Herminium)*, *Periclymenum (Lonicera)*, *Pseudoacacia (Robinia)*.

[95]

(226) "Generic names ending in *-oides* are to be banished from the domain of Botany."

This is the "refuge of the lazy", a practice abused by botanists "of inferior rank." The termination is the "common and safe refuge of the idle." Linnaeus becomes eloquent in expressing his abhorrence; the association is all wrong. *Echiodes* is not an *Echium* and the name is therefore inadmissible: "Philosophers and physicians ridicule and reproach us for this termination ... if they observed that the author had invented a number of names ending in *-oides*, they forthwith declared that he was no *Botanist*, but a '*Botanicoides.*'" Linnaeus was obviously somewhat sensitive to the opinion of those others who were not even *Botanicoides*, and he was eager to do the right thing. Today this requirement appears no longer in the Code, though we have still a reflection of this ghost of the past in Article 21, which states that "the epithet of a subgenus or section must not be formed from the name of the genus to which it belongs by adding the ending *-oides* or *-opsis*, or the prefix *Eu-*." The number of examples is great: *Buglossoides* (*Lycopsis*), *Bellidioides* (*Chrysanthemum*), *Ricinoides* (*Croton*), and many more.

The abhorrence of the ending *-oides* went so far with some of the Linnaean scholars that they used the ending on purpose if they wanted to create a token, not a generic name, provisionally indicating the generic nature of a taxon. We find such names e.g. with Jacquin (1760, 1763) and Rottbøll (1772). The latter's *Schoenoides*, *Scirpoides* and *Cyperoides* indicated unnamed genera resembling *Schoenus*, *Scirpus* and *Cyperus*, which he intended to name later (actually in 1773). In several cases such names in *-oides* have, incorrectly, been accepted as regular generic names.

(227) "Generic names made up of other generic names with a syllable added at the end are not satisfactory."

This aphorism objects to the use of names ending "in *-ella*, *-ulla*, *-ulus*, *-ellus*, *-ula*, *-aster*, *-astrum*, *-istrum*, *-ium*, *-aria*, *-arium*, and a thousand more. O for the honest practice of old time!" ... "... your grandsons shall be my judges, and I can answer for it that they will abandon them." The answer was wrong even then; many such names continued to be in use or were coined anew. Examples of substitutions by Linnaeus: *Alsinella* (*Sagina*), *Fraxinella* (*Dictamnus*), *Plantaginella* (*Limosella*), *Valerianella* (*Valeriana*) and even names like *Linaria* (*Antirrhinum*), *Ficaria* (*Ranunculus*), *Fagopyrum* (*Helxine*). Obviously, many names were rejected for more than one reason: *Ranunculus* and *Ficaria* were combined for taxonomic reasons as well.

[96]

(228) "Generic names ending with a similar sound give a handle to confusion."

This is not just the mild form of objection to orthographic variation which we find in our present Code. One must also beware of choosing names derived metaphorically from one and the same stock (*Acacia, Casia, Cassia, Cassida*), of names differing in only two letters (*Ligustrum, Ligusticum, Levisticum*) and even of names ending with similar words like *–dendron* or *–theca*. Obviously, if this rule is stringently applied, the results are appalling. However, Linnaeus was a genius at creating brief independent generic names: *Toxicodendron* became *Rhus*, *Chamaerhododendron* became *Azalea*, *Hypophyllocarpodendron* became *Protea*, etc.

(229) "Generic names which have not a root derived from Greek or Latin are to be rejected."

Another opening for an almost unprecedented number of changes not only by Linnaeus, but also by several of his followers. A great many name–changes have resulted from this aphorism; many cases of *nomina conservanda* stem from this.

The basic reason was of course to preserve the use of Latin: Botanists should agree to use one and the same language for one and the same science. For Linnaeus, who was still so much a man of the seventeenth century in many respects, *the* language of science was Latin. There are obvious practical advantages in this attitude, and one important element of it has been preserved until the present day: the obligatory Latin diagnoses for new taxa in most plant groups. It was, however, somewhat far–fetched to rule out, on this account, names of Latin form derived from non–Latin roots. Linnaeus was not at all a linguist, and his sentiment is understandable when he says: "also individuals among the moderns have written of their discoveries in their own languages, so that the novice might grow old over his literary studies ere he is competent to study the sciences ..." "I foresee barbarism knocking at our gates."

"Greek generic names must inevitably be tolerated, since the science of plants was built up first of all by the Greeks ... Moreover the Greek tongue expresses a meaning more concisely than most other languages ..."

Linnaeus could not understand that the use of modern languages in the eighteenth century was often not a *testimonium paupertatis*, as he suggests, but a reaction against the exclusiveness of science, an attempt to spread

[97]

education and a road to further progress. The word 'barbarous' speaks for the esoteric attitude. The Enlightenment, that crisis in human thinking of the eighteenth century, resulted in a breakthrough towards a spreading of culture and knowledge away from this elitist garb.

In some cases, where he could secondarily interpret them as of possible classical derivation, the barbarous names were retained: "*Datura* from Latin *dare*, [to give], because it is 'given' to those whose sexual powers are weak or enfeebled. *Musa* I derive from the goddess of study, or from Antonius Musa ..." Thus the Arab word 'mouz' which had no connection whatever with the Greek Mousa, was sanctioned by pure chance. *Datura* was originally Sanscrit *dhustura*. It is understandable that many could not follow these inconsistencies and that Linnaeus was often accused, unjustly, of having invented these rules to have a licence for changing as he wished.

(230) "Generic names of plants which are also used in the nomenclature of zoology or mineralogy, if they were adopted by Botanists at a later date, must be restored to their original significance" [rather: "returned to their first owners"].

The most striking part of this rule is that Linnaeus accepts here the principle of priority. However, orthographic variants of names of animals are also not acceptable if later: *Buglossum* versus *Buglossis*, for instance.

(231) "Generic names which are also used in the nomenclature of anatomists, pathologists, medical practitioners or craftsmen will have to be dropped."

Examples of names to be avoided because of this rule are *Clitoris* (*Clitorea*), *Epiglottis* (*Astragalus*), *Prunella* (*Brunella*), *Calceolus* (*Cypripedium*).

(232) "Generic names which are contradicted by some species of the genus are bad." "*Holosteum*" (all-bone) is a herb no part of which is hard ..."

(233) "Generic names which are also used in the nomenclature of Classes or Natural Orders should be dropped."

Names like 'Alga,' 'Filix,' 'Palma,' 'Planta,' 'Herba' are obviously undesirable as generic names.

(234) "Generic names which are diminutives formed from articles of domestic use and the like are not very satisfactory."

[98]

One more reason to reject '*Calceolus*': because it is "simply equivocal with" *Calceus*.

(235) "Generic names which are adjectival are less satisfactory than those which are substantives."

The reason given for this is again that such names make no sense: *Armeniaca* is highly equivocal, *Vulneraria* suggests that the plant is a sovereign remedy, *Superba* assigns a quality to the plant in question (*Dianthus*), etc. Names ending in *-aria* are permitted "since in our age we can hardly hope for better ones taken from Latin."

(236) "Generic names should not be misused in order to perpetuate the memory of Saints and men distinguished in some other branch of learning or to secure their favour."

This sentiment is still reflected in our present Code: Recommendation 20A(h) says "not to dedicate genera to persons quite unconnected with botany or at least with natural science."

Linnaeus's comment in the *Critica* is extensive and revealing. A generic name is a serious thing, and the honor of being a dedicatee should go only to the botanists themselves. It is unworthy to use this practice to seek favour from the great.

"And so I reject these names of saints, miscellaneous public characters, persons in high places, physicians, and I lay down that they are outside the province of botany." "Yet I shall not on that account show myself to be but a barbarian in savagery (*immanitate*) [sic, see Boerman's analysis of Linnaeus's character above]. For, although I was born at the edge of the world in a remote country, nevertheless the names of such distinguished anatomists and physicians have reached my ears: but my plea is that they have not done so in connection with botany. See Pontedera, Disserationes, 203."

Christophoriana Tournefort becomes *Actaea, Salvinia*, after a professor of Greek, *Marsilea*; although, *Begonia*, after a naval superintendent, is graciously allowed to stay. On the other hand, Linnaeus was not so impractical as to forget the Cliffords and the Luisa Ulrikas of this world:

(237) "Generic names taken from poetry and mythology, consecrated names of Kings, and names of those who have advanced the study of botany I retain."

[99]

Hence *Musa* (wrongly!), *Satyrium* (the satyrs, lustful gods of the woods), *Helenium* (Helen, wife of Menelaos), *Cliffortia, Collinsonia.*

The remaining aphorisms on generic names are positive and specify which can be retained and how new ones are to be formed. It is not necessary to mention them here in the same detail as the rules by which Linnaeus rejected older names. The rejections were the main feature of this second aspect of the generic reform: name–changes based on nomenclatural formalities. Looking at the above formidable list of prohibitions it is understandable that this part of the Linnaean reform met with the strongest opposition. It was not wholly successful; many names rejected by Linnaeus are still in use, although now attributed to those post–Linnaean authors who first validated them. The main positive result was that Linnaeus introduced a set of generic names which were euphonious, brief and easily remembered. Linnaeus was a typical reformer and had the courage to be

---

C A P. III.

De *Vrtica.*

URticam ab urendo dictam effe confentiunt Grammatici, quòd igneæ fit naturæ, unde admota cuti vel levi tantùm tactu, pruritum ac puftulas excitat, quomodo hoc præftat paulo poft oftendemus. 'Ακαλύφη vel 'Ακαλήφη Græcis dicitur, ఆభ τὸ μὴ ἔχειν καλὰν ἀφὴν quod injucundo fit tactu, & pruritum cieat. *Athenæus.* Dicitur & κνίδη quod lanugine noxiâ vellicet, pungat, & fuo morfu fenfum laceffat, à verbo κνίζειν, quod pungere & vellicare fignificat.

Urticæ quatuor tantùm fpecies novimus, duas racemiferas, duas piluliferas, Racemiferas voco quæ flores fuos & femina in quibufdam velut racemulis è foliorum alis egreffis geftant; Piluliferas quæ eadem in pilulas feu globulos congefta, eòdem tamen fitu, proferunt: illarum femina minora funt; harum majora, fplendentia, & Lini feminum æmula. Racemiferæ funt
    1. Urtica vulgaris major *J. B.*
    2. Urtica minor annua *ejufdem.*
Piluliferæ,
    3. Urtica Romana *Ger.*
    4. Urtica Romana altera Parietariæ foliis *Hort. Parif.*
Præter has, alias exoticas, & nobis nondum cognitas, ex Hiftor. Marggravii & Horto Malabarico proponemus.

    1. *Urtica Brafilienfis,* Pinò *indigenis dicta* Marggr. *An* Batti Schorigeriam Hort. Malab.?

Marggr.
Ex *radice* parva, filamentofa, in octo aut novem pedum altitudinem affurgit, *caule* ftriato, aliquantulum pilofo & craffo. *Folia* habet hinc indè pofita, folitaria, vel juxta fe invicem, quorum quodlibet innititur pediculo fefquipedem longo, aut etiam longiori, ex albo paulum rufefcenti. Folia autem Urticæ noftrati fimilia, magna, in ambitu dentata, triangularibus dentibus, & raris pilis
P 2

Fig. 17. Description of the genus *Urtica* in J. Ray, *Historia plantarum,* vol. 1 [1686]. *Reduced.*

so, a courage stemming perhaps from a lack of appreciation of the other man's point of view, but courage all the same. One thing is clear: Linnaeus had no deep respect for the principle of priority in nomenclature.

The Linnaean generic reform as embodied mainly in his *Genera plantarum* had a third, and more positive, aspect: the reform of the generic definitions. Linnaeus's aim in the *Genera* was to provide clear and mutually comparable, no–nonsense diagnoses of the genera. Stearn (1960) has given a review of the genesis of the work and has provided, as an illustration of the superiority of the Linnaean generic definitions over previous ones, a comparison between the Tournefortian description of the genus *Lilium* and that of Linnaeus. The definitions of the genus *Urtica* by Ray, Tournefort and Linnaeus, as given in figs. 17, 18 and 19 illustrate clearly the superior information content and style of the Linnaean description.

Genus IV.

Urtica. *Ortie.*

Urtica eſt plantæ genus, flore A, C apetalo, plurimis ſcilicet ſtaminibus B calyci inſidentibus, conſtante & ſterili : embryones enim D iis ſpeciebus Urticæ innaſci ſolent quæ flore carent, abeuntque deinde vel in capſulam E, I bivalvem F, K, ſemine fœtam G, L, in globulos quandoque congeſtam H, vel abeunt in volſellam M qua comprehenditur ſemen N.

Urticæ ſpecies ſunt.

Urtica urens, maxima C. B. Pin. 232. *Urtica vulgaris, major J. B. 3. 445. Urtica urens, altera Dou. Pempt. 151.*

Urtica urens, maxima, caule rubente C. B. Pin. 232. *Urtica rubra Tabern. Icon. 535.*

Urtica vulgaris, minimè urens Mentz. Pug.

Fig. 18. Description of the genus *Urtica* in Tournefort, *Institutiones rei herbariae* [1700].

"The clear typographical layout, the elimination of verbs such as *est*, *occupat* and *abit*, and the much greater detail given for all floral parts … immediately catch the attention. Such improvements in technique made Linnaeus's *Genera plantarum* the model for later works on the genera of plants." (Stearn 1960, p. x).

Stearn has further shown (but see also Pennell 1930) that the generic definition (the *character naturalis*) of Linnaeus was usually based on a very accurate description of the flower and the fruit of the chief species (see

also *Philosophia botanica* no. 193: *fructificationis primae speciei*) which has in general
to be regarded as the historical type species of the relevant generic name.

935. URTICA.* *Tournef.* 308.

*. *Masculi Flores.*

CAL. *Perianthium* tetraphyllum : *foliolis* fubrotundis, concavis,
obtufis.

COR. *Petala* nulla.
Nectarium in centro floris, urceolatum, integrum, inferne
angultius, minimum.

STAM. *Filamenta* quatuor, fubulata, longitudine calycis, paten-
tia, intra fingulum folium calycinum fingula. *Antheræ* bilo-
culares.

* *Feminei Flores* vel in eadem, vel in diftincta planta.

CAL. *Perianthium* bivalve , ovatum, concavum, erectum, per-
fiftens.

COR. nulla

PIST. *Germen* ovatum. *Stylus* nullus. *Stigma* villofum.

PER. nullum. *Calyx* connivens.

SEM. unicum, ovatum, obtufo-compreffum, nitidum.

D d 4   936.

Fig. 19. Description of the genus *Urtica* in Linnaeus, *Genera plantarum*, ed. 5 [1754].

The first edition of the *Genera plantarum* was published early in the year
1737. It was dedicated to Herman Boerhaave, the great Leiden physician
to whom Linnaeus owed his introduction into the medico–botanical Dutch
Establishment of the day. Linnaeus published a revised edition in 1742. By
far the most important edition for nomenclature today is the fifth, published in August 1754 (eds. 3 and 4 were not edited by Linnaeus); this is the
edition which is linked nomenclaturally with the *Species plantarum*, the
starting-point book for the nomenclature of most groups of plants. The
Code states in Article 13: "It is agreed to associate generic names which first
appear in Linnaeus' *Species plantarum* ed. 1 (1753) and ed. 2 (1762–63) with the
first subsequent description given under those names in Linnaeus' *Genera
plantarum* ed. 5 (1754) and ed. 6 (1764)." This means that all generic names
contained in the *Genera plantarum* ed. 5 are treated as validly published on
1 May 1753. For details with respect to the typification of the genera and the
actual correspondence between the *Species* and the *Genera* ed. 5 see Stearn's
introduction (1960) to the facsimile reprint of the fifth edition.

[102]

The *Genera plantarum* was Linnaeus's most important book, even more than
the *Systema naturae*, with respect to the practical introduction of his ideas.
The generic reform was on the whole successful. The philosophy that the
genus is the basic unit in taxonomy remained in force until the coming
of evolutionary biology and biosystematics. The acceptance or rejection
of Linnaeus by his contemporaries and by those immediately succeeding
them can best be measured by the degree of acceptance of the generic
reform. The sexual system was more spectacular but dealt in effect only
with categories that were implied rather than explicitly given. We have
seen above that Linnaeus himself stated in aphorism 212: "All names used
in designating a plant are either tacitly understood, as those of class or
order, or explicitly given, as those which denote genera, species and varieties." The genera are the basis of Linnaean taxonomy and nomenclature.
His reform was daring and thorough, based on an exceptional and practical
knowledge of plants; although influenced by somewhat outmoded ideas,
it had exactly the salutary effect which he wanted it to have: consistency
and simplicity. These two were prime needs for taxonomy in 1737.

3. *Binary nomenclature*

For a good understanding of the importance of Linnaean binary nomenclature for species it is essential to realize the difference between Linnaeus's
system, which was a simple coding device, and the widespread classical and
renaissance usage of binary names, which was a reflection of classificatory
logic applied to genera with few species.

Theophrastos and Dioscorides used a single generic name to denote
species of monotypic genera. It was also current practice to use the generic
name to denote the main species of a genus, and to add epithets only for
the other species. For instance, 'Apsinthion' is *Artemisia absinthium* with
Dioscorides, but *Artemisia maritima* is *Absinthion thalassion*. This was not strict
practice, but quite common. The use of only the generic name to designate
the species of a monotypic genus was in agreement with the rules of Aristotelean classificatory logic. On the whole the binary nomenclature of
classical authors was a reflection of the natural practice, already referred
to above, of having a comprehensive and a differentiating category called
genus and species. The species designation was, as in the vernacular,

usually simply a modifier of the generic 'name' or term. This type of binary nomenclature was therefore a phenomenon arising naturally from the vernacular which had sufficient flexibility as long as a genus had only a small number of species. A review of this early history of binary nomenclature is given by Váczy (1971).

Medieval and renaissance botany had to deal with a somewhat more involved situation because of the increased number of taxa that had to be dealt with, but very often the specific names could still be binary. Many such binary names appear for instance in C. Bauhin's *Pinax*. Some genera, however, had too many species, and the species designations then consisted of more than one epithet. There was no hard and fast rule except that a species was named in the scholastic tradition "per genus et differentiam." A complicating circumstance is that many pre–Linnaean Latin names of genera consisted of two words, which then looked like binary specific names. Tournefort and Linnaeus insisted upon the consistent use of generic names of one word only. A further complication is that Linnaeus often retained early binary names in his own specific nomenclature. In principle, however, the pre–Linnaean binary names were diagnostic polynomials consisting of two terms only because no more were necessary.

Linnaean binary nomenclature is fundamentally different because it is a system of code designation. Linnaeus did with the species names what had been common practice for the generic names: he made them into brief, handy, but arbitrary designations without any diagnostic meaning per se. Heller (1964, 1968) has shown in extensive studies of Linnaean binary nomenclature that it goes back to Linnaeus's early practice of using abbreviated bibliographical references consisting of two words, each abbreviated, of which the first referred to the author's name and the second to the title of the publication. This binary system (binary is used here as exactly synonymous to binomial) of bibliographic reference is found in Linnaeus's earliest books, such as the *Hortus cliffortianus* and the *Flora lapponica*, both dated 1737. Essentially this consistent system of abbreviated bibliographical references was a space–saving device, illustrating Linnaeus's insistence on conciseness such as is evident in particular also in the *Species plantarum* (Sprague 1955). Stearn refers here—lightly—to Linnaeus' origin as a Smålander: the

Fig. 20. First page of the bibliography appended to the *Prolegomena* of Linnaeus, *Flora lapponica* [1737], showing the binary system of references to the literature consisting of the abbreviated author's name and an epithet designating the title of the publication.

AUTHORES

in opere allegatos diuidimus in *Exteros,*
Suecos & propria scripta.

EXTERI.

Bauh. hist. BAUHINI *Johannis.*
Ebrod. 1650.1651. fol.
Historia plantarum vni-
uersalis. Tomi tres
ob descriptiones sæpe & figuras.

pin. BAUHINI *Caspari.* Basil.1623. 4to
Pinax theatri Botanici.

pro synonymis.

prod. Prodromus theatri Botanici. Basil.
1671. 4to

ob descriptiones & figuras rariorum.

Boerh. lugdb. BOERHAAVII *Herm.* Lugdb.
1720. 4to
Index alter plant. Horti Lugduno-
Bataui.

ob nomina & systema.

Cluf. pan. CLUSII *Caroli.* Antw. 1683. 8vo
Historia rariorum plant. per Pan-
noniam.

ob Descriptiones & Figuras plant.
Alpinarum.

Col.

Fig. 20

people from that region were the Swedish Scots. Actually it was, first of all, one more manifestation of an extremely systematic mind, accustomed to thinking in symbols and emphasizing the role of memory (fig. 20).

The analogy between the early bibliographic references and the later binary specific names is further stressed by the use of numbers. This feature, however interesting, is not essential and need not concern us here. Stearn (1957) and Heller (1964) discuss the Linnaean numbering devices in some detail.

We have seen above that Linnaeus himself, in his *Philosophia botanica*, mentions his *Pan suecicus* of 1749 (see also Ramsbottom 1959) as the first work in which he used 'trivial names,' that is, single specific epithets in our modern sense. In fact, however, their first occurrence is in the *index* of his *Öländska och gothländska resa* of 1745.

This book is a diary and records the various features of interest observed by Linnaeus on his trip of 1741. In the body of his work Linnaeus uses the traditional full phrase names (*nomina specifica*), but in the index each species is cited by the name of the genus, its number in the *Flora suecica*, and a single word which often expresses some characteristic but which may also be derived from the name of another author or be indicative of the use made of the plants. Heller and Stearn are of the opinion that this practice, in an index, is essentially a papersaving device.

Linnaeus himself indicates this in the preface to his *Pan suecicus* of 1749. This dissertation is a study of the use of Swedish plants as fodder. The results of the study are given in tables of which the conciseness is explained in the preface as follows (translation Stearn 1957): "If we take the *Flora suecica* Stockholm, 1745, and for each herb, in order to save paper, we put the generic name, the number of the *Flora suecica* and some epithet in place of the differential diagnosis, the matter is easily put in handy form."

The combination of the generic name and the species number had been Linnaeus's first paper–saving device in indexes (e.g. in the *Flora suecica* itself), but this system had no further merit beyond that of ready reference within a book; numbers have a low mnemonic value. The combination of number, generic name and epithet, however, contained a definite mne-

Fig. 21. Page of the index to Linnaeus, *Flora lapponica* 1737, showing the use of binary species designations to refer to *synonyms* (phase names) under *Muscus*. These binary designations are here coined by Linnaeus as early as 1737 as a reference device. Similar sets of binary names appear in this same index under *Gramen* and *Herba*.

INDEX.

Fig. 21

monic link to features of the plant itself. These trinomials were used in several other works as well, but the most important step was of course the dropping of the number.

Binary names without the numbers are used in most of Linnaeus's botanical dissertations from 1751 onward. In the *Nova plantarum genera* (19 Oct. 1751) the epithets, printed in italics, are given in parentheses immediately after the generic name:

"LECHEA (*minor*) foliis lineari–lanceolatis ..." In the *Plantae hybridae* (23 Nov 1751) they are used as they are today, without further mention of the *nomen specificum*; again they are obviously used as convenient abbreviations. The same is true of the *Plantae esculentae* (22 Feb 1752). In the monograph of *Euphorbia* (6 May 1752) the epithets are not even enclosed in parentheses: Euphorbia *antiquorum* aculeata sub nuda ..."

In the *Species plantarum* (1753) the specific epithets ('trivial names') are printed in the margin in the body of the work itself. In the preface Linnaeus explains their use as follows (translated by Stearn 1957, p. 155): "I have put trivial names in the margin so that without more ado we can represent one plant by one name; these I have taken, it is true, without special choice, leaving this for another day. However, I warn most solemnly all sensible botanists not to propose a trivial name without adequate specific distinction, lest the science fall back into its earliest crude state."

The species numbers are still retained but play no rôle. Reference is by binary names. The trivial names are placed in the margin again for pragmatic reasons: they catch the eye. The epithets for the species given in the *Pan suecicus* are used only in part in the *Species plantarum*. Choate notes (see Heller 1964, p. 53) that of the 754 binary names used in the *Pan suecicus*, only 322, or 43% reappear unchanged in the *Species plantarum*. Linnaeus soon realized, however, that the epithets should be retained, and later on he only rarely changed them. There are minor changes in the epithets in the 10th edition of the *Systema naturae* (1759) and in the second edition of the *Species plantarum* (1762–1763), but on the whole the same epithets remained in use for the same species even though the species numbers might change.

The *nomina trivialia* or specific epithets did not replace the *nomina specifica legitima* or phrase names: Linnaeus never abolished the latter. They served different functions: the epithets were code designations for ready reference, catch–words, the phrase names were diagnostic statements in agreement with scholastic classificatory logic. The fundamental difference is especially clear from Linnaeus' practice with monotypic genera. The diagnosis of a species which is the only one in its genus is superfluous, and the *nomen specificum legitimum* is the same as the generic name. A species *designation*, however, can be given because this is a coding device and necessary for consistency. A glance at the many monotypic genera of the *Species plantarum* will show that Linnaeus is indeed consistent. The designation of the single species of *Triopteris*, for instance (p. 428) is *Triopteris jamaicensis*; the legitimate specific name is cited as "1. Triopteris *Hort. Cliff.* 169."

Linnaeus soon discovered how useful the device of trivial names had proved to be. Heller translates the following passage from one of Linnaeus's autobiographies: "L. first discovered trivial names, and applied them to all species ... Previously one could never remember *differentias specificas*; plants could never be specified without *diffuso genere dicendi*, whereas now it is done as easily as one names a person." It is an apt comparison: the generic name, equivalent to the family name, may be changed, but the specific epithet or the given name will be retained.

Contemporary reaction to binary nomenclature reflects the general reaction against the many other Linnaean reforms, and is not so much a judgment on the usefulness of binary names. Even before the publication of the *Species plantarum* in 1753 the world of botany had recognized the magnitude of Linnaeus's impact on science and had become sharply divided over it. The adoption of binary names for species took some time. Leaving aside Linnaean pupils in the strict sense of the word, such as Loefling and Nathorst, the first authors to use 'trivial names' in the Linnaean sense were perhaps J. Burman in his Index to Rumphius' *Auctuarium* (1755) and in his *Wachendorfia* of October 1757, N. L. Burman in his *Specimen botanicum de geraniis* of 17 August 1759, and N. J. Jacquin in his *Enumeratio systematica plantarum* of 1760, all four books published in Holland. Leiden and Amsterdam were early strongholds of the Linnaean reform, dating back to the years when he so successfully convinced van Royen, Gronovius, Boerhaave and Johannes Burman of his great gifts.

Decisive for the use of binary nomenclature in England were Hudson's *Flora anglica* of 1762 and especially the eighth edition of Philip Miller's *Gardeners Dictionary* (1768). Miller, an admirer of Linnaeus from the time of the latter's visit to England in 1736, adopted the Linnaean binary names only in the last of his own editions of the famous *Dictionary*. The adoption of these names in such a widely used work did much to popularize Linnaean nomenclature, not only in England but also abroad. Miller's example was soon followed by others, e.g. by Thomas Martyn in his *Catalogus horti botanici cantabrigiensis* of 1771.

In France Linnaeus had early followers in Louis Gérard (1733–1819) and Antoine Gouan (1733–1821). Gérard did not yet use binary nomenclature in his *Flora gallo-provincialis* of 1761, however, but Gouan did in his *Hortus regius monspeliensis* of 1762.

Victory for binary nomenclature was almost complete by the time of Linnaeus's death in 1778. It is impossible to say which of his activities and innovations did most towards the ultimate victory of his works. The major publications, such as the *Genera plantarum*, *Species plantarum* and *Systema naturae*, would have created order in plant taxonomy and its literature even without the help of binary specific names. On the other hand, this apparently simple and obvious device was so successful and of such direct help towards achieving stability in nomenclature that its rôle in making Linnaeus's work the generally accepted basis for future taxonomy should not be underestimated. The use of binary specific names marked a fundamental dividing line in the actual practice of taxonomy, a division canonized by the *International Code of Botanical Nomenclature* which, since 1905, has accepted the *Species plantarum* of 1753 as the starting point book for botanical nomenclature. The fact that a later starting point had to be adopted for several special groups does not alter the key position of the *Species plantarum* in botanical nomenclature, a position which it derives principally from its introduction of binary nomenclature (fig. 22). For a general introduction to and an analysis of this work I refer to the Ray Society facsimile published in 1957 and 1959. This reprint contains an extensive introduction by W. T. Stearn which is by itself a botanical classic, as well as a wealth of technical information in various indexes and appendices by Heller and Stearn.

Linnaeus published one more edition of the *Species* in 1762 and 1763. This edition is greatly enlarged and contains binary names for many new taxa

Fig. 22. Page 983 of the *Species plantarum* [1753] showing: 1. the absence of a phrase-name for the species of a monotypic genus (*Buxus sempervirens*); 2. the use of varietal epithets; 3. the use of an old generic name as specific epithet (*Betula Alnus*); 4. the consistent binary form of the references to the literature; 5. the simple 'key' function of a subdivision of a genus (*Oppositifoliae*); 6. the provision of descriptive notes for new or incompletely known taxa (*Betula lenta*); 7. one of the rare notes on generic delimitation (under *Betula Alnus*).

3. BETULA foliis cordatis oblongis acuminatis serratis. *lenta.*
Betula julifera, fructu conoide, viminibus lentis. *Gron.*
virg. 115. •
Habitat in Virginia, Canada. ♄
Folia cordato-ovata, acuminata, tenuissime & argute
serrata, glabra. Amentum *fructus ovatum, sessile:*
squamis acuminatis, integris.

4. BETULA foliis orbiculatis crenatis. *Fl. lapp.* 266. *t.* *nana.*
6. *f.* 4. *Fl. suec.* 777. *Amœn. acad.* 1. *p.* 4. *t.* 1.
Hort. cliff. 442. *Roy. lugdb.* 85. *Hall. helv.* 158.
Gmel. sib. 1. *p.* 170. '
Betula pumila, foliis subrotundis. *Amm. act.* 9. *p.* 314.
t. 14. *ruth.* 209.
Habitat in Alpibus Lapponicis, *paludibus* Suecia, Rus-
siæ. ♄

5. BETULA pedunculis ramosis.   *Alnus.*
Alnus. *Fl. lapp.* 340. *Fl. suec.* 775. *Hort. cliff.* 441.
Roy. lugdb. 85. *Gmel. sib.* 171.
α. Alnus rotundifolia glutinosa viridis. *Bauh. pin.* 428. *glutinosa.*
Alnus. *Cam. epit.* 68. *Lœs. pruss.* 10. *t.* 1.
β. Alnus folio incano. *Bauh. pin.* 428.   *incana,*
Habitat in Europa. ♄
Limites inter Aluum *&* Betulam *nullos a natura po-*
sitos esse docuere species 2 *&* 3.

BUXUS.

1. BUXUS. *Hort. cliff.* 441. *Hort. upf.* 283. *Mat. med.* *sempervi-*
423. *Roy. lugdb.* 400.   *rens.*
α. Buxus arborescens. *Bauh. pin.* 471.   arborescens
Buxus. *Dod. pempt.* 782.
β. Buxus humilis. *Dod. pempt.* 782.   suffruticosa,
Buxus foliis rotundioribus. *Bauh. pin.* 471.
Habitat in Europa *australi.*

URTICA.

* Oppositifoliæ.

1. URTICA foliis oppositis, amentis fructiferis globosis. *pilulifera.*
Hort. cliff. 440. *Hort. upf.* 282. *Roy. lugdb.* 209.
Mat. med. 420. *Sauv. monsp.* 307.
Urtica urens pilulas ferens. *Bauh. pin.* 232.
Urtica 1. d'o.coridis semine lini. *Dod. mem.* 4. *p.* 323.
Urtica romana. *Lob. ic.* 522.
β. Urtica altera pilulifera, parietariæ foliis. *Dod. mem.* 4. *p.*
323.   Q q q 4   Urtica

Fig. 22

published by other authors between 1753 and 1762. Another important Linnaean publication in which many species received their binary names for the first time was the tenth edition of the *Systema naturae* (1758–1759). The first volume of this edition is the starting point of binary nomenclature in zoology.

4. The Linnaean collections

In Linnaeus's time the art of making herbaria was well established. Linnaeus's work, especially the *Species plantarum*, is mainly based on herbarium material and on specimens which he had seen growing in the wild or in gardens. Linnaeus travelled very little and never visited regions outside northwestern Europe. Paris was his *Ultima Thule*. Rather than relying too heavily on the literature, however, Linnaeus was always actively assembling herbarium material from other regions. One of the results of the travels of his many pupils was a considerable growth of his herbarium. He also exchanged seeds and plants with keepers of other gardens and added material to his herbarium which he had himself grown from seed. Apart from his own herbarium, Linnaeus made use of several other collections for his many publications; a thorough knowledge of the material available to Linnaeus is therefore of prime importance for the interpretation of his taxa. Stearn (1957) gives a detailed review of the Linnaean herbaria, citing also the relevant literature.

Linnaeus's main herbarium, although no longer complete, is now at The Linnean Society of London. It was started around 1727 and grew rapidly during the period of travelling in Sweden and the stay in Holland. When Linnaeus wrote his *Species plantarum* the herbarium had become an excellent working instrument; at that time the contents and arrangement of the herbarium must have agreed closely with the book. Linnaeus's correspondents were many in number and came from all over the world; a list of them, though very incomplete, is given in the preface to the *Species plantarum*. Linnaeus himself also gave away 'duplicates,' although unfortunately not as freely as he received them. The main reason for this was that the number of duplicates was very limited. These 'duplicates' are sometimes very valuable because a duplicate was not simply another specimen from a single gathering, but another specimen of the same species or variety.

Recipients of these duplicates were mainly Swedish contemporaries: most of these specimens are now in the Linnaean collection at Stockholm, others are at Uppsala. Incidental Linnaean specimens will be found in other herbaria such as those of Haller and Jussieu at Paris, but on the whole they are of little importance.

Linnaeus left his herbarium to his wife with the provision that his son was not to enjoy the use of it. As a result of this rather cynical provision, which was obeyed, strangely enough, by the mother of Carl filius, the herbarium was locked away from human hands but exposed to mould and the rats. Ultimately the younger Linné obtained access to the collection, but he then found that he had to discard many damaged sheets. It is not quite clear what happened, but the main result was that the link between the herbarium and the *Species plantarum* was greatly weakened. It should be realized, however, that Linnaeus himself had added greatly to the herbarium after 1753, and that his annotations are so brief and often cryptic that this connection with the book had become obscured even during his lifetime.

The most amazing part in the history of the herbarium was still to follow, however. After the death of the younger Linné (November 1783) his mother, still alive, offered it for sale to Joseph Banks in London. Banks suggested to the young James Edward Smith (1759–1828) that he should buy it, and the sale was concluded. In October 1784 the collections reached London, with the full cooperation of the Swedish authorities. Extensive details of this story, which, even for the eighteenth century, remains remarkable because of the lack of action by the Swedes to preserve this part of their national heritage, will be found e.g. in Jackson's biography of Linnaeus. It must be said, though, that the herbarium could not have come into better hands. The Linnaean dominance in England was practically unchallenged. The last quarter of the century brought a revival of British taxonomy exemplified by the creation of The Linnean Society of London on 26 February 1788. The collections were accessible, at any rate in principle, to all botanists, although between 1796 and 1829 they were kept rather out of reach in Smith's country residence in Norwich. After Smith's death in March, 1828, The Linnean Society bought the herbarium from the estate. As a result the herbarium, library and many of the manuscripts, all acquired by Smith with the herbarium itself, became lovingly cared for and easily accessible to any plant taxonomist who took the trouble to come to London. The stimulating influence on British taxonomists of the presence of these invaluable collections in their midst can hardly be over-estimated. The final act of making this body of information even more readily available to the world of taxonomy came in the sixties of our own century, through the world–wide diffusion of cheap and high–quality microfiche photographs of the complete herbarium.

For details on the Linnaean specimens in Uppsala and Stockholm I can refer to the publications of Juel (1921) and Lindman (1908–1910) respectively. The Lapland herbarium, rather small, and given by Linnaeus to Johannes Burman, was later acquired by Benjamin Delessert, and is now at the *Institut de France* in Paris.

Several other herbaria were consulted by Linnaeus during his lifetime. They are all listed by Stearn (1957) and need not be discussed here in any detail. As a student Linnaeus had already had access to the herbarium made by Joachim Burser (1583–1639), which is preserved at Uppsala and which provided him with information on the interpretation of many of Caspar Bauhin's taxa. Burser had been closely associated with Bauhin and received authentic material from him. Linnaeus's interpretation of the *Pinax* (1623) often rests upon the Burser herbarium.

Needless to say, the herbarium which Linnaeus found at Clifford's estate, de Hartecamp, and to which he added himself, is of great importance for the interpretation of the plants described in the *Hortus cliffortianus*. This herbarium was acquired by Joseph Banks and is now at the Natural History Museum of the British Museum, London. A famous case resting on the strength of evidence from this herbarium is the interpretation of Linnaeus's *Amaryllis belladonna* (see Dandy and Fosberg 1954).

4

The Linnaean systems

1. *Classes plantarum*

Linnaeus published three systems of his own, of which the sexual system has had the greatest impact. He set down his rules for systems in his *Fundamenta botanica* of 1736, but elaborated them further in his much less known though equally interesting *Classes plantarum*, published in Leiden in 1738. The *Classes plantarum* bears as a subtitle *Fundamentorum botanicorum pars II* (fig. 23) and consists of a review of 16 'universal' and 13 'partial' systems of plants of other authors as well as of his own, all based on the 'fructification.'

In his preface, dated Leiden 20 March 1738, Linnaeus states: "Nil pulchrius, nil magis utile & necessarium in botanicis desideratum & inventum est, quam systematica plantarum Methodus, quae ignarum in vasto Vege-tabilium Regno constitutum recta ducit ad desideratam plantam ejusque nomen. Quid umquam Botanica vel quis Botanicis absque methodo?"

Linnaeus elaborates his thesis that the 'empiricists' muddle along by looking through herbaria, books and illustrations, but that the taxono-mist, thanks to his logical system, eliminates step by step major groups of alternatives, thus quickly identifying his plant. There are many systems, one better than another perhaps, but they all aim at an efficient disposition of the taxa. There are two main kinds: artificial and natural.

"Naturalia dicuntur quae classes naturales servant, in quibus classibus nullae admittuntur, nisi quae inter se affines sunt plantae, tota facie et natura convenientes." In other words: the classes of the natural system contain plants which are interrelated because they agree fully in *facies* and *natura*. By *facies* Linnaeus means 'habit,' including general vegetative charac-teristics, by *natura* he means the structure of the fructification.

"Artificialia vero constant Classibus, quas ingrediuntur varia indiscriminatim plantarum genera, inter se toto coelo diversa, nisi quod conveniant unica ista nota Classi a Systematico praefixa."

Or, freely: artificial classes contain very diverse genera, totally different except that they agree in possessing a single characteristic chosen by the taxonomist as the criterion of the class.

The book itself contains extensive treatments of 29 systems of which sixteen are universal, treating the whole plant kingdom; the remainder are partial, treating special taxa only. Linnaeus presents these systems in the form of a key in which it should be noted that system 16, 'Fragmenta' (of a natural method), is defined as universal and based on the whole fructification.

The treatment of each system is thorough and objective. A brief summary is given of the main principles ruling the system; then follow bibliographical references to the books observing the system, a key to the classes and lists of the classes themselves. These lists contain the names of the genera included in the classes, with their Linnaean equivalents. An index at the end gives the place of each Linnaean genus in each of the sixteen universal systems. The book is a perfect example of clear, objective, and concise presentation of taxonomic information, and as such it ranks with the *Hortus cliffortianus* and the *Species plantarum*.

Linnaeus himself is represented by three universal systems and two partial ones:

14. Methodus à calycis speciebus,
15. Systema à sexu: staminibus & pistillis [sic, Linnaeus uses here 'systema' rather than methodus],
16. Fragmenta methodi naturalis,
24. Methodus graminum,
29. Methodus filicum.

2. *Methodus calycina*

Linnaeus presented an artificial method based on the structure of the

Fig. 23. Title–page of the *Classes plantarum* [1738], describing the systems based on the fructification. The book is presented as the second part of the *Fundamenta botanica*, aphorisms 53–77 of which deal with this subject matter. [II. Systemata].

CAROLI LINNÆI

Med. Doct.

Soc. Ac. Imper. Nat. Cur.

CLASSES
PLANTARUM·

Seu

SYSTEMATA PLANTARUM

Omnia a *fructificatione* defumta,
quorum XVI Univerſalia & XIII Partialia,
compendioſe propoſita

Secundum

CLASSES, ORDINES ET NOMINA GENERICA CUM
CLAVE CUJUSVIS METHODI ET SYNONYMIS
GENERICIS.

FUNDAMENTORUM BOTANICORUM PARS II.

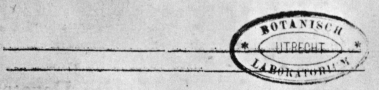

LUGDUNI BATAVORUM,
Apud CONRADUM WISHOFF, 1738·

Sk

Fig. 23

'calyx' in addition to his sexual system, mainly for the benefit of beginners in natural history. It appears in detail in the *Classes plantarum* and is mentioned only in passing in the *Philosophia botanica*. It is an exercise which reminds us of the one which Adanson undertook later, on a more elaborate scale and to create a basis for his natural system.

The calyx, says Linnaeus, is the part of the fructification which first presents itself to our eyes, which protects the flower and—often—the fruit, and which is shed only when the fruit matures. Young botanists will have the least difficulty in setting up a system if they base it on the calyx. There are five species (Aristotelian use of the word!) of calyx: the *spatha* (as in Palms, Araceae, but also Liliaceae and Amaryllidaceae), the *gluma* (Gramineae, Cyperaceae, and e.g. *Typha*), the *amentum* (Amentiferae, but also Gymnosperms, and some Compositae), the *involucre* and the *calyptra*. Linnaeus's use of the word calyx is broad because it is defined as the representation of the *cortex* of the plant in the fructification (Phil. bot. 86). The *Philosophia* gives further definitions of the terms used to describe the 'species of calyx,' such as

"*Amentum* ... Calyx ex Receptaculo communi paleaceo–gemmaceo
Spatha ... Calyx *Spadicis* longitudinaliter ruptus ..."

The key to the orders of the system shows that the 'perianthium' is the most common type of calyx: this actually is more in agreement with the present use of the word.

The *systema calycina* never really caught on. It is doubtful that it was as simple and readily understandable for the 'tyro' as Linnaeus stated; his later neglect of this system seems to confirm this.

3. The Sexual system

All Linnaean works follow the sexual system of classification as set out first in a key in the *Systema naturae* of 1735. At the basis of this system is Linnaeus's evaluation of the rôle of reproduction as a universal function. "For Linnaeus reproduction contained the secret working–plan of the Creator" (Engel 1964).

Linnaeus's interest in the sexuality of plants was kindled by his teacher Rothman at the gymnasium at Växjö (Savage 1936, Stearn 1957). Rothman attached great importance to the structure of the flower; he seems to have been acquainted with Vaillant's *Sermo de structura florum* (1718) and may well have drawn Linnaeus's attention to this paper. Linnaeus himself wrote down his ideas on this subject as early as 1729, in a manuscript entitled *Praeludia sponsaliorum plantarum* (fig. 24), and elaborated upon it in the fifth chapter of the *Fundamenta* and the *Philosophia*.

For a penetrating analysis of this manuscript and of the genesis of the sexual system in Linnaeus's mind I refer to a recent publication by Larson (1967). There is no doubt that the conviction that reproduction was a primary feature of the essence of vegetable life goes back to Linnaeus's earliest days.

A detailed description of the sexual system appears in the *Classes plantarum*. A whole page is devoted to the jubilant announcement in outsize type: "V. Systema a staminibus quod Nostrum est."

In the introductory paragraphs Linnaeus explains that previous systematists neglected the stamens and the pistils, but that nature guides him to

Fig. 24. Title–page of Linnaeus's manuscript *Praeludia sponsaliorum plantarum* of 1729 [reproduced from Uggla 1957]. *Reduced.*

use these for his system. The second statement is the most important because it asserts that the stamens and the pistils are the 'essence' of the flower:

"Commendabant se munere quo fungebantur, quum his solis omnis plantarum propagatio innitebatur, latebat in his tam nullis ipsa floris Essentia; Flos enim nil *est* nisi *Actus generationis plantarum*; generatio haec absolvitur solis staminum *Antheris*, pistillorumque *Stigmatibus*, adeoque sine his nullus fructus."

"These (stamens and pistils) were claiming attention by their function, since the whole generation of the plants depended on them alone; in these apparently insignificant (*tam nullis* see *Syst. Nat. Introit.*) parts lay hidden the very essence of the flower, for the flower is nothing else but the generative act of plants; this generation is completed only by the anthers of the stamens and the stigmata of the pistils. Without these there is no fruit" [translation John Heller.]

Furthermore: "Classes vel ordines naturales admisit tot, quot ulla methodus alia, numerus tamen genio ubique fruitur suo; obstacula quae methodo contraria erant collegi, candidus imperti [impertii; the words are taken from Horace]; Naturalem methodum nec hanc, nec aliam vocaverim ullam."

"It admits as many natural classes and orders as any other method, but in the numbers [of classes] it enjoys complete freedom. I have collected the exceptional cases [of genera] which contradict the method and I have acknowledged them openly; I would not call this method Natural, nor any other either" [translation John Heller.]

The key (fig. 25, see also fig. 26) taken from the *Classes plantarum* shows the main division of the sexual system into 24 classes on the basis of the number of the stamens, their relative lengths, their distinctness or fusion, and their presence or absence in certain flowers.

The 24 classes were divided in *ordines* on the basis of the number of carpels. We have seen above that the arrangement of the genera in the *ordines* was as much as possible in accordance with the fragments of his natural system; in many cases Linnaeus found that these fragments fitted quite well into his sexual system. No wonder that he attributed such a high value to it and

Fig. 25. Key to the classes of the sexual system, Linnaeus, *Classes Plantarum* [1738].

Clavis methodi Sexualis.

Flores funt vel

Vifibiles cujus omnes partes diftincte tradi
queunt; his vel

Stamina & Piftilla in eodem flore, tum

Staminibus nulla fui parte inter fe
connatis

æqualibus vel abfque certa pro-
portione longitudinis, his

Stamen unicum ——— ———Monandria	1
Stamina duo ——— ———Diandria	2
Stamina tria ——— ———Triandria	3
Stamina quatuor ——— ———Tetrandria	4
Stamina quinque ———Pentandria	5
Stamina fex ———Hexandria	6
Stamina feptem ——— ———Heptandria	7
Stamina octo ——— ———Octandria	8
Stamina novem ——— ———Enneandria	9
Stamina decem ———Decandria	10
Stamina duodecim ———Dodecandria	11
Stamina plura (fæpe viginti)	
calyci inferta———Icofandria	12
Stamina plura, calyci non	
inferta ——— ———Polyandria	13

inæqualibus ita ut duo femper
breviora fint; tum

duo longiora funt filamenta . Didynamia	14
quatuor longiora filamenta - Tetradynamia	15

Staminibus aliqua fui parte cohæren-
tibus, vel

Filamentis coalitis in unum corpus Monadelphia	16
——— coalitis in duo corpora Diadelphia	17
——— coalitis in plura corpora Polyadelphia	18
Antheris coalitis in cylindrum Syngenefia	19
Staminibus coalitis cum piftillo,	
feu ei infidentibus. ——— ———Gynandria	20

Stamina & Piftilla in diftinctis a fe invicem floribus: vel in una eademque

planta ambo ——— ——— ———Monoecia	21
in duabus diftinctis plantis, feparata - Dioecia	22
alia feparata, alia in eodem flore fimul Polygamia	23

Vix vifibiles, cujus partes diftinctæ (a nobis)

tradi nequeunt ——— ——— ———Cryptogamia	24

Clavis hujus triplicem explicationem, fecundum nomina, fecundum analogiam fexus, & fecundum ftructuram fructificationis dedimus in Syftemate Naturæ trium regnorum.

Monogygynia, Digynia eft Piftillum unicum, duo &c.

Ordinum ampliorum fubdivifiones in Methodo fexuali & Syftemat.
Nat. dedimus.

Fig. 25

that he was basically not at all convinced that the sexual system itself was after all so unnatural. Linnaeus realized very well that the method presented some practical problems, especially with smaller flowers and with cryptogams. In his *Systema naturae* (1735, Obs. 17 in Regn. veg.) he writes: "I predict that botanists surely will say, that my method presents too great a difficulty notably for examining the very small parts of a flower, which one can hardly see with the naked eye. *I reply*: If everybody interested would have a 'microscopium' (magnifying glass), a most necessary instrument, at hand, what work would there be left? I myself, however, have examined all these plants with the naked eye, and without any use of a 'microscopium.' However, the last class seems as it were to have been excluded by the Creator from the theory of stamens, and so I have not described them according to their number, for nature does not allow to join them together on account of their stamens. See the works of the Illustrious *Micheli*."

In his next observation (18), Linnaeus explains the refinement accomplished by his subdivisions: "In order not to let the orders appear too long and therefore too difficult, I have distinguished them, according to their fructification, into auxiliary subdivisions. Among them the group of *Pentandria monogynia* are most noteworthy, where the Umbellatae are dealt with, which I have arranged according to the method thought out by the illustrious *Artedi* for the Umbelliferae. ... This method bears the palm among all others in this family" [translation Engel and Engel 1964].

The German artist G. D. Ehret (1708–1770), on his visit to Holland in 1736, made an engraving of an illustrated version of the Linnaean sexual system. Two editions are known, the one reproduced in Taxon 3: 175, of which only one specimen is known (at Uppsala), and the one, undated, often found in combination with the first edition of the *Systema naturae* (see also Uggla 1939). This illustration was repeatedly used in other publications by or on Linnaeus; the version given here (fig. 41) is that appearing in David de Gorter, *Leer der plantkunde of* 1782.

Linnaeus brought the system, all ready for printing, to Holland. He found it very practical for classifying the many new plants he encountered there, and in later years he often repeated that his sexual system had been

Fig. 26. Key to the classes of the sexual system as given in Linnaeus, *Systema naturae*, ed. 10, vol. 2 [1759]. Note in this key the anthropocentric descriptive phrases which are made superfluous by the technical definitions printed in italics.

CLAVIS SYSTEMATIS SEXUALIS.

NUPTIÆ PLANTARUM.
Actus generationis incolarum Regni vegetabilis.
Florescentia.
ʃPUBLICÆ.
Nuptiæ, omnibus manifestæ, aperte celebrantur.
Flores unicuique visibiles.
ʃMONOCLINIA.
Mariti & uxores uno eodemque thalamo gaudent.
Flores omnes hermaphroditi sunt, & stamina cum pistillis in eodem flore.
ʃDIFFINITAS.
Mariti inter se non cognati.
Stamina nulla sua parte connata·inter se sunt.
ʃINDIFFERENTISMUS.
Mariti nullam subordinationem inter se invicem servant.
Stamina nullam determinatam proportionem longitudinis inter se invicem habent.

1. MONANDRIA.	7. HEPTANDRIA.
2. DIANDRIA.	8. OCTANDRIA.
3. TRIANDRIA.	9. ENNEANDRIA.
4. TETRANDRIA.	10. DECANDRIA.
5. PENTANDRIA.	11. DODECANDRIA.
6. HEXANDRIA.	12. ICOSANDRIA.
	13. POLYANDRIA.

SUBORDINATIO.
Mariti certi reliquis præferuntur.
Stamina duo semper reliquis breviora sunt.
14. DIDYNAMIA. | 15. TETRADYNAMIA.
AFFINITAS.
Mariti propinqui & cognati sunt.
Stamina cohærent inter se invicem aliqua sua parte vel cum pistillo.

16. MONADELPHIA.	19. SYNGENESIA.
17. DIADELPHIA.	20. GYNANDRIA.
18. POLYADELPHIA.	

DICLINIA (a δὶς bis & κλίνη thalamus ʃ. duplex thalamus.)
Mariti & Feminæ distinctis thalamis gaudent.
Flores masculi & feminei in eadem specie.

21. MONOECIA.	23. POLYGAMIA.
22. DIOECIA.	

CLANDESTINÆ.
Nuptiæ clam instituuntur.
Flores oculis nostris nudis vix conspiciuntur.
24. CRYPTOGAMIA.

CLAS-

Fig. 26

and still was primarily designed for rapid identification; it served the function of a key to the whole plant kingdom.

The only place where Linnaeus gave keys down to the genera was in the *Systema naturae* (e.g. ed. 10, vol. 2. 1759). The *Genera plantarum* and the *Species plantarum* did not contain such keys; those in the *Systema* are not all dichotomous but they are certainly usable. The keying out of the genera in the *Systema* is somewhat similar to that of the species per genus in the *Species plantarum*: by means of terse diagnostic phrases. It is for this reason that the various editions of the *Systema* best served Linnaeus's ideal of rapid identification. One had to turn to the *Genera* and *Species plantarum*, however, for further details, bibliographical references and synonymy.

In his justifications for the sexual system, such as the stamens and the pistil being the essence of the flower, Linnaeus showed a curious mixture of empirical intuition and old-fashioned apriori reasoning. He simply considered it bad taste not to have a philosophical justification for a 'method,' although his first objective was undoubtedly to create an eminently practical system. The basic tenets of Linnaeus's mind were not uncompromisingly Aristotelian–scholastic; this was only the shape he gave to his thoughts and methods, in agreement with contemporary practice. Basic was his belief that species, genera, and natural orders had been created as such by God, that they were unchangeable and therefore recognizable by man. True, in later years he changed his opinion on the species to some extent, but not really in principle. His much repeated statement (before 1761) that there are as many species as were created in the beginning was just a way of stressing that species are distinct entities, maintaining themselves by propagation. His insistence on natural genera was even more fundamental, because here no objective criterion such as self–reproduction was available. Even so, the delimitation of the genera had to be found in the 'fructification.'

The real reason why Linnaeus thought the sexual system to be superior was that it left the genera intact. He did not mean simply the genera themselves; the sexual system is concerned with taxa of higher rank. He certainly also meant the arrangement of genera in more or less natural groups in the higher echelons.

[124]

4. *Fragmenta Methodi naturalis*

Although Linnaeus modified his ideas on the natural system slightly during his lifetime, none of these amendments affected his basic attitude towards it as expressed for the first time in extenso, in his *Classes plantarum* (485–488). The conviction that species were stable units propagating themselves without change, a seventeenth–century notion resulting from the abolishment of any lingering ideas on *generatio spontanea*, is at the basis of Linnaeus's concept of what is "natural." His use of this word agrees more or less with "created as such." In the beginning of the eighteenth century one could not call this an old–fashioned concept. On the contrary, the discovery of "all life from the egg" and of the continuity of generations, free from the spectacular mutations in which so many had believed, was a definite and positive achievement. Linnaeus's concept of life rested on an experimental scientific basis. He extrapolated his views on the nature of the species to genera and ordines and was actually convinced that these were also natural in the sense of 'created as such.' He was enough of an empiricist, however, to state of the genera and ordines that they would be known only if all included taxa were known. For the genera he saw the key to recognition of their natural delimitation in a search for their essence, which could be derived from the structure of the fructification. For the ordines, however, the realization that his knowledge was very incomplete weighed more heavily. All through his life Linnaeus was confronted with a stream of new forms, many of them of groups previously unknown. Plants from the Cape such as the Proteaceae may be cited as an example: many of these new and completely different taxa came to his knowledge during his productive years and were a warning to him not to jump to conclusions about knowing the 'natural' delimitation of the higher taxa. Linnaeus's attitude was nominalistic only in so far as he recognized the nominalist character of many of the higher taxa *as known to him*; in his basic thinking he remained an essentialist, believing that objective delimitation would eventually be possible. We have seen above that 'nature' and 'essence' are often almost equivalent in the writings of Linnaeus; the natural, or the created, could be known only through its essence. The botanists of the Enlightenment, on the contrary, did not share this quest for the 'essence,' but concentrated on overall description as a means to 'catch' nature. The main difference between these two ways of thinking is that between

[125]

diagnosis and description; it is the analysis along apriori established lines of thought as against biological research along more inductive lines.

In practice the difference in result was negligible. Linnaeus's essentialist fragments of a natural method are not fundamentally different from the natural methods developed by Adanson and the Jussieus (Stafleu 1963). The main reason is that Linnaeus's natural method was just as much based on an intuitive approach to involved character complexes as that of his opponents; the difference was mainly to be found in the justification.

Linnaeus stated in his *Philosophia botanica* (although in other words) that the natural method was based on overall affinity. He actually used the word affinity. In the *Classes plantarum*, however, his presentation was still less sophisticated; the main contents of his 13 dicta can be paraphrased as follows (fig. 27):

1. The natural method is the first and the last desideratum in taxonomic botany. While it has been as highly praised by wiser botanists as it was deprecated by the less learned, it has so far not been discovered.

2. Botanists often use the 'natural method' as an argument to praise one system or to deprecate another. The private opinion of botanists varies greatly on the degree of naturalness of the various systems.

3. Once all the natural orders have been culled from all given systems, the number of plants whose orders have been discovered will surely be smaller than one would easily believe, though so many 'completely natural' methods have been proclaimed.

4. Linnaeus affirms that he himself has also worked at a natural method and that he has grasped quite a few points to add; he could not carry them through but would continue searching as long as he lived. In the meantime he will report on what he knows. He who can complete the picture by describing the few plants that remain, will do botany a great service.

5. Any other method proposed as natural should be tested against the Linnaean *Fragmenta*. The more agreement there is, the more deserved is the epithet 'natural.'

6. A method which preserves more natural orders is more natural than one which keeps a smaller number of them intact.

Fig. 27. The first nine (of thirteen) aphorisms of Linnaeus's *Fragmenta methodi naturalis* published in the *Classes plantarum* [1738].

FRAGMENTA
METHODI NATURALIS.

1. Primum & ultimum in parte Syſtematica Botanices quæſi-
tum eſt Methodus Naturalis; Hæc adeo a Botanicis minus
doctis vili habita; a ſapientioribus vero tanti ſemper æſti-
mata, adhuc licet detecta nondum.

2. Quid magis frequens apud Botanicos quam unius methodi
ſummus honos, alterius vero ſummus neglectus; quod illa
magis naturalis ſit, hæc autem minus; licet res contrario
modo ſæpe ſe habeat, & a fama methodi & idiotiſmo Botanici ſolum multoties pependit pretium.

3. Collectis omnibus, ex omnibus datis ſyſtematibus, ordinibus naturalibus, certe in pauciorem rediguntur numerum
plantæ, quarum ordines detecti ſunt, quam quis facile
crederet, licet tot proclamatæ ſint methodi naturaliſſimæ.

4. Diu & Ego circa methodum naturalem inveniendam labo-
ravi, bene multa quæ adderem obtinui, perficere non potui,
continuaturus dum vixero; interim quæ novi proponam:
qui paucas, quæ reſtant, bene abſolvit plantas, omnibus magnus erit Apollo.

5. Cum aliquis naturalem methodum jactet, ſecundum hos ordines eam examinent Botanici, plantas enim has ſi conjun-
xerit, nec peregrinas immiſcuerit, digna eſt methodus ſuo
nomine, hos vero ſi ſeparaverit, contra.

6. Methodus quæ plures ordines naturales ſervavit quam altera, magis naturalis dicatur altera, & vice verſa.

7. *Clavis* methodi non dari poteſt antequam omnes plantæ relatæ ſunt ad ordines.

8. Non ſatis eſt in definitione ordinis dediſſe notas communes,
niſi & his interſint, quæ etiam eam ab omnibus aliis diſtin-
guant.

9. Claſſes nullas propono, ſed ſolos ordines, detectis ordinibus,
dein in claſſicis labor facilis erit.

Hh 2

10. Nulla

Fig. 27

489 *Fragmenta Methodi Naturalis.* 490

I. *ORDO.*

Arum
Dracontium
Calla
Acorus
Saururus
Piper

Et innumeræ aliæ utriusque Indiæ ad genera etiamnum non relatæ, quas Plumier & Rheede delinearunt.

II. *ORDO.*

Corypha
Borassus
Coccus
Chamærops
Phœnix
Caryota

Omnesque Palmæ aliæ a Plumiero & Rheede depictæ.

III. *ORDO.*

Musa
Thalia
Alpinia
Costus
Canna
Maranta
Amomum
Curcuma
Kæmpferia

IV. *ORDO.*

Orchis
Satyrium
Serapias
Herminnum
Neottia
Ophrys
Cypripedium
Epidendrum

Et numerosa ista familia Americes a Plumiero delineata, ad genera nondum amandata.

V. *ORDO.*

Iris
Gladiolus
Antholyza
Sisyrinchium.

VI. *ORDO.*

Sagittaria
Alisma
Butomus

Forte & ad has referre licet *Stratioten* & *Hydrocharin*, nec adeo ab his abludit *Triglochin*.

Hh 3 VII. *OR-*

Fig. 28

7. It is impossible to give a key to the natural method before all genera have been assigned their proper places.

8. When defining an order it is not sufficient to list the common characters; one should also list the characters which distinguish the order from all others.

9. Linnaeus proposes only orders, not classes. As soon as the orders are known it will be simple to arrange them in classes.

10. The orders in the *Fragmenta* are themselves not necessarily in a natural order; Linnaeus confined himself to indicating the genera which belong together in the same order.

11. Those who are capable are invited to improve, extend and complete this method; those who cannot do this should leave the method alone. Those who can are superbotanists.

12. No apriori rule is in force here, and not one part or another of the fructification [should be singled out]. The real 'character' (read 'description') will be found but merely in the simple symmetry of all parts as often indicated by the peculiar characters (this is equivalent to stating that there is agreement in character complexes, an integral relationship of all parts).

13. Those who seek to build a key should realize the prime importance of the position of the growing tip of the young plant in the seed and the way the seed germinates. The method of Cesalpino should be followed here.

In the 1738 version of the *Fragmenta* the orders have no names yet (fig. 28). We find them e.g. in the *Philosophia* (fig. 29). Interesting features of the 1738 version are the brief critical notes such as the one under order no. 31 (*Capparis, Breynia, Morisona, Crataeva*): "Hac praecedentibus (30) valde affines sunt." Order 30 comprises the *Rhoeadales*, but it is the use of the word *affines* which is most remarkable here. In agreement with the above-mentioned tenet no. 7, the *Classes plantarum* contains no key to the natural orders; however, in the year of its publication, 1738, Linnaeus helped Adriaan van Royen in Leiden to prepare such a key for his *Florae Leydensis prodromus* (fig. 33).

If we take the genera of Linnaeus's *Columniferi, Contorti, Luridae, Verticillatae, Multisiliquae, Tricocca, Caryophyllei* and *Preciae*, all groups of which Linnaeus had a fair knowledge in 1751, it appears (Stafleu 1963) that of the 142 genera,

Fig. 28. The first part of Linnaeus's fragment of a natural system given in the *Classes plantarum* [1738].

22. UMBELLATÆ.
Eryngium
Arctopus
Hydrocotyle
Sanicula
Aftrantia
Tordylium
Caucalis
Artedia
Daucus
Ammi
Bunium
Conium
Selinum
Athamanta
Peucedanum
Chrithmum
Cachrys
Ferula
Laferpitium
Ligufticum
Angelica
Sium
Bubon
Sifon
Oenanthe
Phellandrium
Cicuta
Coriandrum
Ethufa
Bupleurum
Scandix
Chærophyllum
Sefeli.
Imperatoria
Heracleum
Thapfia
Paftinaca
Smyrnium
Anethum
Carum

Pimpinella
Ægopodium
Apium
Anifum
Lagœcia.
23. MULTISILIQUÆ.
Pæonia
Aquilegia
Aconitum
Delphinium
Garidella
Nigella
Ifopyrum
Helleborus
Caltha
Ranunculus
Myofurus
Adonis
Anemone
Hepatica
Pulfatilla
Atragene
Clematis
Thalictrum.
24. BICORNES.
Ledum
Azalea
Andromeda
Clethra
Erica
Myrfine
Memecylum
Santalum
Vaccinium
Arbutus
Royena
Diofpyros
Melaftoma
Pyrola.
25. SEPIARIÆ.
Nyctanthes

Jafminum
Liguftrum
Brunsfelfia
Olea
Chionanthus
Fraxinus
Syringa.
26. CULMINIÆ.
Tilia
Theobroma
Sloanea
Bixa
Heliocarpus
Triumfetta
Bartramia
Muntingia
Clufia
Dillenia
Kiggelaria
Grewia
Corchorus.
27. VAGINALES.
Laurus
Helxine
Polygonum
Biftorta
Perficaria
Atraphaxis
Rheum
Rumex.
28. CORYDALES.
Melianthus
Epimedium
Hypecoum
Fumaria
Impatiens
Leontice
Monotropa?
Utricularia?
Tropœolum?

29. CON-

Fig. 29

118 (83%) were put in the correct family according to modern standards. If we take the modern equivalents of the rank of order for his *ordines*, the number of correctly placed genera is 131, or 92%. Linnaeus does not give any indication of his guidelines and criteria, except those contained in the 13 canons mentioned above. The general criterion was an overall similarity, especially but not exclusively of the structure of the fructification. What he in fact did was to evaluate this overall similarity more or less intuitively on the basis of his profound knowledge of the plants. Theoretical considerations hardly played a role. Linnaeus's 'Columniferi' can be equated with the suborder *Malvineae* of Engler, with the exclusion of the *Tiliaceae* (*Malvaceae, Bombacaceae, Sterculiaceae, Byttneriaceae*). An analysis of this Linnaean natural order reveals that 15 out of 19 genera were correctly placed, two genera (*Camellia* and *Stewartia*) are now assigned to the *Theaceae* and two other genera (*Turnera* and *Mentzelia*) are placed in families which are now widely separated from the *Malvineae*. In his *Species plantarum* (1753) and *Genera plantarum* ed. 5 (1754) this group reappears for the most part, understandably, under the *Monadelphia*; exceptions are, for instance, *Turnera* and *Mentzelia*.

By 1764 (Gen. pl. ed. 6) Linnaeus had received more non–European material and included in all 33 genera in his *Columniferae* (he had changed the ending) of these 27 (82%) belong to the *Malvales* and 26 (79%) to the *Malvineae*.

A curious early essay by Linnaeus on a fragment of the natural method is the rare brochure published privately in 1736 with the support of Clifford: *Musa cliffortiana florens Hartecampi 1736 prope Harlemum*. This publication was printed as a gift for friends; relatively few copies of it were known until it was republished in facsimile. When Linnaeus worked at the Hartekamp a banana tree flowered for the first time in the Netherlands in Clifford's garden. The booklet is virtually a monograph of *Musa paradisiaca* (*cliffortiana* is evidently not a trivial name avant–la–lettre, but a simple linguistic *epitheton ornans*) and contains the earliest elaboration and explanation of quite a few of the aphorisms of the *Fundamenta botanica*. After a nomenclatural discussion Linnaeus provides a taxonomic setting for his genus in the chapter called '*theoretica.*' He mentions in passing that it belongs to the *Polygamia monoecia* in 'his' system, but then discusses amply its position in the natural method (fig. 30). It belongs to the *Classis palmarum*, which is defined and

Fig. 29. Part of Aphorism 77 of the *Philosophia botanica* [1751] showing, among others, the natural families Umbelliferae (22), Ranunculaceae (23), Ericaceae (24).

Spatha nobis eft calyx membranaceus a latere fecundum longitudinem dehifcens.

Spadix verò receptaculum fructificationum commune e pedunculo productum, ad bafin femper fimplex, pluribus floribus, fecundum longitudinem varie annexis, inferviens. Hinc fequens propono Syftema.

Claſſis
Palmarum.

CLASSIS PALMARUM.

Ordines hujus claffis quatuor conftituimus. A. B. C. D.

Ordo pri-
mus.

A. SPATHA *unica, fimplex.* SPADIX *fimpliciſſimus.*
   1. ARUM. vide *Characteres* noftros *Naturales* fub *Gynandria Polyandria.*
   2. CALLA. vide *Char. Nat.* fub *Gynandria Polyandria.*
   3. ACORUS. vid. *Char. Nat.* fub *Hexandria Monogynia.*

Ordo fe-
cundus.

B. SPATHA *unica, compoſita.* SPADIX *ramoſiſſimus.*
   1. CHAMEROPS. *Chamæriphes.* Pont. X.
   CAL: *Spatha* univerfalis, compreffa, femibifida.
   COR: tripartita. *Petalis* ovatis, acutis, erectis, apice inflexis, coriaceis.
   STAM: *Filamenta* fex, fubulato-compreffa, bafi leviter cohærentia, corollâ breviora. *Antheræ* lineares, didymæ, adnatæ interiori parieti filamentorum.
   PIST: *Germina* tria, fubrotunda. *Styli* totidem diftincti, breviffimi, perfiftentes. *Stigmata* acuta.
   PER: *Baccæ* tres, globofæ, uniloculares.
   SEM: folitaria, globofa.

CO-

Fig. 30. Page 10 of Linnaeus, Musa cliffortiana florens Hartecampi 1736 prope Harlemum [Leiden 1736]. This monograph of the genus *Musa* contains also a description of the natural *Classis Palmarum*, its division into four 'ordines' and a description of a number of the included genera. *Reduced.*

which contains four natural orders, A, B, C, and D. A corresponds to our present *Araceae* (*Arum, Calla, Acorus*), B to our *Palmae*, C to the *Zingiberales* (but with *Iris*) and D to the *Orchidaceae*. Apart from providing diagnoses for the four orders (something which he never did in his later *Fragmenta*), Linnaeus takes the opportunity to describe several new genera, such as '*Chamerops*,' *Corypha, Costus* and *Amomum*, all based on the plates and descriptions of these plants in Rheede's *Hortus malabaricus*. The remainder of the book is the actual monograph of the genus *Musa* and of its only species, with several varieties. The main importance of the document, however, lies in the emphasis on the natural system and on the elaboration of it for this special case. The book is, to my knowledge, the only publication of Linnaeus in which he follows strictly the order of his own *Methodus* of 1736.

The statement (*Phil. bot. 77*) that the plant world is like a geographical map shows that Linnaeus realized that the natural system would be characterized by multiple relationships. The natural orders would contain genera which would have different relations with various other orders: Donati's metaphor of a *reticulum* says in fact the same. This is an improvement over the old *scala naturae*, the idea of a single chain of being. In his later years Linnaeus elaborated on his ideas in his lectures at Uppsala. One of his pupils, Giseke, published his own notes on these lectures and those of Fabricius as Linnaeus's *Praelectiones in ordines naturales plantarum* (Hamburg 1792). The book contains a wealth of details but was out of date by the time it was published. It is furthermore impossible to know which part comes from Linnaeus and what was added by Giseke. Linnaeus's main thoughts of his later years are, however, discernible. One of the most interesting features of the book is the *Tabula genealogico–geographica affinitatum plantarum secundum ordines naturales Linnaei* [*quam*] *delineavit Paulus Dietericus Giseke 1789*, evidently an effort by Giseke, which shows the Linnaean orders as circles of different size arranged in two dimensions, in accordance with their affinities. This chart, which was made without any phylogenetic ideas in mind, is very ingenious and has a modern flavour. Pulle's graphic representation of the plant kingdom in his *Compendium* (1938), for instance, seems to have been inspired by Giseke's chart.

5. *The origin of taxa*

The last version of the natural system prepared for publication by Linnaeus himself was that of 1764, published as an appendix to the sixth edition of the *Genera plantarum*. The list of the ordines is preceded by an extremely interesting set of aphorisms on the natural orders which Linnaeus had not previously published and which reveal the evolution of his general taxonomic thinking in later years.

One of the most repeated of Linnaeus's dicta is the one on the stability of species: "Species tot numeramus quot diversae formae in principio sunt creatae," or, we count as many species as different forms were created in the beginning. We encounter this in the *Fundamenta botanica* (no. 157) as well as, in a more elaborate form, in the *Philosophia*. We have seen that in Linnaeus's youth the discovery that there is no *generatio spontanea*, and that like produces like, was relatively new. The fact that species are delimited by continuous generation, and that they never spring from dead material or from widely distant other beings, was much more of a novelty at his time than is now generally realized. Linnaeus's belief in the way the creator had operated ('in the beginning') was more or less in agreement with the result of late seventeenth–century research on the nature of generation.

In the course of his life Linnaeus modified his ideas in this respect. At first he was quite impressed by Marchant's discovery of a mutation in *Mercurialis* (1719) and by his own discovery of the peloric *Linaria*. In the comments on aphorism 157 in the *Philosophia*, however, the doubts seem to have been stilled. Evidently his ideas went in another direction, although this did not become clear until 1762, in the dissertation *Fundamentum fructificationis*, and in a more general way in 1764 in the appendix to the *Genera plantarum*. This 1764 statement on the nature of the natural orders is given here in Stearn's translation (with his parenthetical remarks) (1959); it is revealing with respect to Linnaeus's ideas on the mechanism of 'creation,' but also a fitting summary of his mature thoughts on the natural system itself.

1. The Creator of the Universe in the beginning clothed the vegetable *Medulla* (core, essence, primary matter) with diverse constituent possibilities (principles, beginnings, basic elements) of a *Cortex* (skin, covering, outside), whence sprang as many individuals of different form as [there are] Natural *orders*.

2. The Omnipotent blended the classes of plants (derived from 1 above), whence came as many genera of the orders as [there were] plants.

3. Nature blended the Genera (derived from 2 above), whence [came] as many *Species* of the same genus as exist today.

4. Chance blended the *Species* (derived from 3 above) whence [came] as many *Varieties* as occur here and there.

5. These processes (see 1–4 above) took place because of the laws of the Creator which lead from simple things to complex: the laws of nature in producing hybrids; the laws of man in observing what has taken place.

6. The botanist must observe these laws as far as he can.

[7.] The Beginner must learn to allocate *Varieties* to *Species*, since a detailed knowledge is the first step to a sound understanding.

[8.] The Botanist must allocate *Species* to *Genera*, since from that comes [knowledge of] the fraternal affinity of plants. Let the Veteran attempt to allocate *Genera* to [Natural] *Orders*, since thereby he gains an insight into the Nature of the vegetable kingdom; this, however, is difficult because of want of knowledge of matters still hidden, e.g.

    Tamarix . . . . . . *Cactus*, if not *Reaumuria*

    Actaea . . . . . . *Paeonia*, if not *Cimicifuga*

9. A multitude of *Genera* is a burden on the memory to be lightened by *System*.

System will indicate the plant without [the aid of] a teacher. Natural orders without a key do not constitute a method. And so an artificial method has only diagnostic value since it is not possible or it is hardly possible to find the key to the natural method.

10. Natural orders indicate the nature of plants. Artificial orders are effectual [only] for the diagnosis of plants.

11. He who founds natural genera should refer them to natural orders when possible.

[12.] Those who in the absence of [a complete] Natural Method arrange plants according to the fragments of one [i.e. the incomplete parts available of a Natural Method] and reject the Artificial Method seem to me like those who pull down a useful vaulted building and build another in its place but cannot provide the roof of the vault.

The pronouncements on the 'natural method' bring no essentially new statements. Linnaeus is still of the opinion that the time for the natural system has not yet come because knowledge is still insufficient.

There are fragments, but one cannot even compose a key. His scholastic attitude is shown in the sentence: "Natural orders indicate the nature of plants" because as usual 'nature' and 'essence' are the same.

The really new ideas, however, are expressed in the first four aphorisms. Bremekamp (1950, 1953a) analysed these aphorisms and pointed out some consequences. 'New ideas' mean new in Linnaeus's line of thought. The way in which these thoughts are expressed was already old-fashioned in 1764. Linnaeus, it must be repeated, was in many ways a man of the past. Bremekamp points to his affinities with the theologian Swedenborg and warns us not to think that Linnaeus belonged to the group of advanced physicists: he had no contact with this section of the rapidly advancing frontiers of the natural sciences. He still clothed his statements in theological verbiage: the form was definitely antiquated—the contents only at times. Linnaeus gives here his ideas on the origin of the hierarchy of taxa. It is clearly not an evolutionary but a creationist theory. There is no reason to see in Linnaeus a precursor of transformism.

A considerable number of vegetable prototypes were created first. This number is the same as that of the natural orders: in 1764 Linnaeus recognized 58 such orders, of which one, at least, was unnatural, the *Miscellaneae*. By a second act, however, the Creator 'blended the classes' and obtained several thousands of vegetable prototypes of the second order, that is: genera. With 60 primary prototypes there would be at least 3600 secondary prototypes. Linnaeus's ideas on the diversity of genera, however, would allow further variation in the fructification, and it may be assumed that in this way Linnaeus reached the—for him—possible total of some 10.000 created genera.

A definite departure from the creationist views, however, is embodied in the third dictum, that *Nature* blended the genera (Nature being the created, not the creator), thus producing the species. The Latin phrase is "genericas has miscuit Natura," in which we may look upon the use of 'miscere' as 'hybridize.' Linnaeus postulated therefore that species originated through natural hybridization of the genera. It is not quite clear how he envisaged this in practice: did all species arise originally from intergeneric hybridization, or was the 'blending' restricted to individuals within one species? The answer to this question is irrelevant in view of the completely artificial nature of this Linnaean brainchild. The only experimental background is that of early examples of hybridization cited in Gråberg's dissertation

(1762), *Fundamentum fructificationis*. These examples, however, are taken from a world in which species do exist already, and do not illustrate the original process.

Linnaeus's ideas on hybrids were, and had to be, very primitive. Really good examples of vegetable hybrids were unknown to him (as were, evidently, Koelreuter's epochmaking experiments and publications of 1761 and 1763), but he knew the hybrids between the horse and the donkey. Bremekamp points out that this is the reason why Linnaeus held that hybrids were matroclinal. These hybrids between horse and donkey always resemble the mother much more than the father. This is of course not at all a general rule, but Linnaeus held it to be fundamental.

Theophrastus and Cesalpino maintained that basically a plant consisted of a *medulla* (which was the seat of its essence) and a *cortex*. This cortex could consist of xylem, phloem (*liber*), cortex in sensu stricto and the epidermis. Linnaeus held that in the flower the calyx represented the cortex, the corolla the phloem, the stamen the xylem (and therefore part of the cortex!) and the pistil the medulla: the ovules were the true carriers of the essence (*Syst. nat.* ed. 10. 2: 826).

The medulla was in the first instance the carrier of the vegetable essence, the cortex of diversity. In his first dictum Linnaeus states that the creator clothed the medulla with diverse constituent possibilities ("vestiit vegetabile medullare principiis constitutivis diversi corticalis ...") which resulted in the, say 60, prototypes of the natural orders. Considering that the fructification and especially the fruits of the sixty orders shared that diversity, it must be assumed, with Bremekamp, that Linnaeus had in view also a sixtyfold diversity of the medulla agreeing with the original diversity of the cortex. This diversity can be seen as a secondary modification of the originally uniform medulla.

This original uniformity rests really upon the basic function attributed to the medulla by the ancient writers, whose belief was shared by Linnaeus. The medulla, in the modern view a relatively unimportant part of the plant, was centrally located and, mainly for that reason, was thought to be the principal carrier of the essence of vegetable life. The original uniformity is therefore understandable. The 'mixing' of the 60 different types of cortex with 60 types of secondarily modified medulla produced 3600 genera. In these genera, however, the new cortex would again modify, for the second time, the medulla. This would mean that in the process of speciation 'by nature' it was again possible to obtain a 60-fold variety: the number of species could in principle be 60^3, or 216.000, which amply satisfied Linnaeus's needs. The creator was therefore responsible for the actual creation of (at least) 3600 prototypes (if we assume for the moment that Linnaeus distinguished 60 natural orders) and for the setting in motion of the process of speciation.

This logical structure has very little contact with reality or empiricism and is much more the result of a *weltfremd* metaphysical speculation than of inductive research. Logically, if one holds that the stamens represent part of the cortex and the ovary the medulla, it is possible to argue in favour of 60^3 number of species. The allegedly 'natural' hybridization of the 3600 genera, however, would imply wholesale intergeneric hybridization, a phenomenon which by itself is very rare and on such a scale purely imaginary. Anyhow the genera before and after the speciation would seem to be different entities and the arguments taken from actual examples all refer to the genera *post hoc*. It is impossible to see this process of speciation as anything but a completely deistic-mechanistic concept of a unique process. If the genera 'ante' and 'post' were correlated, this would mean that all genera would have as many species as there are natural orders, and every natural order would have sixty genera. All this is very far from what is or was ordinarily accepted or acceptable. The theory is open to fundamental criticism:

"If we confine ourselves to the kingdom of plants, we may state that by no means all plants are provided with medulla and cortex, which means that the theory is applicable to a part of the plant kingdom only. The fact that not all hybrids are matroclinal means that it is built on an unfounded generalisation, and the circumstance that in paragraphs 1 and 2, where natural means are insufficient to produce the desired effect, the aid of a super-natural power is invoked moreover, places the theory outside the domain of natural science" (Bremekamp 1953).

After this crushing verdict Bremekamp explains that this refers merely to Linnaeus's explanation and not to the factual contents of his dicta. Of major importance here is that Linnaeus postulated the existence of four major ranks in a hierarchy of taxa: natural order, genus, species and variety, and that the differences between these ranks are fundamental. "The latter is expressed in a parabolic way by referring the origin of the orders to an act of creation, that of the genera to a direct intervention of God, that of the species to the regulating activity of nature, and that of the varieties to indeterminate influences." Linnaeus's earlier dictum, according to which all species had been created, is a similar expression of a conviction that species are constant, but an expression clothed in theological garb.

The explanation and argumentation of the fundamental problems of taxonomy by Linnaeus is mostly outdated and often almost or entirely outside the sphere of the natural sciences. The basic facts observed by the empiricist Linnaeus were often presented in a now unattractive form. It is good, however, not to lose sight of the facts registered by Linnaeus, such as his fragments of a natural system. These facts were based on experience, but his theological or pseudophilosophical inclinations often played havoc with the presentation of the facts. For Linnaeus the differences between groups of different rank are of a qualitative nature. It was impossible to prove this thesis; even now we are making slow progress towards an answer supported by evidence.

In his ideas on the hierarchy of taxa Linnaeus shows again the ambivalence which is so characteristic of all his work: on the one hand an antiquated theory at variance with the facts and based on almost irrational aprioris; on the other hand genuine observation and intuitive evaluation of complex situations.

Linnaeus should be granted the last word on his taxonomic method. The preface to the second part of his *Mantissa*, dated 1 September 1771, contains this summary, composed in "the twilight of his life." It is given here in Svenson's translation (1945):
"Some botanists talk loudly about the *Natural Orders* in place of a method, but so long as there is no essential character of an order, by which the genera can be combined or distinguished from those of different orders, these orders remain as a bell without a clapper. However, their use in other respects may be of the greatest importance."

Part II
THE LINNAEANS

5

Linnaeus's pupils and dissertations

Not less than 186 dissertations were defended under the 'presidium' of Linnaeus during the years of his professorship at Uppsala (1741–1776). It could be said therefore that Linnaeus had at least 186 pupils. It is evident that these pupils differed greatly: many of them were simple physicians who had to defend a thesis in order to obtain their degree, others became outstanding natural scientists themselves. The dissertations were published on the day on which they were to be defended, or a little earlier, and invariably cite the name of the defendant (the pupil) and the name of the praeses, Linnaeus. A full list of the dissertations was given by J. D. Lidén in 1778 and reproduced by Stearn (1957). Further information will be found in Soulsby (1933) and in Pulteney (1781), who gives brief abstracts. The dissertations were reprinted in Linnaeus's *Amoenitates academicae*. The reprints were edited by Linnaeus and often contain additional or changed information; it is often necessary to consult both the original and the *Amoenitates* version of a dissertation, especially in matters of nomenclature.

The authorship of the dissertations has been a matter of dispute, mainly because later authors were not acquainted with the practice and customs of academic disputation at Swedish universities in the eighteenth century which was still a carry-over from medieval times and had strong scholastic overtones. The student went through a number of proofs and examinations which were not public, but the final formal ceremony at which he obtained his degree was a public disputation in Latin in which he defended a thesis for which his professor had usually provided the material. The scientific contents of the printed dissertation were the responsibility of the professor; it was the duty of the defendant to show his proficiency in Latin and his mastery of the art of discussing in a syllogistic style. The

[143]

contents of the thesis were actually almost irrelevant, as long as one could talk about them. This system was not at all uniquely Swedish, but rather continental European. It was abandoned gradually in the course of the nineteenth century, when the importance of independent scientific research at last gained a full victory over scholastic disputation on what were essentially a priori statements. Universities were until quite recently conservative institutions, even though groups of students sometimes voiced progressive ideas on other than their own traditions. The system in force in Linnaean times in Sweden still lingers on to a very limited extent, but very clearly, at, for instance, present day Netherlands universities. In order to obtain his doctor's degree the student does not merely present his doctoral dissertation, which is always an independent piece of scientific work, but he must add to this thesis (which is the hard core of his achievement) a number of so-called 'stellingen,' theses on various subjects of his training in an aphoristic style. The contents of these theses in *sensu stricto* are often not the spiritual property of the defendant, but have been given to him by other scientists (although nowadays usually not by the professor himself). The rôle of these theses, which have hardly any meaning or importance, is to serve as a subject for disputation at the official ceremony. This is essentially the same situation that existed in Linnaeus's time, except that the dissertation itself, which is also a subject of discussion, is now duly written by the student himself.

The authorship of the Linnaean dissertations poses no problem: the author is Linnaeus, and names published in them must be attributed to him. It is clear, however, that the share of the pupil in preparing the thesis was variable. It might be simply a case of translating the given text into Latin and seeing it through the press (the system had as an additional advantage for the praeses that the defendant paid the printing bill), or anything between this and what would almost amount to an independent work. Examples of the latter type of student are D. H. Söderberg (with *Pandora et Flora Rybyensis* 1771), P. Loefling (*Gemmae arborum* 1749), F. Hasselquist (*Vires plantarum* 1747), A. Sparrman (*Iter in chinam* 1768), and probably several others as well. Krok (1925, p. 460–461) lists 37 Linnaean pupils of whom he assumes (no proof is given) that their rôle in producing the dissertations was more important than that of a mere defendant.

Exceptionally gifted pupils like Loefling cannot, however, be taken as a standard, and for the reasons mentioned above, as well as for several others advanced by Rickett (1955), Stearn (1957) and Nordenstam (1961), it is necessary to regard the Linnaean dissertations in their original form, as well as amended in the *Amoenitates*, as the spiritual property of Linnaeus.

Not every Linnaean pupil, however, obtained a degree with him. Notable examples are Giseke, Fabricius, Fr. Ehrhart and Thunberg. On the whole it is possible to divide Linnaeus's most outstanding pupils into two groups: the 'botanistes–voyageurs' and the 'botanistes de cabinet,' a division which is obviously not limited to the Linnaean school.

Among the more sedentary but successful pupils of Linnaeus we can mention for instance the German J. C. D. Schreber (1739–1810), who took his degree in 1760 on a dissertation entitled *Theses medicae*. The subject of this thesis is very typically Linnaean: the anatomy and physiology of plants. Every plant is said to consist of a *medulla* and a *cortex*, the former carrying the essence of vegetable life and producing the seeds and vegetative propagules, such as bulbils and other buds, the latter taking care of nutrition. The *medulla* is the unifying agent for the genera; it is the basis of the common properties of the species belonging to one genus. The matter of hybridization and of the rôle played in this process by the *medulla* and the *cortex* are also mentioned. This dissertation contained the germs of Linnaeus's theory on the hierarchy of taxa.

Schreber spent less than a year with Linnaeus, mainly at Hammarby during the summer of 1760. Back in Germany he became professor of botany and director of the botanic garden at Erlangen. In his later years he edited and published several later editions of Linnaean works, the *Materia medica*, the eighth edition of the *Genera plantarum* (the important revised edition of 1789–1791), an edition of the *Amoenitates*, etc. His special subject in later years were the grasses. Schreber became a powerful proponent of the Linnaean ideas in Germany. Other German pupils of Linnaeus were P. D. Giseke, mentioned above because of his *Praelectiones*, and Friedrich Ehrhart, originally an amateur without university training, who spent several years with Linnaeus (1773–1776) "in the twilight of his life." Ehrhart's rôle in taxonomy was unassuming but, through his numerous writings he contributed to the spreading of the Linnaean thought and methods in Germany, and especially towards the further elaboration of the undercurrent of empiricism (Wein 1931).

Johann Andreas Murray (1740–1791), born in Sweden but of German and Scottish descent, was also one of Linnaeus's pupils. He studied at Uppsala, where he took his licentiate, from 1756 to 1759. In 1760 he went to Göttingen, where he took his doctor's degree in 1763, and there he taught botany from 1764 until his death. Murray was a true Linnaean and published several later editions of the botanical part of the *Systema naturae* (*Systema vegetabilium*). "Murray hielt sich berufen, die Ansichten seines grossen Lehrers gegen jeden Angriff zu verteidigen" (Wein 1931); and was "... derjenige ..., der unbekümmert und ohne jede kritische Stellungnahme anderer Auffassungen seines Lehrers für dessen Sexualsystem eingetreten ist" (Goerke 1967). With Murray at Göttingen and Schreber at Erlangen, the botanical teaching in two of the most renowned German universities was in the hands of Linnaean pupils. The quality of Murray's botanical work was not very high and his later influence was negligible.

Two important Swedes of the more sedentary type can be mentioned briefly: Peter Jonas Bergius (1730–1790), another Smålander, and Erik Acharius (1757–1819). Bergius studied originally at Lund and had first been inclined to become a minister or a lawyer. His stammering, however, made him choose medicine. In 1749 he came to Uppsala and the next year he defended a thesis on *Semina muscorum*. This dissertation is now only of historical value; he considered the sporangia equivalent to anthers and the groupings of antheridia and archegonia (not recognized as such), as they appear e.g. in *Polytrichum*, as female flowers. The musci are ranged with the ferns, the algae and the fungi among the plants which have flowers without fruits (though they are stated to have seeds). After having obtained his medical degree in 1754 Bergius became a practising physician in Stockholm. In 1761 he was appointed professor of natural history and pharmacy at the *Collegium medicum* in the same town. He kept this position (with minor administrative improvements in rank) until his death on 10 June 1790, but he retained his considerable medical practice as well.

Bergius assembled a rich botanical cabinet and library which he left, with an ample endowment, to the Swedish Academy of Sciences. This legacy provided the basis for the Bergius foundation (1791) as well as for the Bergius professorship at the Academy. The endowment enables the Academy to maintain the Bergianska Trädgården, where Bergius's herbarium and library are now housed. Bergius himself collected only in Sweden, but his herbarium contains plants from a great many collectors all over the world.

Bergius' output as a botanist was relatively modest, certainly if compared

[146]

with the works of his teacher Linnaeus and of his later Uppsala colleague C. P. Thunberg. His first major botanical treatise, *Descriptiones plantarum ex capite Bonae Spei* of September 1767, was mainly based on a collection of plants made at the Cape by Mikael Grubb (1728–1808), a director of the Swedish East India Company. Bergius named one of his new genera in honour of him: *Grubbia* (Descr. p. 90–91).

Linnaeus's only son, Carl, born January 20, 1741, was also one of Linnaeus's pupils. He studied at Uppsala, where he later followed a university career until his early death on November 1, 1783. In the years 1781–1783 Linnaeus filius made a trip to the major western European centers of learning. In the later years of his father's life there was evidently an estrangement between the two men because the elder Linnaeus left his herbarium to his wife with the provision that his son was not to use it.

Linnaeus filius' botanical output was modest and in no way spectacular. Best known is his *Supplementum plantarum* of 1781, which contained descriptions by his father and contributions by Friedrich Ehrhart and some others, as well as original work by the author himself. Apart from the *Supplementum* Linnaeus filius published some minor treatises on plants from the Uppsala garden and contributed a number of descriptions to William Aiton's *Hortus kewensis*. During his professorship his most illustrious pupil was Olof Swartz, who defended his dissertation *Methodus muscorum illustrata*, in 1781.

Erik Acharius was Linnaeus's last pupil. He studied at Uppsala from 1773–1776 and defended the last Linnaean dissertation at which Linnaeus himself was praeses: *Planta aphyteia* (1776). The new generation made itself heard: Erik Acharius, who would later become the founder of scientific lichenology, defended a thesis on a plant sent from the Cape by Pehr Thunberg in 1774. Pliny's dictum: 'semper aliquid novi in Africa' was (and is) still in force. The "Planta Aphyteia" is *Hydnora africana* Thunb., a parasite on roots of *Euphorbia* species from the Cape region (Karroo). Acharius' later work on lichens was done after the Linnaean era and falls outside the scope of this essay. The refinement of research on cryptogams in the early nineteenth century was one of the major factors in bringing to an end the Linnaean tradition.

The travellers were a totally different group of Linnaean pupils. Linnaeus himself did not travel to any extent. After he settled in Uppsala in 1741 his only trips were some brief excursions in Sweden. In his youth he had made his one great journey of exploration, the *Iter lapponicum*; he had also travelled in the various regions and islands of middle and southern Sweden, such as Öland and Gothland, and he had spent his three years abroad, mainly in Holland. Although he could have had the opportunity to travel himself also after 1741, for instance, to the Cape or the Indies (through his Dutch protectors), this seems never to have been a real temptation. Linnaeus was essentially a cabinet botanist; however, he was sufficiently eighteenth-century in his outlook to send his pupils abroad. He had seen so many marvellous new plants and animals during his Holland days that he was fully convinced of the need for extensive exploration of the world outside Europe. In his autobiography Linnaeus calls his travelling pupils his 'apostles,' an appropriate name, because several of them did not return from their journeys, but met an early death by disease or brute force. The expression is revealing for Linnaeus's character and for the way he looked upon himself.

One of the reasons why Linnaeus could send so many of his pupils abroad is found in his association with the Count of Tessin. He and Magnus Lagerström, the director of the Swedish East India Company at Göteborg, did much to facilitate the participation of naturalists in travels to the East. Other pupils, however, travelled because they were invited to do so by foreign scientists or by governments acquainted with Linnaeus's fame.

The first pupil to sail was Christopher Ternström (1703–1746), whose mission was partly religious and partly exploratory, and whose destination was the Far East. Employed by the Swedish East India Company, he died on the way out to China on the island of Poeloe Candor, off present-day Vietnam.

More successful was Pehr Kalm (1716–1779), who had studied at Åbo and Uppsala. Kalm had already travelled in Sweden, Finland and Russia in the years 1742–1745, when he was selected to explore North America, with the charge to introduce new useful plants from that temperate region, and more especially to find strains of *Morus rubra* fit for introduction into Sweden. Kalm stayed in North America from 1747 until 1751 and afterwards became professor of natural history and 'economical resources' in Åbo. He published a three-volume work on his travels: *En Resa till Norra America* (1753–1761). Kalm gave Linnaeus a specimen of each of his species; this set became for him the major source of new information on the North American flora. (For an extensive discussion of plant collectors in America as background for Linnaeus see Ewan (1970).)

Frederik Hasselquist (1722–1752) made a long voyage to Egypt and the Orient from 1749 until 1752 (he died at Smyrna). Hasselquist's main object was Palestine, but he travelled widely all over the Middle East. After his death at Smyrna on the way back his manuscripts and rich collections were seized by his creditors, but ultimately they were bought by Queen Luisa Ulrika of Sweden. The manuscripts and a duplicate set of the specimens were handed to Linnaeus, who published Hasselquist's *Iter palaestinum* (1757) and a *Flora palaestina*, the latter as a dissertation which was defended by B. J. Strand in 1756 (Uggla 1953, Bodenheimer 1953).

Pehr Osbeck (1723–1805) was not a pupil of Linnaeus, but a ship's chaplain who sailed to China, spent some months there and made some collections which he afterwards gave to Linnaeus. He published a diary which has definite scientific merit: *Dagbok öfwer en Ostindisk Resa åren 1750–1752* (Stockholm 1757).

The star performer among the swarm of Linnaean disciples was Pehr Loefling (1729–1756), a pupil to whom Linnaeus himself seems to have been genuinely attached. Loefling took his degree with Linnaeus on 18 November 1749 on a dissertation entitled *Gemmae arborum*, of which it may be assumed that Loefling's share in the writing was considerable. Even so Linnaeus considered it as his own, as appears for instance from his letter to Gesner of 13 February 1750 (de Beer 1949) in which he writes, referring to the *Gemmae arborum*: "I have described the buds of all our trees, which are wonderfully diverse in different species ...."

The thesis deals with the buds of trees and shrubs which give rise to flowers, to leaves, or to both. Loefling points out the analogy with flower bulbs and proposes a common term for both: *hibernacula*, because they are the plant organs which serve to protect the young growth during the winter. He classifies 180 species of trees and shrubs on the basis of structural characteristics of their buds, thus providing a key for identification when the leaves have been shed. This *methodus gemmarum* is also intended to facilitate the establishment of a natural system based upon all parts of the plant:

"*Methodus naturalis* plantarum fuit primum & ultimum quaesitum Botanicorum, ad quam rite excolendam, non modo Fructificationis adcuratissima inspectio necessaria est, sed & consideratio totius plantae ejusque partium, quae ansam dabit sagaci Botanico perscrutandi naturalem illam catenam ordinemque, quo summus Conditor plantas creavit."

It is difficult to say who speaks here, Loefling or Linnaeus, but the intention is clear: the natural method rests upon a scrutiny of all charac-teristics. It is very interesting to note here the use of the word 'catena,' chain, for the arrangement of the natural orders: this is the great chain of being, an idea usually rejected by Linnaeus in favour of his comparison of taxa with the countries on a map of the world. Here, however, a linear arrangement of the orders is presupposed, although not further elaborated. The dissertation contains on its last page (I consulted only the version in the *Amoenitates* vol. 2, p. 224) a highly interesting elaboration of Linnaeus's thoughts on the basic morphology of the plant body, discussed earlier in connection with his theory of the hierarchy of taxa. The calyx and the ordinary leaves are derived from the *cortex*, the tender corolla from the equally tender phloem, the stamens from the wood: "probat *consistentia, situs, plenitudo* florum e vegetatione vegetiori, ubi ex molli libo indurescere lignum non permisit fortior propulsio." The pistil is the center of the flower, is derived from the *medulla*, and gives rise to the fruit "nisi prius staminum essentia lignea absorpta fuerit ab humore medullari pistilli."

Another interesting point about the *Gemmae arborum* is the frequent use made of trivial names. The dissertation was defended only a few weeks before N. L. Hesselgren's *Pan suecicus* (9 Dec. 1749) ('suecus' in later editions) in which Linnaeus used his binary system of nomenclature consistently for the first time. In the *Gemmae arborum* we encounter *Daphne Laureola, Vaccinium Oxycoccos* and *Aesculus Hippocastanum*, to mention only a few; however, this usage is not consistent, although the two–word specific designations seem to be much more of the nature of trivial names than of diagnostically sufficient specific names. The *Gemmae arborum* is in many respects highly original: it is based on direct empirical research and contains an excellent descriptive morphology and terminology. It remains a pity that it is impossible to know to whom the originality should be ascribed: to Loefling or to his revered master.

Loefling stayed in Uppsala in 1750. Fries relates that he assisted Linnaeus in writing the *Philosophia botanica*, and that his habit of asking difficult questions greatly helped Linnaeus in making his meaning clear. In 1751 the Spanish government invited Loefling to come to Spain to study the flora and to organize botanical research. He remained there until 1753, made collections, and wrote many letters to Linnaeus. Early in 1754 he sailed for the Spanish territories in northern South America. His explorations are in part related in his *Iter*, but he was doomed to die all to early: he met his death on 22 February 1756 at the mission station of Murrecurri ('Merercuri' in the literature) in what is now Venezuela. The *Iter hispanicum* was published by Linnaeus in 1758; it contains the text of his letters to Linnaeus and his descriptions of Spanish and American plants. For a modern account of Loefling and his travels see Ryden (1965).

Of the numerous Linnaean travelling apostles only a few more can be mentioned here. For an instructive map of the world showing the routes of the most important 'Lärjungar' see Fries (1951).

Pehr Forsskål was born in Helsingfors and studied in Uppsala and Göttingen. He joined a Swedish expedition to the near East. Forsskål collected extensively in Egypt and Saudi Arabia, and died from the plague at Jerim, in Yemen. The sole survivor of the expedition, Carl Niebuhr, saw Forsskål's manuscripts through the press; the most important of these documents was the *Flora aegyptiaco–arabica*.

Daniel Carl Solander (1733–1782) was, unlike Forsskål, a 'full' pupil of Linnaeus; Uggla (1955) states that there is no doubt that the Master considered Solander to be one of his most promising pupils. Linnaeus apparently hoped that Solander would become his successor, a circumstance which was even more attractive to him because his eldest daughter and Solander were, at one time, quite fond of each other. Rauschenberg, however, the author of a recent and extensive biography of Solander, is not particularly impressed by this romantic story and doubts whether there ever was such an ardent relationship (1968).

Solander lived and studied at Uppsala from 1750 until 1759, without taking a degree. He published Linnaeus's *Elementa botanica*, a now rare pamphlet published in Stockholm in 1756 and reprinted with minor modifications in the tenth edition of the *Systema naturae* (2: 825–827. 1759). The treatise is a concise but to all intents complete summing up of Linnaeus's thoughts on the structure of plants. It is not a dissertation and contains Linnaeus's ideas rather than those of Solander, whose later writings do not show any leaning towards theoretical biology.

Two London amateur botanists, John Ellis and Peter Collinson, both faithful correspondents of Linnaeus, had asked Linnaeus to send one of his pupils to London. Solander went to England in 1760, was appointed first to a post at the British Museum, and became, later, librarian to Joseph Banks. While in Banks's service he went with him as a naturalist on Cook's first voyage on the *Endeavour* (1768–1771), a voyage heavily supported

[151]

Lichtdruck: J. Löwy, Wien.   Nach dem Gemälde von P. Krafft jun.
(pinx 1808) im Besitze der Universität Upsala.

Thunberg.

Fig. 31

by Banks himself; in 1773 Solander also accompanied Banks to Iceland.

Kalm, Thunberg and Solander were really the only Linnaean 'apostles' who returned home successfully with rich collections and in good health. Solander's collection, however, was the property of Banks and was never made available to Linnaeus, a circumstance not exactly appreciated by the Swedish master. He is said to have several times spoken of his pupil as "the ungrateful Solander"; Linnaeus, however, was then in the years of increasing mental decline. One of the reasons why Solander's travels were so much more successful than those of Forsskål, Hasselquist and Loefling was the superior organization of Cook's voyage, which in turn was due to its solid financial backing. Travelling and exploring by ship was in any case much safer and healthier in the eighteenth century than travelling great distances over land. Cook's exploration, in which Solander took part, heralded a new era in botanical exploration, namely that of the opening of the Pacific and the sending out of expeditions on well-equipped ships for scientific and geographical purposes. We shall come back to him when discussing Joseph Banks.

Solander's successor at Banks's library, Jonas Dryander (1748–1810), also a student from Uppsala, did not travel to any extent. We shall come back also to him when discussing the Banksian era in British systematics.

One of the most successful of Linnaeus's apostles was undoubtedly Andreas Sparrman (1748–1820), who travelled to China with the East Indian Company in 1765–1767 and to the Cape, April–September 1772 (with Thunberg), and who accompanied Georg Forster on Cook's second voyage (1772–1775), staying on in South Africa until 1776. He also participated in the Swedish Africa expedition of 1787–1788, sent out to find a suitable place for a Swedish settlement on the African west coast. Sparrman obtained his degree under Linnaeus on 30 November 1768, on a dissertation on his voyage to China. His own botanical publications are few and modest; many of his collections were used by Linnaeus and Linnaeus filius, but his main set went to the Academy of Sciences at Stockholm.

One of the last and the most successful of Linnaeus's pupils was another

Fig. 31. CARL PETER THUNBERG (*b.* Jönköping, Sweden, November 11, 1743; *d.* Thunaberg near Uppsala, Sweden, August 8, 1828), Swedish explorer and botanist, travelled in Holland, France, South Africa, Japan, Java and Ceylon 1770–1778; professor of botany at Uppsala University 1781–1828. [Reproduction of an oil-painting by P. Kraft jun. (1808) at the University of Uppsala. (I. Dörfler, *Botaniker–Porträts* no. 39. 1907)].

Smålander, Carl Peter Thunberg (1743–1828) (fig. 31), who was destined to occupy his chair in later years. Thunberg studied natural sciences and medicine under Linnaeus at Uppsala between 1761 and 1770. He took his degree in 1767 on a thesis entitled *De venis resorbentibus*, but obtained a regular medical degree only in 1772, in absentia, when he was residing at the Cape of Good Hope.

In 1770 Thunberg received a travelling grant ("Kåhres stipendium") to continue his studies in the natural sciences and medicine in Paris. This led to an absence of nine years, during which he travelled through Europe, South Africa, Ceylon, the East Indies and Japan. In Amsterdam, on his way to Paris, Thunberg made the acquaintance of Johannes Burman and his son, Nicolaas Laurens Burman. After his stay in Paris Thunberg returned to Amsterdam and was offered an opportunity to go to Japan in the service of a group of Dutch merchants (Poll, Deutz and Hoven), to collect plants for the Amsterdam botanical garden and for their own collections. In order to be admitted to Japan, Thunberg had to pass as a Dutchman; he therefore spent three years in the Dutch colony at the Cape of Good Hope, becoming acquainted with the Dutch language and collecting plant material. After that he spent half a year on Java, and in August 1775 he arrived in Japan (Nagasaki). After his return from Japan, in November 1776, he spent another half year on Java. In July 1777 he arrived at Ceylon; in February 1778 he left for Holland, stopping over at the Cape for a fortnight. Back in Amsterdam (October 1778) he reported to his commissioners, and in December he made a short trip to London, visiting Banks, Smith and the Forsters. In January 1779 he started the return journey to Sweden, arriving in Uppsala in March.

During his absence, in 1777, Thunberg had been appointed botanical demonstrator at the botanical garden under the professor of botany, Linnaeus filius. In 1781 he was appointed extraordinary professor and in 1784 full professor of botany and medicine, succeeding the younger Linnaeus; Thunberg held this post until his death in 1828. During these years he made several short trips within Sweden, but no more major journeys.

Thunberg was a prolific author. Krok (1925) lists 139 publications, among them several of great importance: *Nova genera plantarum* (1781–1801), *Flora iaponica* (1784), *Museum naturalium academiae Upsaliensis* (1791–1821), *Prodromus plantarum capensium* (1794, 1800) and a *Flora capensis* (1807). Many of Thunberg's publications were dissertations defended by his pupils but for which he was himself fully responsible. The *Nova genera plantarum* and the *Museum* are series of such dissertations. Some of the pupils may again be supposed to have contributed substantially to their own dissertations: they are listed by Krok (1925, pp. 715–716). Thunberg built up a considerable herbarium which, unlike that of Linnaeus, stayed at Uppsala. Thunberg remained a Linnaean scholar all through his life: he was not an original thinker, but a dedicated floristic botanist, an excellent traveller, and an inspiring teacher. With the deaths of Acharius (1819) and Thunberg (1828) the last Linnaean pupils disappeared from the Swedish botanical scene. The Linnaean school, in narrow sense of the term, had then prospered for almost a century.

One Swedish botanist, not a pupil of Linnaeus himself but of his son, should be mentioned briefly: Olof Peter Swartz (1760–1828). Swartz travelled quite a bit, in Sweden, North America, the West Indies and along the coast of South America. On his return from his West Indian voyage (1784–1786) Swartz spent some time in London to name his collections with the help of the library and herbarium of Sir Joseph Banks and with the assistance of his countryman, Jonas Dryander. The results of this collecting trip were published at first in the *Nova Genera et Species plantarum seu prodromus ...* of 1788 and later in the *Flora indiae occidentalis* of 1797–1806. Swartz had made a special study of the flora of parts of Jamaica into which western botanists had not previously penetrated. His harvest was rich: 61 new genera and 955 new species which were not all truly new because some of them had been previously described in manuscript by Solander. The book faithfully follows the Linnaean tradition and is linked by means of cross–references (Latin numbers behind genera) to the natural families of Giseke's *Praelectiones*. The majority of Swartz's publications, however, appeared after 1789 and have therefore to be left out of account here. Swartz's private herbarium later became the nucleus of the present herbarium at the Naturhistoriska Riksmuseum in Stockholm.

6

The Netherlands and Austria:
A faithful beginning

1. Netherlands

The gospel of simplicity, efficiency and brevity in the identification of plants was spread not only by Linnaeus's apostles, but even more widely by the force of his publications. The real impact on descriptive botany came from the *Systema naturae* and the *Genera* and *Species plantarum*: an impact which remained strong all through the eighteenth century, and which, despite a gradual dwindling throughout the nineteenth century, has not disappeared even today. We have only to look at the central place occupied by the Linnaean works in botany as well as zoology to realize that we still live with Linnaeus.

The first epoch–making Linnaean publications, the *Systema*, the *Genera*, *Fundamenta*, *Critica*, *Bibliotheca*, and the *Classes* were all published in Holland. Linnaeus's decision to go to Holland to finish his early training and to obtain his degree had been determined by two main factors: Dutch botany and botanists were leading taxonomy in the discovery and description of the extra–European plant world, and Holland was a main centre of printing and publishing.

The Dutch golden age of botany had reached its peak in the first third of the eighteenth century with Johannes Burman (1707–1779) at Amsterdam and, especially, with Herman Boerhaave (1668–1738) at Leiden. Their fame was worldwide. Both had the great advantage of having the living collections of plants in the Amsterdam and Leiden botanical gardens close at hand, collections unsurpassed in numbers and quality at the time when Linnaeus decided to go to Holland. Boerhaave was a European figure, more renowned now perhaps as a physician, but as a botanist too he was a man of no mean achievement (see Lindeboom 1968, Stearn 1970). Linnaeus had some initial difficulty in penetrating the social defenses of this celeb-

[157]

METHODI NATURALIS
PRAELUDIUM,

seu

CONSPECTUS SYSTEMATIS
AD NATURAE CODICES
CASTIGANDI.

I. PALMAE.

1. *Spadice ramoso.*
Corypha.
Chamaerops.
Coccus.
Phoenix.
Cycas.

2. *Incompletae.*
Acorus.
Dracontium.
Calla.
Arum.
Saururus.
Piper.
Zannichellia.
Ruppia.

3. *Spatha bifida.*
Vallisneria.
Najas.
Stratiotes.
Hydrocharis.

4. *Ringentes.*
Musa.
Canna.

Costus.
Maranta.
Thalia.
Alpinia.
Amomum.
Curcuma.
Kaempferia.

5. *Gynandrae.*
Epidendrum.
Cypripedium.
Serapias.
Satyrium.
Orchis.
Herminium.
Ophrys.
Neottia.
Limodorum.

6. *Triandrae.*
Iris.
Gladiolus.
Sisyrinchium.
Ixia.
Xyris.

✳✳ ✳✳   II.

Fig. 32

rity, but as soon as he succeeded in this Boerhaave realized that there was something special about the manuscripts of the young Swede. Once Linnaeus obtained Boerhaave's sanction all roads were open to him, and his Dutch career unfolded with the regularity of the flower of *Linnaea borealis.*

Holland still carried on the great tradition of the Plantyns and Elseviers in printing and publishing. Leiden and Amsterdam were centers of book production and book trade, comparable only with Leipzig and Paris. A book published by one of the main Dutch firms such as Theodoor Haak, Conrad Wishoff, or Samuel Luchtmans in Leiden, or Salomon Schouten in Amsterdam, would certainly be well produced and widely distributed. Linnaeus could not have made a better choice in the early thirties: the botanists and publishers in Holland readily grasped the importance of his work and provided the impact for its success. The Linnaean victory, therefore, had its start in Holland.

Professor of botany and medicine at Leiden after Boerhaave was Adriaan van Royen (1704–1779), himself a pupil of Boerhaave. Van Royen lectured at Leiden University from 1732 onward. He was a versatile, highly gifted, erudite personality whose social fame rested, in part, on his long Latin orations in verse on botany and medicine, delivered at various academic occasions. His botanical output was limited; in later years he turned completely to medicine. At the time of Linnaeus's stay in Holland van Royen was working on his main botanical work, the *Florae leydensis prodromus,* which was published in 1740. This *Prodromus* is not a flora in the usual sense but an enumeration with ample synonymy, bibliographical references, incidental notes and descriptions of the plants grown in the Leiden botanic garden. The arrangement follows a natural system (fig. 32 & 33), the key to which was constructed by Linnaeus and van Royen together. This key is one of the first of its kind and leads to twenty natural classes. Every class is amply described and discussed; van Royen was the first author to do this for a natural system. The Monocotyledones, for instance, comprise three classes: the *Palmae, Lilia* and *Gramina.* Van Royen's concept of the *Palmae* (as a class) shows great similarity with that of Linnaeus as worked out in his *Musa cliffortiana.* There were six orders which did not receive names of their own, but were designated by diagnostic epithets: *Palmae spadice ramoso*

Fig. 32. First part of Adriaan van Royen's attempt at a natural system from his *Florae leydensis prodromus* [1740].

[159]

CLAVIS CLASSIUM.

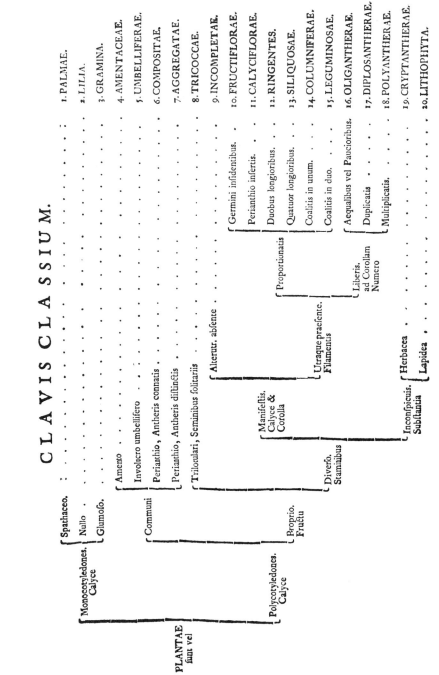

Fig. 33

(real Palms and *Cycas*), *Palmae incompletae* (*Araceae, Piper* e.a.), *Palmae spatha bifida* (*Vallisneria, Naias, Stratiotes, Hydrocharis*), *Palmae ringentes* (*Zingiberales*), *Palmae gynandrae* (*Orchidaceae*) and *Palmae triandrae* (*Iridaceae*).

Van Royen duly cites Linnaean publications and accepts in general the Linnaean generic nomenclature and circumscription. This is an important criterion for the Linnaean influence; before the introduction of the *nomina trivialia*, the Linnaean reform made itself felt mainly in two ways: generic delimitation and nomenclature on the one hand, the artificial system on the other. Van Royen did not accept the latter but fully accepted the generic reform which, in so many ways, was the really revolutionary element in Linnaeus's writings.

In his preface van Royen explains his system of nomenclature and makes it clear that Linnaeus, with his *Critica botanica*, has made it possible to end the confusion in generic names. For the specific names he uses, wherever possible, the names from the *Hortus cliffortianus* or the *Flora lapponica*. Van Royen states that Linnaeus has been the first to give consistent diagnostic phrase names to species and that for this reason he follows his example.

Van Royen's *Methodus naturalis praeludium* is a good effort and comparable to Linnaeus's *Fragmenta*. The twenty Classes (not given by Linnaeus) are for the greater part quite natural and correspond in the main to higher taxa still recognized today. The descriptions contain characters derived not only from the fructification but from the vegetative parts as well.

The Linnaean influence on van Royen's book is evident from another feature: the bibliographical references. It has been explained above that Linnaeus, for instance in his *Hortus cliffortianus*, used a binary system of literature references which consisted of the abbreviated author's name followed by an 'epithet' designating the title of the book. *Bauh. pin.* was C. Bauhin's *Pinax Theatri botanici*. Linnaeus made an exception for his own books, to which he did not refer by means of 'Lin.' but by means of a reference, also binary, consisting of abbreviated elements from the title, e.g. *Mus. Cliff.* for *Musa Cliffortiana florens*. Van Royen adopts this system and uses, when possible, the abbreviations of the *Hortus cliffortianus*. The only difference lies in the references to Linnaeus's books; van Royen wrote *Linn. crit., Linn. Mus.*, etc.

Another Leiden botanist, also a contemporary of Linnaeus, who spread

Fig. 33. Adriaan van Royen's key to natural families as given in his *Prodromus florae leydensis* [1740]. *Reduced.*

[161]

his ideas at a very early stage was Jan Frederik Gronovius (1690–1762). His rôle in promoting Linnaeus as well as his publications has already been mentioned.*

Gronovius was an amateur botanist of considerable skill who published a modest treatise on *Camphora* in 1715 and who built up, in the eighteenth-century tradition, an important library and herbarium of his own. This herbarium, when sold by public auction at Leiden on 9 October 1778, numbered nearly 300 volumes of plants. Gronovius received a considerable set of North American plants from the Virginian botanist John Clayton (1686–1773). Clayton, who had come to North America in 1705, was clerk of Gloucester County, Virginia, and an enthusiastic amateur botanist. Gronovius, who pays due tribute to Clayton's observations and manuscript names, worked on the collection with the assistance of Linnaeus and published the results in his *Flora virginica*, the first part of which was published in Leiden in 1739 (fig. 34) and the second part in 1743. This *Flora virginica* is the first work by an author other than Linnaeus himself, in so far as I know, in which the sexual system is followed. Gronovius also accepts, when possible, the Linnaean generic and specific nomenclature, mainly taken from the *Hortus cliffortianus* and the *Flora lapponica*. In the introduction, which has the form of a letter to Clayton, Gronovius refers to Linnaeus's share of the work and to the Linnaean method. The book was of great importance for early North American botany: it contained descriptions and diagnoses of a considerable number of North American plants, in the Linnaean tradition, and it served for a long time as the basic flora for the 'Virginian' region, that is the greater part of the East coast of the present United States. A second edition was published by Gronovius' son, Laurens Theodoor Gronovius (1730–1773), in the year of his father's death (1762). This edition contains many additions based on new material received by Gronovius and on new publications. It faithfully follows the Linnaean system, although it provides no trivial names.

Another important work by J. F. Gronovius, also in the Linnaean style, was the *Flora orientalis* of 1755, in which he described the plants from the Rauwolf herbarium preserved in the Leiden university library. Leonard

* For an extensive study of the relationship between the two men see Nordström (1955).

Fig. 34. Title-page of J. F. Gronovius, *Flora virginica* [1739] the first book by an author other than Linnaeus in which the sexual system is followed [from facsimile edition 1946].

FLORA VIRGINICA

Exhibens

PLANTAS

Quas

V. C.

JOHANNES CLAYTON

In

VIRGINIA

Obſervavit atque collegit.

Eaſdem

Methodo Sexuali diſpoſuit, ad Genera propria
retulit, Nominibus ſpecificis inſignivit, &
minus cognitas deſcripſit

JOH. FRED. GRONOVIUS.

PARS PRIMA.

LUGDUNI BATAVORUM,
Apud CORNELIUM HAAK, 1739.
Fig. 34

Fig. 35. JOHANNES BURMAN; *b.* Amsterdam, Netherlands, April 26, 1706; *d.* Amsterdam, Netherlands, January 20, 1779. [Engraving at the age of 30 by J. Houbraken of a drawing by J. M. Quinkhard; *Conservatoire botanique de Genève*]. *Reduced.*

Rauwolf was a sixteenth–century explorer (c. 1540–1596) of the near East who brought home one of the earliest herbaria.

The Amsterdam garden was in the hands of the Burmans: Johannes Burman (1707–1779) (fig. 35 & 36), with whom Linnaeus had stayed in 1735, and through whom he had met Clifford, and his son Nicolaus Laurens (1733–1793), whose professional contacts with Linnaeus stem from the days spent in Uppsala.

The Burmans came originally from the Rhine region near Cologne, but members of the family had taken refuge in the Netherlands after the Reformation. Johannes' uncle Pieter Burman (1667–1741) was a historian and classical scholar of great fame, professor at the universities of Utrecht and Leiden. His brother Frans (1671–1719), father of Johannes, was a professor of theology in Utrecht. Johannes Burman was born in Amsterdam in 1707 and was educated in the house of his uncle Pieter after his father's death (1719). He studied medicine at Leiden and became a pupil of Boerhaave. After obtaining his Leiden degree on a medical dissertation he practised medicine in Amsterdam from 1728 onward and was invited to teach botany in the botanic garden from that same year on, assisting the regular professor of botany at the Amsterdam Athenaeum, Frederic Ruysch. Burman became a regular professor in 1738: at the time when Linnaeus visited him he was only in charge of the garden and a 'lecturer.' Through his family and that of his wife (Adriana van Bueren) Burman was soon accepted as belonging to the Amsterdam Establishment, a circumstance of which he made the most in obtaining plants for his garden. This garden had already been greatly enriched by the Commelins but enjoyed a further expansion under Burman. His efforts went so far as to stimulate the creation of a first botanic garden on Java in Batavia (Djakarta). His international reputation at the time is well illustrated by the cognomen which he received in the German academy of sciences called the *Leopoldina*: Dioscorides III. Burman was, especially in his earlier years, a hard worker, and he published on a grand scale. In 1737 he published his *Thesaurus zeylanicus*, based on collections of plants made in Ceylon by Paulus Hermann and Jan Hartog. This publication shows, understandably, no trace of Linnaeus's influence. In the next two years, however, Burman published his magnificent *Rariorum africanarum plantarum decades* I–X (Amsterdam 1738–1739), with 100 engravings by Hendrik Claudius, who made the original drawings for the Amsterdam burgomaster Nicolaas Witsen during a stay at the Cape of Good Hope. The nomenclature is here often in agreement with that of the *Hortus cliffortianus*; Burman accepts the Linnaean generic reform as brought about by the *Genera plantarum* and attempts, though not yet consistently, to coin his phrase names in a purely diagnostic way in the Linnaean manner. In Amsterdam as well as in Leiden, therefore, Linnaeus's influence made itself felt almost from the beginning.

Burman's most sumptuous publications, however, are those which he published for others: he took care of the Dutch edition (1025 plates) of Weinmann's *Phytanthoza iconographia* of which the plates were published first as 'Duidelijke vertoning' but for which the edition with text was issued as *Taalrijk register* (see Lawrence in Rudolph 1965). Two further works of great importance published by Burman were Rumphius' *Herbarium amboinense* and a selection from Plumier's plates with text by Burman: *Plantarum americanarum fasciculi X*. In addition Johannes published keys to the Linnaean names for the plants of the *Hortus malabaricus* (1796), and the *Herbarium amboinense* (1755, 1769), and several smaller publications.

Two of these smaller publications are of special importance for the history of the Linnaean influence in taxonomy. The first is the key to Rumphius' *Herbarium amboinense*, published in the *Auctuarium* (1755); it contains a number of Linnaean binary names, including even some new ones coined by Burman himself and marked 'B.' (fig. 37). The second publication is a folio pamphlet of eight pages and a large folded copper engraving, dedicated to Burman's colleague at the Utrecht garden, Evert Jacob Wachendorff, published in October 1757 and entitled *Wachendorfia*. The genus *Wachendorfia* (Haemodoraceae) occurs in the Cape region and has —at present—five species. Burman was not the first to describe it: Breyne had already done so in his *Prodromus* (p. 3. t. 9 fig. 1. 1739) but had not put his plant in a genus of its own, but in *Sisyrinchium*. Burman describes the genus *Wachendorfia* on the basis of living material from his garden and from herbarium material collected by Oldenland. There are two species which are given the trivial names *Wachendorfia thyrsiflora* and *W. paniculata*. The specific epithets are put in the margin, as in the *Species plantarum*. As far as I know Burman is the first author other than Linnaeus (or one of the pupils in the dissertationes) who used the binary system of nomenclature in his publications. It is remarkable how slowly the trivial names found their way into the literature. This Linnaean innovation was accepted with much more hesitation than any of the other revolutionary proposals; however, in Amsterdam and with Burman, in a tribute to a remarkable Utrecht botanist, binary nomenclature started its victorious course.

Burman was not at all theoretically inclined; his influence, however, was considerable, mainly because of the great number of new plants from

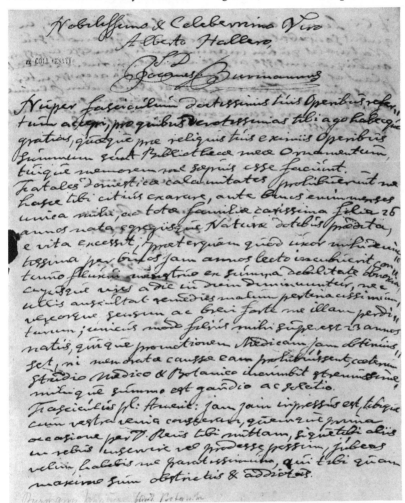

Fig. 36. Letter written by Johannes Burman to A. von Haller on Sept. 1, 1758. Burman mentions the death of a daughter; this was Johanna Elizabeth Burman (April 6, 1732–May 29, 1758), the first child from his marriage with Adriana van Bueren; the son mentioned is Nicolaus Laurens Burman. [*Conservatoire botanique de Genève*]. *Reduced.*

[167]

Fig. 37

the Cape and from the Indies which he described or of which he published descriptions or illustrations made by others. In doing this, after 1738, he made use of the Linnaean system and nomenclature wherever possible; he provided Linnaean keys to important pre–Linnaean works, as stated above, and made manuscript material of Plumier and Rumphius available to the general public. Johannes Burman thus became one of the great promoters of Linnaean taxonomy and nomenclature.

Johannes' son Nicolaas Laurens, born in 1733, studied at Leiden, where he received his doctor's degree on 17 August 1759 on a thesis entitled *Specimen botanicum de Geraniis*: a worthy subject for the son of the man who had done so much to promote Cape botany. This monograph of the genus *Geranium*, in a wide sense, is remarkable in several respects, but most striking is again the use of Linnaean binary nomenclature. Trivial names are given in the margin in the same way as in the *Species plantarum* and in *Wachendorfia*.

After obtaining his degree the young Burman went to Uppsala to spend some months with Linnaeus. In 1760 he started a medical practice in Amsterdam, but he was soon called upon to assist and later (1780) to succeed his father as professor of botany and director of the Amsterdam botanic garden. The younger Burman was not such a prolific author as his father: apart from his dissertation he produced only one important work, his *Flora indica* of 1768, fully in the Linnaean tradition.

The *Flora indica* is of importance because at a relatively early date (1768) it gave an enumeration, in the Linnaean style, of what was then known about the nomenclature and taxonomy of the flora of the Indies. There are brief descriptions of about 1305 species, of which 241 are proposed as new (Merrill 1921). The main collections on which the work is based are those of Piso, Hermann, Garcin, Breyne, Oldenland, Hartog, Kleinhof, Outgaerden and Pyron—most of them in the private herbarium of the Burmans. The term 'India' referred to the tropics in general, especially to India, Ceylon and the East Indies, but also to the West Indies and the Neotropics. Merrill mentions that about 300 species are listed from India itself (although Javan material was among them), 115 from Java, 90 from Ceylon, 50 from China, 15 from Japan, 20 from Persia. There are also species from the Moluccas, taken from Rumphius, and furthermore from Brazil, Mexico, Peru,

Fig. 37. A page from J. Burman, *Index universalis* [1755] to Rumphius, *Auctuarium*, in which Burman uses binary nomenclature and publishes two binomials himself (*Phaseolus marinus* and *Aurantium maximum*). Reduced.

Canada, Arabia, Egypt and the Cape of Good Hope. In a way the book is therefore the first general tropical flora in the Linnaean style. Merrill's analysis has shown how much new information was brought forward by Burman, but also how the uncritical Burman trusted previous Linnaean publications for those taxa of which he had no specimens.

The *Flora indica* was published in March or April 1768, shortly after Linnaeus's first *Mantissa*. The two works deal in part with the same taxa based upon the same collections. Burman and Linnaeus maintained close contact, and all through the time when the book was being printed Linnaeus received advance copies of the loose sheets and plates. This is the reason why he could quote quite a few of Burman's new taxa in his *Mantissa* (See Stearn 1961a for further details). The *Flora* contains also a *Prodromus florae capensis* which contains about 260 legitimately named new species from the Cape (Dandy 1961) in very concise form. Thus the *Flora indica*, in its main body as well as in its appendix, contains the names and descriptions of over five hundred new taxa either from the tropics or from the Cape. It was based on a thorough—although not always critical—knowledge of the contemporary literature, as well as on a herbarium which was at the time perhaps the richest in the world in herbarium material from these regions. The *Flora indica*, notwithstanding its many incorrect references, therefore remains a document which counts in taxonomy today; from a historical point of view, it was an almost unequalled attempt to produce a general tropical flora.

With the *Flora indica* the younger Burman's botanical activities had nearly come to an end. In 1773 he published a brief article on a Cape Crucifer, *Heliophila*; he also published a *Florula corsica* on the basis of a manuscript by Jaussin. During the last decades of his life (he died in 1793) he did not publish anything botanical; as far as creative work was concerned he sank into insignificance. James Edward Smith, in a letter to T. J. Woodward published by Lady Smith (1832), paints an unflattering picture of the evidently somewhat pompous younger Burman in 1786: "... Burman shelters his ignorance under his professional dignity, and is very difficult of access. I could not get a sight of his herbarium, nor did he seem to be acquainted with some very well known botanical facts. How different is van Royen!"

After the death of Burman's wife in 1810 the collections and library were put up for auction. Benjamin Delessert acquired the herbarium, which

then numbered 29.000 specimens, many of them types, and brought it to
Paris. It is now part of the general herbarium of the *Conservatoire Botanique* at
Geneva. (For biographical details on the Burman family see Burman
Becker, s.d.).

Botany thus flourished in Amsterdam and Leiden in the early part of the
Linnaean era. The young Linnaeus himself had divided his time between
these two centers and de Hartecamp. At Utrecht he spent one day, only
to discover that there was no botanical activity to speak of; the aged
Serrurier (x–1742) did little or nothing but his successor, Evert Jacob
Wachendorff (1703–1758), brought life to the Utrecht garden. Wachendorff
was appointed ordinary professor of medicine, botany and chemistry [sic]
in 1743 and kept this position until his—early—death in 1758. His modest
claim to fame rests on a highly original *Horti ultrajectini index* (1747) which
lists an impressive number of species from this small garden. Wachendorff's
Index is fully in the Linnaean tradition with respect to the nomenclature
and taxonomy of the genera and the species; the Linnaean generic reform
was fully accepted and the generic names are given with simple references
to the second edition (1742) of the *Genera plantarum*. The species are listed
wherever possible by the phrase names given by Linnaeus in the *Hortus
cliffortianus* and *Flora suecica*, by van Royen in his *Prodromus*, or by Gronovius in
his *Flora virginica*. The system of bibliographical references is the binary one
proposed by Linnaeus in the *Hortus cliffortianus*. The great difference, however, is the system: Wachendorff, like van Royen, makes an attempt at a
natural system based upon a combination of characters derived from the
flowers, fruit and seed (cotyledons). Linnaeus, in his *Philosophia botanica*
(no. 69), states that Wachendorff tried to make a natural method "with
the help of the Greek language." A somewhat mocking but not untrue
characterization of Wachendorff's system, which is mainly notable because
of its almost fantastic names of classes. These names are often so complicated that they will remain obscure even for the more than casual reader.
Adanson (1763) and Ehrhart (1791) have provided a helpful analysis. The
Anomoiodiperiantae [plantae] are for instance plants of which the number of
sepals is different from that of the petals, but with as many stamens as
there are petals; the *Pollaplostemonopetalae* are plants of which the number of
stamens is 2, 3, 4 or 5 times that of the petals.

Wachendorff has nineteen classes which he presents in a universal key
leading to all genera. Such a key (fig. 38), for the greater part dichotomous,

PLANTAE SUNT:

I. Floribus manifeftis. Phaneranthae.
  λ. Seminibus bi- vel pluri-valvibus, feu foliis fe-
   minalibus fimplici aut uno pluribus. Polycotyledones.
    1. Floribus fingulis fibi fufficientibus; hinc
    completis feu perfectis: partibus fcilicet cun-
    ctis floris effentialibus, id eft, ftaminibus fi-
    mul atque piftillis, praeditis. Teleianthae,
    A. Floribus duobus perianthiis, corolla fcili-
    cet & calyce, inftructis. Diperianthae.
     a. Floribus fimplicibus: fingulis fcilicet fin-
     gulis feu pedunculis, feu thalamis infiden-
     tibus, feu denique calycibus exceptis.
     Monanthae.
      α. Staminibus ad petala, eorumve fegmen-
      ta, relativis. Schefeopaloftemones.
      I. Staminibus ad corollae divifiones nu-
      mero paribus. Ifoftemonopetalae.
       A. Staminibus numero ad corollam
       iisdem feu fimplicibus. Haplofte-
       monopetalae.
        1. Seminibus nudis. Gymnofper-
        mae
         A. Flore ovario infidente. Epi-
         carpanthae.
         a. Seminibus duobus. Difper-
         mae.
          α. Stylis duobus. Diftylae.
          (hae Pentaftemones quo-
          que funt & Pentapetalae)
           2   I*. Um-

Fig. 38

was still a rarity at the time. The great pity is that it is so involved and difficult to follow. In this key Wachendorff used many other terms (also explained by Ehrhart) which sometimes have a definite modern flavour, such as 'Angiospermae' and 'Gymnospermae,' but of which others are again difficult to understand. The system was therefore not very attractive, and it is no suprise that Wachendorff found no followers. His main aim was to found a system with natural classes on the basis of all parts of the 'fructification' (including therefore the structure of the seed). The main characteristics used are presence or absence of flowers, number of cotyledons, number of stamens with respect to the number of calyx and or corolla lobes, free or connate stamens and their relative lengths, distribution of male and female flowers and the completeness or incompleteness of flowers. The result is not very impressive. The classes are on the whole rather unnatural. A good exception is the class called *Cylindrobasiostemones*, a name somewhat less enigmatic than the others because it refers to the *Malvales*. The classes are subdivided in what can be called orders which are more often in agreement with generally recognized natural families. These orders are again subdivided, sometimes several times, with the result that there are some 250 groups of genera.

Wachendorff's book was the only significant botanical publication to come out of Utrecht during the century. However, in other parts of the Netherlands in the second half of the eighteenth century botany was also on the decline. N. L. Burman in Amsterdam was much less productive than his father Johannes, David van Royen in Leiden (1727–1799) was insignificant when compared with his uncle Adriaan. The gardener Nicolaas Meerburgh (1734–1814) at Leiden produced some elephantine books with ghastly illustrations (see e.g. Fuchs, 1962–1963), but did not add anything further.

In Groningen, Tiberius Lambergen (1717–1763) taught botany in the Linnaean tradition and tried to emulate the rich collections of the Amsterdam and Leiden gardens. However, he left little in print. His successor, Petrus Camper, was not too keen on systematics: "However, the perpetual changing of the composition of a system which is so characteristic of the foreman of all present-day botanists, Linnaeus, shows

Fig. 38. E. J. van Wachendorff, *Horti ultrajectini index* [Utrecht 1747]; first page of general key to the plant kingdom.

clearly that the principles of botany are not yet based on the laws of nature" (quoted by Andreas 1971).

In Franeker, the Friesian university, David Meese (1723–1771) published some short treatises—e.g. a *Flora frisica* (1760), an early local flora fully in the Linnaean tradition, but in Dutch except for the phrase names and still without trivial names. In 1763 he published two parts of a general botanical textbook, of which the most interesting feature is perhaps that the whole text is in Dutch as well as in Latin. In England, France and Germany alike there was a certain waning of Latinity in botany in the second half of the century. Meese was the first Dutchman to show this phenomenon which is so typical of the Enlightenment. I have shown elsewhere (1963) that the use of the vernacular was part of the escape from the bonds of tradition and served the purpose of spreading knowledge among wider groups of people (see also p. [209]).

An excellent example of this trend towards writing on science in the vernacular with a wide public in mind is provided by Maarten Houttuyn (1720–1798) and his elaborate Dutch 'version' of the twelfth edition of Linnaeus's *Systema naturae*, actually a wholly independent work, entitled *Natuurlijke Historie of uitvoerige Beschrijving der Dieren, Planten en Mineraalen, volgens het Samenstel van den Heer Linnaeus* (1773–1783) (fig. 39). Houttuyn was a Dutch physician at Amsterdam with evidently as much leisure as enthusiasm for natural history. His book consists of not less than 37 sizeable volumes, of which 18 deal with the animals, 14 with plants and 5 with minerals. Soulsby (no. 73) remarks correctly that "this voluminous compilation is only slightly based on the *Systema naturae*, under which it is so often cited, but [that] it influenced largely many similar works in other countries." Christmann and Panzer's *Vollständiges Pflanzensystem* (1777–1788) was, for instance, mainly based on Houttuyn's work.

Even though professing to follow the *Systema naturae*, Houttuyn actually opts for a major division of the plant kingdom on the basis of a natural system. Of all such systems so far proposed—he discusses the works of Adanson and others in great detail in a somewhat biassed historical introduction—he chooses that proposed by Linnaeus himself in the 12th edition of the *Systema*, with some minor modifications. Even so, he discusses the sexual system in great detail and illustrates it with a plate obviously

Fig. 39. Title-page of the first volume of the botanical part of Maarten Houttuyn, *Natuurlijke Historie* [1773]. The name of the author does not appear on the title-page.

NATUURLYKE HISTORIE
OF
UITVOERIGE BESCHRYVING
DER
DIEREN, PLANTEN
EN
MINERAALEN,
Volgens het SAMENSTEL van den Heer
LINNÆUS.
Met naauwkeurige Afbeeldingen.

TWEEDE DEELS, EERSTE STUK,
DE PALMBOOMEN.

Te AMSTERDAM,
By de ERVEN VAN *F. HOUTTUYN.*
MDCCLXXIII.

Fig. 39

adapted from the famous Ehret plate of 1736 (reproduced Taxon 3: 175.)·

The taxonomic part of the book is extremely detailed and contains a wealth of incidental information not brought together in this form elsewhere.

The total botanical work contains some 8600 pages of text, 105 excellent copper plates illustrating 275 species of plants and the description of well over a hundred new species of plants. The *Natuurlijke Historie* as a whole comprises well over 21.500 pages of text. On publication it was an immediate success, as is shown by the fact that the botanical part was soon reissued as *Handleiding tot de plant- en kruidkunde* and by the Christmann and Panzer translation into German.

Merrill has provided a modern evaluation of Houttuyn's many new taxa (1938, 1939). The main significance of the work, however, was not scientific–technical; as an attempt to bring botany and zoology to a wider public it was a conspicuous example of the eighteenth–century movement towards general education and the spreading of knowledge. As such it did much to diffuse Linnaean thought and method among the increasingly growing body of eighteenth–century intellectuals and *curiosi*.

One further Dutch botanist carrying on and spreading the Linnaean tradition should be mentioned, if only because of his very particular personal association with Linnaeus: David de Gorter (1717–1783), the son of Linnaeus's promotor at Harderwijk, Johannes de Gorter.

When Linnaeus came to Harderwijk he was evidently attracted to the young David (van Ooststroom 1941), and he accompanied him on some collecting trips. The Rijksherbarium at Leiden possesses some specimens collected on these occasions. David had obtained his medical degree at Harderwijk on 14 April 1734, when he was 16 years old. In 1742 he was appointed lecturer, to assist his father, in order to keep the latter from going to Utrecht. In 1754 David and his father were called to St. Petersburgh as

Fig. 40. Frontispiece of David de Gorter, *Leer der Plantkunde* [Amsterdam 1782]. The engraving faithfully illustrates the eighteenth century attitude towards botany as *scientia amabilis*. The plants in the foreground are beautiful products of the artist's imagination; the formal garden in the background has a romantic flavour, but the caption catches best of all the prevailing sentiment:

"Oh young man, behold wither Linnaeus leads you,
And learn here how to distinguish the trees, herbs and flowers.
However, think of Him who bestowed them upon us: it's God's Providence,
Whose disposition Man can never sufficiently praise."

[176]

O Jongeling! befchouw waar u LINNÆUS leidt,
En leer hier 't onderfcheid der Boomen, Kruiden, Bloemen.
Doch denk, wie ons die fchonk: 't is GODS voorzienigheid;
Wiens schikking nooit genoeg door 't Schepfel is te roemen.

F.R. Reselman pinx.

O.E. DE GORTER Gebt SCHULTZ

Fig. 40

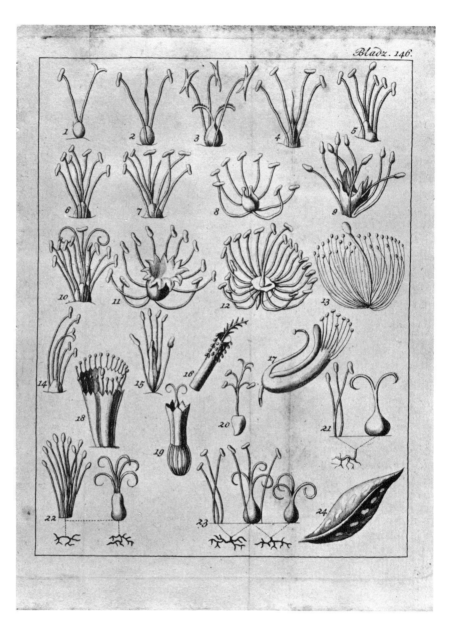

Fig. 41. Illustration of the sexual system of Linnaeus given by David de Gorter in his *Leer der Plantkunde* [Amsterdam 1782]. The drawing is based on an engraving by Ehret of 1736 but deviates from it in the symbolic picture (24) of the cryptogams. The numbers are those of the classes of the Linnaean system. *Reduced.*

personal physicians to Elisabeth of Russia. David returned to Holland in 1761 because of illness, went again to Russia for a few years, settled in Wijk bij Duurstede near Utrecht in 1764 and spent the last years of his life in Zutphen.

David de Gorter was the only botanist of international standing in the Netherlands in the second half of the eighteenth century. He published a number of excellent floras, all in the Linnaean tradition. His first major flora was the *Flora Gelro–Zutphanica* of 1745, accepting the Linnaean generic reform as well as the sexual system. The Russian period is reflected by his *Flora ingrica* of 1761, in which de Gorter uses Linnaean binary nomenclature. The *Flora belgica* of 1767 is the first general Dutch flora in which binary nomenclature is used. Gorter's most elaborate work was his *Flora VII Provinciarum Belgii Foederati indigena* of 1781, especially notable because of its extensive coverage of the cryptogams. The "L.S." starts with "opusculum hoc origenem suam debet Excursionibus Botanicis, quas Anno 1735 comite Ill. Linnaea circa Harderovicum feci," "the excursions which I made with Linnaeus around Harderwijk in the year 1735." A handsome tribute to the stimulating influence of the young Swede. Very interesting is his Dutch *Leer der plantkunde* of 1782 (fig. 40 & 41), in which de Gorter gives extensive descriptions and discussions of Linnaeus's 'natural orders.' He also discusses extensively the phenomenon of interspecific hybridization and comes to the conclusion (in translation): "that there are now possibly also species which were not present in the Universe at the time of Creation." For the delimitation of difficult species he advises in the first place to grow them in the garden and to assess their variability by growing them in different soils. The publication of such an extensive treatment in the Dutch language is again characteristic of the spiritual climate of the day in the Netherlands, which was strongly imbued with the ideals of the French Enlightenment. Meese and de Gorter were both modest but enthusiastic representatives of this movement, which was responsible in its home country for the great change from natural history to biology. We shall find a similar attitude among the botanists of other European countries. In their pure systematics these botanists stayed with the Linnaean system, mainly because of its great direct practical importance, but de Gorter in particular shows some signs of originality.

Two centuries after Dodoens and Clusius had put Dutch botany on the road towards expansion, two centuries in which the Dutch mercantile empire had been built up and in which the colonial expansion had resulted in a rich stream of botanical novelties to its gardens, a setback was almost inevitable. Dutch botany would be at low ebb for nearly a century, until the new expansion of the nineteenth century under the influence of the industrial development and the rapid extension especially of the interests in the Dutch East Indies would provide a new impetus.

However, before we leave Dutch systematic botany, one instance should be cited of its influence beyond the borders of the United Netherlands. Many such instances could be mentioned; Leiden, especially in the first half of the eighteenth century, was a great center which attracted numerous students from abroad. Famous names in botany are, for instance, William Sherard (1659–1728), Albrecht von Haller (1708–1777), Johann Gesner (1709–1790), Nehemiah Grew (1628–1711), William Houstoun (1695–1733), Carl Linnaeus (1707–1778), Patrick Browne (1720–1790), Gerard van Swieten (1700–1772), Johann Bartsch (1709–1738), Nicolaus Joseph von Jacquin (1727–1817) and James Edward Smith (1758–1828). Especially typical representatives of the spreading of the Linnaean influence through Leiden were Gerard van Swieten and Nicolaus Joseph von Jacquin (Stafleu 1970, 1971).

Gerard van Swieten (fig. 42), born in Leiden in 1700 of Roman Catholic parents, studied medicine and pharmacy at Louvain and at Leiden under Boerhaave. The latter counted him amoung his most outstanding pupils. Van Swieten first practised medicine in Leiden and was later appointed professor of medicine, a post, however, which he had to abandon because as a rule Roman Catholics were not welcome to teach at the University. The spiritual freedom characteristic of the Netherlands did not necessarily extend to professional circles. In 1745 van Swieten was invited to become physician to Maria Theresia in Vienna, and in 1749 he was charged with the reorganization of the medical faculty at Vienna. He made a splendid career and published extensively in the field of medicine. Van Swieten advised the Empress on the planning of the gardens of the Schönbrunn palace, which had been completed by 1750. The Dutch gardener Adriaan [van] Stekhoven, from Leiden, was engaged to organize the development of the gardens and the zoo. Stekhoven constructed conservatories and a special hothouse for tropical plants. Richard van der Schot, from Delft, was appointed head gardener and instructed to bring a number of exotic plants from the Leiden gardens and nurseries. Among these plants must have been quite a few South African plants from the rich choice offered by

GERARDUS. L.B. VAN SWIETEN,
August. Imperato. et Imperatric.
a consil. Archiatr. comes

Dessiné par Aug. de St Aubin

Gravé par N. Pruneau 1771.

Se vend a Paris chez l'Auteur rue de la Harpe au Collège de Narbonne.

Fig. 42. GERARD VAN SWIETEN; *b.* Leiden, Netherlands, May 7, 1700; *d.* Schönbrunn, Austria, June 18, 1772; "archiater imperatricis Mariae Theresiae; summus prefectus rei medicinalis austriacae; conditor horti botanici imperialis Fontibelli (Schönbrunn)." [Engraving by N. Prunau, 1771, after a drawing by Auguste de St. Aubin; *Biohistorical Institute, Utrecht*]. *Reduced.*

[181]

JACQUIN (sic.)

Fig. 43. Nicolaus Joseph Jacquin (after 1806 Freiherr von Jacquin); *b.* Leiden, Netherlands February 16, 1727; *d.* Wien, Austria, October 26, 1817; traveller in Central America 1755–1759, professor of chemistry at Schemnitz, Hungary 1763–1768, professor of botany and chemistry in Wien 1769–1797. [Lithograph of unknown origin; *Biohistorical Institute, Utrecht*].
Reduced.

[182]

Leiden. Van Swieten founded the Vienna University botanical garden in 1754 and modelled it after Boerhaave's Leiden garden. The garden was put under the direction of Robert Laugier. In 1752 van Swieten had invited or stimulated N. J. von Jacquin to come to Vienna to finish his medical training. This invitation and his founding of the University botanic garden bring van Swieten, who described not a single plant in his life, into the history of plant taxonomy. N. J. von Jacquin was to become the founder of the Vienna school and, mainly through his many publications, one of the most powerful proponents of Linnaeus's system and ideas.

2. *Austria*

Nicolaus [probably originally Nicolaas] Joseph Jacquin (fig. 43–45) was born in Leiden on 16 February 1727. His father was a relatively wealthy cloth manufacturer of French origin, the Jacquin family having come to Holland late in the seventeenth century. Jacquin was therefore Dutch by birth, and became Austrian by choice.

After having received an early schooling at Leiden and Antwerp, Jacquin studied philosophy at Louvain—in the 'Austrian Netherlands'—and medicine and botany at Leiden. Here he worked under Adriaan van Royen and became acquainted with father and son Gronovius. The remark by Garside (1942) that Jacquin was a pupil of the gardener Nicolaas Meerburgh (1734–1814) must be based on a misunderstanding. By 1750, the year in which Jacquin left Leiden, Meerburgh was barely sixteen years old. Laurens Theodoor Gronovius was four years younger than Jacquin, and the two struck up a friendship. There is a story that Gronovius Jr. stimulated Jacquin's interest in botany by explaining to him the structure of the flower of a species of *Costus arabicus*. Kronfeld (1905), who relates this story, attributes it to J. F. von Jacquin, who is stated to have said of this episode that "it was the spark which kindled his [father's] inexhaustible passion for this science." I have not been able to find confirmation of this anecdote. Jacquin spent the years 1750–1752 at Paris for further specialized medical schooling and came into contact with the professor of botany at the Jardin du Roi, Antoine de Jussieu (1686–1758), and his knowledgeable brother, the famous botanist Bernard de Jussieu (1699–1777). In 1752 van Swieten, a friend of Jacquin's parents, advised Jacquin to finish his medical studies in Vienna. Here again Jacquin pursued his botanical interests by frequent visits to the University botanic garden as well as to the gardens at Schönbrunn. These Schönbrunn gardens were already richly stocked, thanks to van Swieten, van Stekhoven and van der Schot who, through their connections in Leiden, found it not difficult to build up the Schönbrunn collection at a rapid rate. The eighteenth century spirit, however, was to sponsor expeditions in order to obtain new taxa, preferably from the tropics. Franz I, Maria Theresia's husband, organized a collecting trip to the West Indies and the northern parts of South America for which he chose Jacquin as the botanist, to be accompanied by van der Schot. The two men would have the assistance of two Italian technicians, Giovanni Buonamici and Ferdinando Barculli, for the zoological collections. Their assignment was to collect as many living plants as possible for the Schönbrunn gardens, in addition to the usual objects to be collected for the Hof–Naturaliencabinet. Jacquin gives an extensive account of his voyage and of the various consignments of plants and animals on pp. ii–iii of his *Hortus Schoenbrunnensis* (1797).

The party left Livorno on 7 January 1755 and arrived in Martinique on 28 June 1755. During the four years of their stay in the West Indies (cf. Urban 1902), with Martinique as the main basis, the following islands and regions were visited: St. Vincent, Grenada, Curaçao and Aruba, on the mainland Venezuela and Colombia (near Cartagena); and then Guadeloupe, St. Kitts, St. Eustatius, St. Maarten, St. Barthélemy, Haiti (1757–1758), Jamaica (1758) and Cuba. Jacquin returned to Vienna in July 1759. The consignments of living plants had been considerable; herbarium material was scanty, but many drawings and descriptions had been made on the spot.

The immediate result of Jacquin's work for taxonomy were two publications which have remained of importance for the knowledge of the West Indian flora: a small octavo published shortly after his return and a big folio published in 1763.

The small octavo [41 pages], published in 1760, is the *Enumeratio systematica plantarum quas in insulis Caribaeis vicinaque Americes continente detexit novas, aut jam cognitas emendavit*. It was published in Leiden by Theodoor Haak and remained relatively unnoticed, partly because of its rarity and its inconspicuous appearance, but mainly because Jacquin himself did not refer to it in his definitive work of 1763. The *Enumeratio* was simply a *prodromus*; the folio *Selec-*

tarum stirpium americanarum historia of 1763 contained the ample descriptions and the illustrations. The 1760 booklet is of importance here because it employed the binary system of nomenclature at a very early date, barely a year after N. L. Burman's thesis, also published by Haak at Leiden. It contains the descriptions of many new taxa, even though in the most concise and laconic Linnaean style one can think of. The diagnoses are sometimes of the minimum length: one word. Even so, they constitute valid publication of the names of the taxa in question, because these one–word diagnoses (in fact diagnostic 'specific' names of the Linnaean type) always refer to a second species added to a monotypic Linnaean genus. The single word following the binary combination is usually sufficient to distinguish the new species from the old. In the true Linnaean fashion, the species of new monotypic genera have no specific diagnosis, though they do receive an epithet.

Jacquin's link with Leiden is still apparent from the way in which the *Enumeratio* was published. He had sent it to L. T. Gronovius, who saw it through the press. Gronovius was in regular contact with Linnaeus and reported to him the progress of the book. On 17 August 1760 Gronovius wrote to Linnaeus—who was very eager to learn of Jacquin's results— that publication might be expected any time. Even so, Linnaeus received his copy only on 18 December. Linnaeus was enthusiastic: "yesterday I received at last this work, which I awaited so eagerly, and I have seldom seen such a small booklet so rich in golden knowledge, I read it during the evening and could not sleep at night because I dreamed of your beautiful plants."

Jacquin and Linnaeus also kept up a close correspondence. The two men never met, but Jacquin became one of the staunchest supporters of the Linnaean reform. Linnaeus had heard from Sauvages of Jacquin's safe return from the West Indies and opened the correspondence on 1 August 1759: "We [all natural scientists] receive and honor you as the ambassador of Flora itself, bringing us the treasures from foreign worlds, so far neither heard of nor seen."

The correspondence between Jacquin and Linnaeus is fully available to us: the letters written by Linnaeus to Jacquin were published as early as 1841 by Schreiber; those written by Jacquin are at The Linnean Society of London, and available on IDC microfiche. The letters give a vivid picture of the genesis especially of Jacquin's first big folio, the *Selectarum stirpium,* for the details of which I refer to my introduction (Stafleu 1971) to the recently published facsimile edition of this work.

The *Selectarum stirpium americanarum historiae* of 1763 was the book with which Jacquin made his name as a taxonomist. It contains the extensive descriptions of the taxa dealt with, usually too briefly, in the *Enumeratio*. The plates are engravings of Jacquin's original drawings. A special edition containing 264 coloured drawings, copies of the originals, was issued in 1780; but it is excessively rare because only 12–18 copies were published.

Jacquin, like Johannes Burman, was not a theoretician but a practical taxonomist whose aim it was to describe new taxa. The preface to the *Selectarum stirpium* shows that Jacquin was not very much interested in methodological questions. He relates how Plumier and Sloane had been the pioneers of West Indian botany and how Patrick Browne—another Linnaean enthusiast—and he himself at almost every step had found plants described by their illustrious predecessors. Even so, many new taxa were still to be gathered, so many that he purposely neglected the grasses and the cryptogams and concentrated on the plants with more showy flowers. He adopts wholeheartedly and on his own account the sexual system of Linnaeus. He explains that this choice does not imply that he does not realize that "the force of nature not rarely intervenes" and that the sexual system shares certain defects with other systems. His main reasons for accepting the sexual system were that it had been adopted and used by so many others that most plants known at the time of his writing had been conveniently placed in the system, and because it was generally accepted.

Every system, says Jacquin, is but a methodical summary. The natural system is certainly the ultimate aim. The natural affinities can be a guide towards medical properties. However, nature will not accept laws from us which it had not previously made itself. We must diligently study affinities, but who is able to circumscribe his taxa on the basis of affinities alone? As long as everything created has not come to our attention, it would be foolish to trust affinities.

We can bring varieties and individuals together to species, and we have nature as our example. However, as soon as we try to bring species together

Fig. 44. Title-page of N. J. von Jacquin, *Anleitung zur Pflanzenkenntnis nach Linné's Methode. Zum Gebrauche seiner theoretischen Vorlesungen* [Wien 1785] "Introduction to the knowledge of plants according to the method of Linnaeus; for use at his theoretical lectures."

[186]

Nikolaus Joseph Edlen von Jacquin's
Lehrers der Kräuterkunde an der hohen Schule zu Wien

Anleitung

zur

Pflanzenkenntniß

nach Linné's Methode.

Zum Gebrauche seiner theoretischen Vorlesungen.

Wien,
bey Christian Friederich Wappler.
1785.

Fig. 44

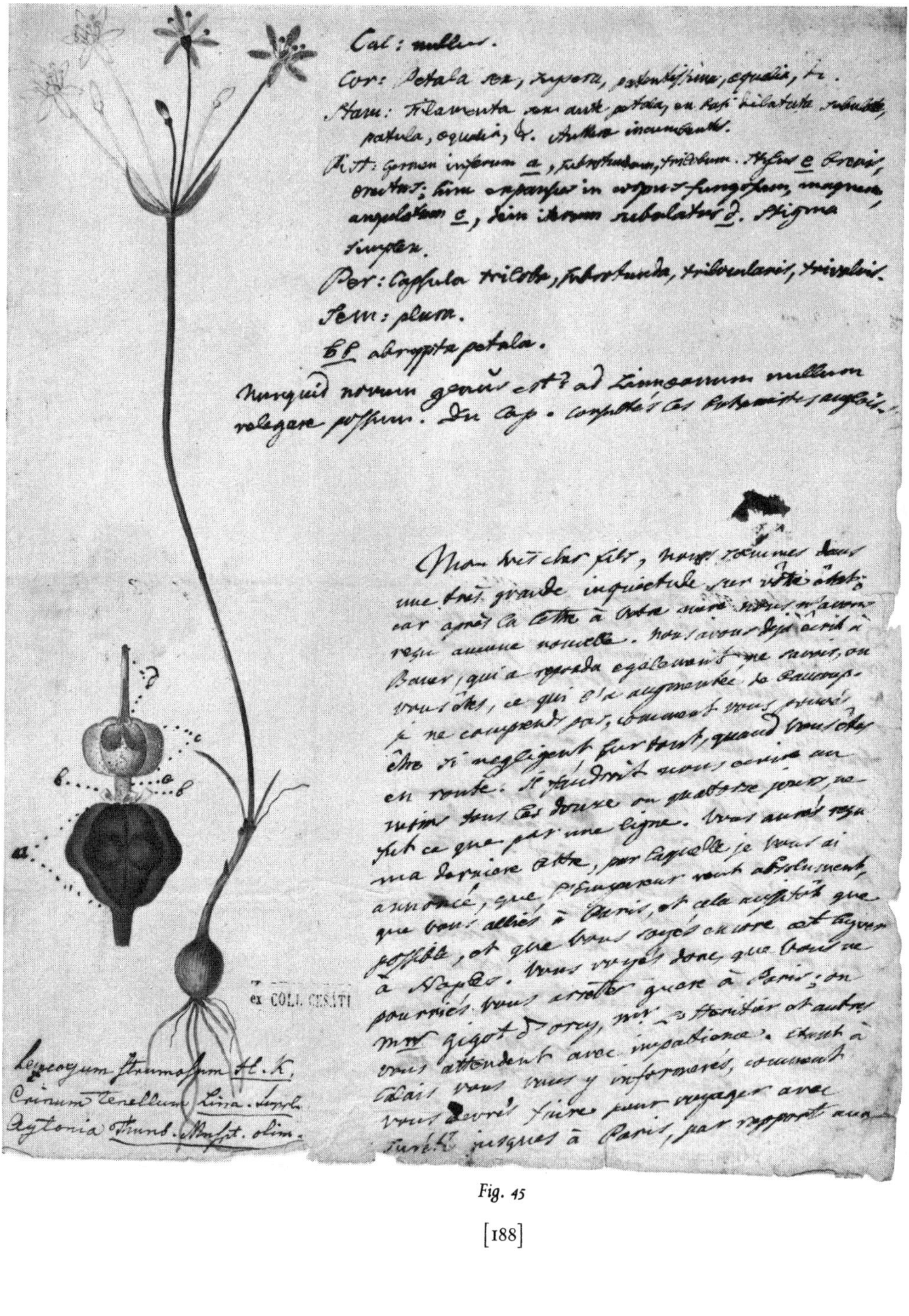

ex COLL. CESATI

Fig. 45

[188]

in natural genera we may quite easily go wrong. Nature jumps over our delimitations and makes fun of human cleverness. We need genera, orders and classes in order to avoid confusion and not be overwhelmed by nature's profusion. A genus is not known until all its species are perfectly understood. The detailed description of new species is therefore the main objective of Jacquin's book.

Jacquin continues with a warning that the habit of growth of certain tropical plants in the European glasshouses differs often from that in the field. Some may grow more luxuriously, others are dwarfed under our conditions. The descriptions in his book will therefore not always agree with the plants as they are known in cultivation.

Another early Jacquin publication in which he used the Linnaean system of binary nomenclature for species was the *Enumeratio stirpium ... in agri vindobonensi* of 1762, a list of plants growing in the Vienna region. This was the first use of Linnaean binomials for the Austrian flora. Some of these binomials clash with names published for the first time in the second edition of Linnaeus's *Species plantarum*. The book came out in May 1762; the first volume of the *Species* in September. Even so, Jacquin later withdrew his name *Scabiosa pannonica* in favor of Linnaeus's later *S. sylvatica*. Because of its priority, this Austrian *Enumeratio* is of some importance in botanical nomenclature.

From 1763–1768 Jacquin was a professor of chemistry at the mining academy of Schemnitz (then in Hungary, now Banska Stiavnica, Czechoslovakia), but in 1768 he was recalled to Vienna to become professor of botany and chemistry, as well as director of the University botanic garden. He kept these posts until 1797, when he retired and was succeeded by his son Joseph Franz (1766–1839). Jacquin Sr. was made a baron in 1806 and died in Vienna on 26 October 1817.

Jacquin, as we have seen above, was not a great theoretician. However, in his second Vienna period he published an *Anleitung zur Pflanzenkenntniss nach Linné's Methode. Zum Gebrauche seiner theoretischen Vorlesungen* (Wien 1785) which gives us an idea of his ideas on taxonomy during the best years of his life. The title indicates that the Linnaean method is followed. It is possible, says Jacquin, for one hundred botanists to make one hundred

Fig. 45. Letter written by N. J. Jacquin at Vienna on October 29, 1789, to his son in London. Jacquin Sr. expresses his concern about the well-being of his son because the latter was obviously not a very good correspondent. [*Conservatoire botanique de Genève*]. Reduced.

systems which are all different and which may all be useful. If we look at two different 'species' we will often find it possible to fill the gap between them with intermediary forms. "Wir ... lernen, die Natur schreite langsam durch fast unmerkliche Stufen fort, ohne einen lehren Raum zu lassen. Also gibt es keinen in der ungeheuren Kette der Dinge, und der, den wir darin wahrzunehmen meynen liegt viel mehr in den beschränkten Gränzen unserer Verstandskräfte." The principle of plenitude makes its appearance here in more definitive form than with Linnaeus. Jacquin continues to explain that the chain of being is not simple, "und bildet also nicht eine einfache, sondern eine unendlich, in unter einander geflochtene Kettenstücke, abgetheilte und unterabgetheilte Kette." The logical outcome of this strong emphasis on the continuity of nature is a nominalist attitude with respect to taxa above the rank of species:

"Lasset es uns bekennen, die Natur bringt die Dinge nicht nach Classen, Ordnungen, oder Gattungen hervor. Sie zeugt Arten, zwischen welchen unser Geist Trennungen zu Entdecken glaubt welche nie in der Natur waren. Gibt es ja eine natürliche Gattung, so ist es eine solche, die nur eine einzige Art in sich begreifft, und dann ist sie auch nur eine blosse Art ..."

"Our mind thinks to discover gaps which were never present in nature ..."; the only natural genera are those which consist of one species. All systems give an incomplete picture, a disrupted part of the great chain of nature:

"Sie biethen uns nur ein durch unsere Einbildungskraft [imagination] tausendfältig verstummeltes und verzerrtes Scheinbild [imaginary picture] der Natur an. Alles ist darin willkührlich, die Classen sind es, die Ordnungen und Gattungen nicht weniger ..."

Jacquin therefore holds that all systems are arbitrary. Yet, one needs a system for purposes of information. Such a system must provide a place for each plant, must enable rapid determination, must be able to accommodate new taxa and be accepted by the great majority of botanists. As such the Linnaean system is by far the best.

The reason why Jacquin wholeheartedly accepts the Linnaean system is, therefore, its practical usefulness. His basic tenets are quite different from those of the great master. Jacquin is an extreme nominalist; essentialist thinking is foreign to him, but what attracts him in the Linnaean system is its directness, simplicity and efficiency as a system for storing and retrieving taxonomic information. This great practical usefulness was indeed the main reason for the success of the Linnaean system and was responsible for the fact that it gained general acceptance in several countries, even though the philosophical basis from which it had sprung had been completely abandoned. The only old philosophical idea which continues is that of the principle of plenitude. Jacquin's world of plants remains timeless; nature is a vast unchanging complex which our mind can grasp only very incompletely. The most efficient and practical system will do; all talk about its being 'natural' is nonsense.

Jacquin's main output during his second and longest period in Vienna consisted of an impressive series of illustrated folios. They are too numerous to be listed here; especially fine examples are the *Icones plantarum rariorum* (1781–1793), with many illustrations by e.g. Franz Bauer, and the *Plantarum rariorum horti caesarei schoenbrunnensis* (1797–1804), with 500 coloured engravings, mostly of drawings by Johannes Scharf and Martin Sedelmayer.

Many of the plants described by Jacquin in his later years came from the Cape. Joseph II, son of Maria Theresia, sent Francis Boos and George Scholl to the Cape to collect living plants and seeds. For the detailed story of their travels reference may be made to Garside's publication (1942). The result of these activities was that many new plants reached the Vienna gardens in the second half of the century, many of them amply described in Jacquin's folios. One of his last efforts was his monograph of *Stapelia* (1806). Many splendid specimens belonging to this genus had been brought home by George Scholl in 1799.

Jacquin's son, Joseph Franz, succeeded him as professor of botany and director of the University botanic garden, but his scientific activity fell far short of that of his father. Neither of the Jacquins did very much in the way of building up a school, although both of them maintained social contacts. When the younger Jacquin died in 1839 he was succeeded by Stephan Endlicher (1804–1849), whose scientific views were more modern and who turned away from the Linnaean tradition.

The Jacquin era was a period in which Austrian taxonomic botany flourished as never before; the second half of the eighteenth century was the golden age for Austrian botany. The enthusiastic receipt of Linnaeus's works in Austria had started before Jacquin, in the year 1756, with the publication of Wilhelm Heinrich Kramer's *Elenchus vegetabilium et animalium per Austriam inferiorem observatorum*. This book contains (pp. 1–307) what amounts to the first Lower–Austrian flora following the Linnaean

Lichtdruck : J. Löwy, Wien.

Nach einem im Museo Civico zu
Rovereto befindlichen Ölgemälde.

Joannes Antonius Scopoli M.* D.* et

Phys:. Reg.* Carn.*...

Fig. 46

[192]

system and nomenclature. An exception must be made for the *nomina trivialia*: they do not yet make their appearance, but for the rest the book is wholly in the Linnaean style, with verbatim quotation of the specific phrase names from the *Species plantarum*. Neilreich (1855) marvels at the way in which Kramer, with very limited means, succeeded in presenting a very detailed and precise flora of the region which contained two thirds of the species known in 1855. However, Kramer was soon overshadowed by Jacquin and the group of scholars more or less grouped around him: Scopoli, Crantz, Wulfen, Mygind, and others.

Another very characteristic sign of the impact of Linnaeus's writings on Austrian intellectual life are the so-called Graz editions of the *Amoenitates Academicae* published by Leopold Gottlieb von Biwald (1731–1805) (Widder 1967). This enthusiastic follower of Linnaeus used the Linnaean dissertations as the basis of dissertations of his own pupils. They were reprinted and enriched with *Additamenta* of varying significance. In all, von Biwald published three sets of selections: from the *Amoenitates* volumes 1 and 2 (in two editions, octavo and quarto), a *continuatio* with selections from volumes 3 and 4 and a *continuatio altera* from 5 and 6. Apart from their general interest as a most unusual means of providing texts for disputation, the actual value of the writings rests with the *additamenta*, which unfortunately are seldom studied because of their extreme rarity.

A contemporary of Jacquin who was more directly productive than von Biwald was Johann Anton Scopoli (fig. 46 & 47), born in Cavalese in Tyrol in 1723. Scopoli studied at the University of Innsbruck, which had no professor of natural sciences at the time. As a botanist Scopoli was therefore mainly self-taught. He spent some years at the University of Graz (with von Biwald) and went to Vienna in 1753 for his final examination as a physician, which would give him the right to practise anywhere in the Austro–Hungarian countries. The state committee for the examination was headed by van Swieten. The dissertation defended in 1754 at Vienna University (fide Voss 1882) was Scopoli's *Methodus plantarum enumerandis stirpibus ab eo repertis destinata*, in which he grouped the genera in a diagnostic key

Fig. 46. JOANNES ANTONIUS SCOPOLI (Giovanni Antonio); *b*. Cavallese, Tirol, June 3, 1723; *d*. Pavia, Italia, May 8, 1788; physician in Idria 1754–1767, professor of mineralogy and metallurgy at Schemnitz (Hungary) 1767–1776, professor of chemistry and botany at Pavia (Italy) 1776–1788. [From I. Dörfler, *Botaniker-Porträts* no. 27 (1907) after an oil-painting in the Museo Civico di Rovereto].

retaining the Tournefortian genera and nomenclature. The system itself rests heavily on Haller's work. In that same year Scopoli received an appointment as governmental district physician for Idria in Carniola, then a Habsburgh duchy, now part of Slovenia. Scopoli spent 16 years in this then underdeveloped region under most appalling circumstances. He found opportunity, however, for an extensive botanical, entomological and mineralogical exploration of the region, and published his *Flora carniolica* in 1760, dedicating it to Maria Theresia. The book contains the descriptions of 756 phanerogams and 256 cryptogams and is almost entirely Linnaean in the circumscription and nomenclature of the genera. The species are quoted by their Linnaean phrase names, but binary names are not used.

For the arrangement of the genera, however, Scopoli does not follow the Linnaean sexual system but attempts a natural arrangement following, as is stated in the preface, the attempts of Morison, Hermann, Ray, Boerhaave, van Royen, Haller and Wachendorff. His summing up of the choice is terse and precise: "Methodica divisio duplex; naturalis & artificialis: illa praestantior, nondum perfecta, sedulo inquirenda; Haec illius succedanea, semper utilis, perfecta nunquam; divellit enim socias stirpes, genera multiplicat & Classes Naturales plerumque dilacerat."

The system chosen has much affinity with Linnaeus's first fragments of a natural method. There are 33 classes, most of which are indeed natural to a high degree and easily recognizable today as families or orders. An important and significant difference with Linnaeus is that the 'lower' plants precede the higher ones. The treatments of the cryptogams, especially of the fungi, show remarkable detail. A second edition of the *Flora* came out in Vienna in 1772, much enlarged and covering a much greater area. This second edition is fully 'Linnaean': the sexual system is now followed and binary nomenclature is introduced. For the practical purpose of a flora and for the keying out of the genera, the sexual system is recognized as superior.

In 1767 Scopoli had been appointed successor to Jacquin at the Schemnitz mining academy, a position which he held until 1776, when he was invited to become professor of chemistry and botany at Pavia. Here he published his *Introductio* (1777) and the luxurious folio *Deliciae florae et faunae insubricae* (1786–1788).

Scopoli was a universal naturalist with an unusual field knowledge.

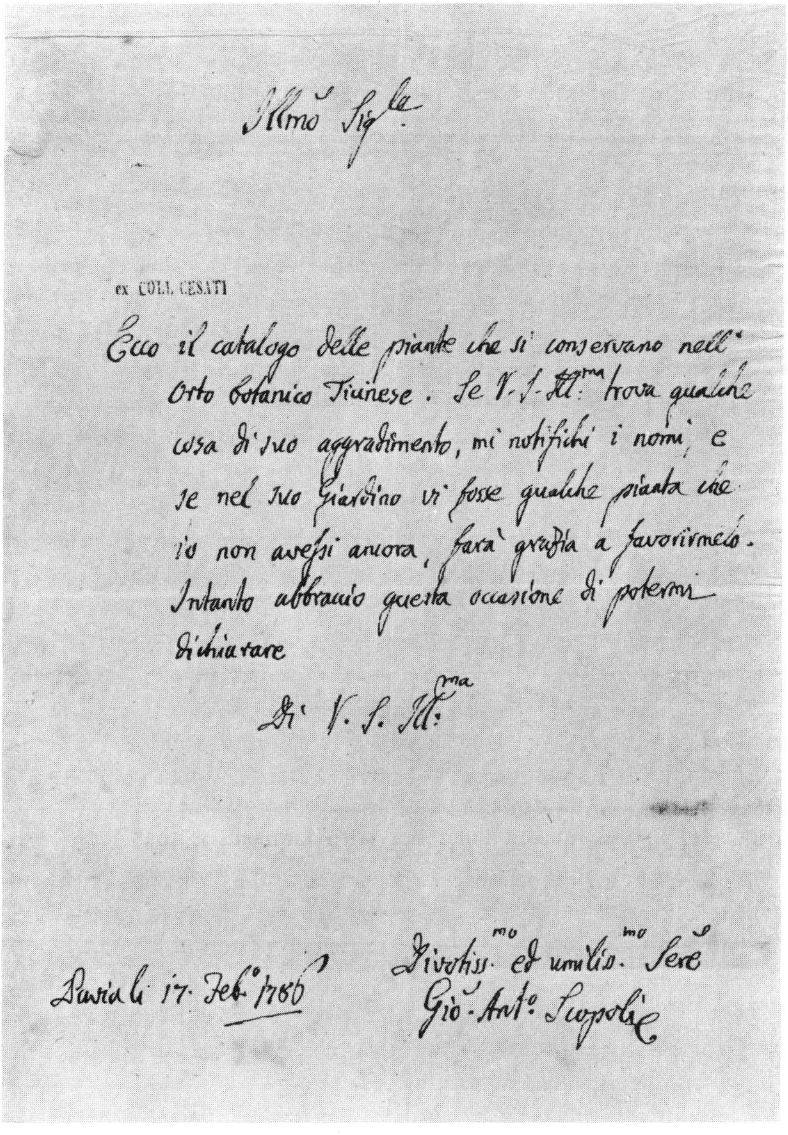

Ill.mo Sig.re

ex COLL. CESATI

Ecco il catalogo delle piante che si conservano nell' Orto botanico Ticinese. Se V. S. Ill.ma trova qualche cosa di suo aggradimento, mi notifichi i nomi, e se nel suo Giardino vi fosse qualche pianta che io non avessi ancora, sarà grazia a favorirmelo. Intanto abbraccio questa occasione di potermi dichiarare

Di V. S. Ill.ma

Pavia li 17. Feb.o 1786

Divotiss.mo ed umiliss.mo Serv.e
Gio. Ant.o Scopoli

Fig. 47. Letter written by G. A. Scopoli on February 17, 1786 to an unknown correspondent. Scopoli sends the seed list of the *Orto botanico Ticinese*. Ticino is an ancient name for Pavia (Italy) [*Conservatoire botanique de Genève*]. *Reduced.*

His publications cover the three realms of eighteenth–century natural history. Of special interest are also his publications on fossils, occasioned by his repeated professional contacts with the mining industry (*Introductio ad diagnosim et usum fossilium* 1763).

The *Introductio ad historiam naturalem* of 1777 is one of Scopoli's most remarkable (though generally ignored) publications. It is a *Systema naturae* in which he lists the genera of the three kingdoms with concise diagnostic descriptions (*characteribus essentialibus donata*). The Linnaean generic nomenclature is followed for botany: Linnaean names are the only ones not provided with an author's name. Scopoli adheres to the Linnaean rules for coining generic names and rejects many of the 'barbarous' names published by Aublet and other authors. The book has therefore become a source of superfluous synonyms. Several of the barbarous names were replaced by names derived from names of botanists. Because it was generally overlooked, however, many of these names were also coined by later authors. This homonymy often resulted in the rejection of the older Scopoli name by conservation of the later name, such as *Logania* R. Brown vs. *Loghania* Scopoli.

Scopoli's theoretical considerations with respect to plant taxonomy, as given in his *Praefatio ad regnum vegetabile* (to the *Introductio*), are a strange mixture of old and new thought. After having repeated, though in other words, Linnaeus's thoughts on the structure of the plant body and the role of fertilization in general, the inevitable conclusion is "hinc Plantae partes essentiales sunt Flos et Fructus." He continues, however:

"Ordo naturalis innititur scientiae germinationis, foliationis, habitus, vitae, partus, nec non situs, numeri, figurae, proportionis, & structurae omnium partium, praesertim Floris et Fructus, ut judiciosa comparatione detectis adfinitatibus, initium fiat a primo Individuo Terris proximo, indeque progressiva & catenata, non vero laterali ad reticulata serie, progredi queat ab una Classe in aliam, usque ad ultimam illam, quae Plantas cum Animalibus certiore foedere jungit."

"Methodus artificialis inimica Naturae, neglectis adfinitatibus, arbitrarie ordinat Plantas juxta unam aliamve notam ex Flore, aut Fructu, vel utroque petitam, Tale est Systema Rivini ..."

It is clear that Scopoli had come under the influence of Adanson. Several of the latter's thoughts are found in these paragraphs. The mixture of scholastic thinking with respect to the single chain from family to

family and the modern approach of overall affinity which is so characteristic of Adanson is also present in Scopoli's paragraphs. He states "Liceat
ergo mihi, exemplo oculatissimi Adansonii, Plantas hactenus detectas,
iuta harum adfinitates, in Tribus dividere, praestantiorum Botanicorum
nomina iis imponere …"

Scopoli then gives a review of all characteristics used by him: his taxonomy rests on the consideration of all parts of the plants. The names of his
36 tribes are derived from names of famous botanists, although the equivalent names from other natural systems are cited. The *Adansonii* are for
instance the *Satyria* (= Orchids) and the *Scitamineae*, the *Linnaei* are the
Calycantherae (Rosaceae and allies), the *Bauhinii* are the Leguminosae. A
certain sardonic humour is evident: the *Anomalae* (e.g. Polygala, Cleome)
are called *Hillii* after the controversial John Hill. The 36 tribes are for the
greater part really natural groups, and so are many of the subdivisions. The
hierarchy of categories is: Tribus, Gens, Divisio, Ordo, Genus; names are
given only to the tribes and of course to the genera.

The general arrangement of the tribes is supposed to reflect the chain
between minerals and animals. For that reason the system begins with
the plants which are, in Scopoli's opinion, closest to the mineral world.
The *Micheli* or *Incompletae* start off with simple lichens like *Pulina* Adanson,
Lepia Scopoli and *Verrucaria* Scopoli, followed by *Byssus*, *Conferva* and *Fucus*.
Then follow the ferns, the spermatophytes, the gymnosperms, and the
mosses. The last tribe, considered to be closest to the animals ("Molluscis
animalibus adeo similes") are the fungi, which are thereby proclaimed the
highest organized vegetable beings. The last genus, no. 1672, is *Tremella*. For
Scopoli fungi were 'plantae dubiae.'

Scopoli's system is now purely a curiosity. He had no followers. His
floristic work and his cryptogamic studies are best known and have
retained their importance. His *Introductio* illustrates the change of ideas in
taxonomy: rigorously conservative in most aspects, but at the same time
showing a tendency to a broader and more inductive attitude. Scopoli
sets forth different ideas in each of his major works: he was a searching
soul but did not find the answer.

Another contemporary of Jacquin and Scopoli was Heinrich Johann
Nepomuk (von) Crantz (1722–1799), for a long time professor of physiology
and materia medica at Vienna University. Crantz was a sharp observer
who published valuable critical revisions of the *Umbelliferae* and the *Cruciferae*

[197]

(1769) as well as an excellent floristic work, *Stirpes austriacae* (1762–1767). His main work is the *Institutiones rei herbariae juxta nutum naturae digestae ex habitu* (2 volumes, 1766), 'Elements of botany on the *authority* of nature,' a good eighteenth–century sentiment. The *Institutiones* is a *Species plantarum* with concise generic descriptions, binary nomenclature for the species, and citation of the Linnaean and other phrase names, accepting in general the Linnaean generic reform. The main difference from Linnaeus lies in the higher taxonomic units. There are fifteen more or less natural classes for which ample and critical descriptions are provided. The genera are keyed out diagnostically but are not specially arranged in named subordinate groups. Sometimes Crantz differs from Linnaeus in the generic delimitation: he combines *Atriplex* and *Chenopodium* in one genus (*Atriplex*) and transfers (without reference) the Linnaean phrase names from the latter to the former. Since the book is quite early, and follows binary nomenclature, it contains a relatively high number of validly published new names. The 'natural system' is not impressive: it follows in general the lines of van Royen, Ludwig and Haller, to whom the book is dedicated.

Crantz was sharply critical of the sexual system. Comparing *Atriplex* and *Chenopodium*, for instance, he could point out that a very natural group had been treated by Linnaeus in widely different groups: *Pentandria digynia* and *Polygamia monoecia*; however, his critical attitude with respect to Linnaeus and Jacquin did not make him blind to the evident advantages of the remaining elements of the Linnaean taxonomic and nomenclatural reform, and he therefore played an important rôle in their diffusion.

The Jacquin epoch was a great one for Austrian taxonomy. It extended well beyond the limits of my essay and was characterized by a rich harvest of taxonomic publications of every kind. The Linnaean tradition runs like a red thread through them all. The sexual system was the only element of the Linnaean reform which did not meet with general acceptance, mainly because of the important French cultural influence. The immediately practical binary nomenclature and clear generic taxonomy and nomenclature, however, were almost at once accepted and made Austria, with the Netherlands, the country where Linnaeus's thoughts found the earliest and almost universal acceptance.

7
Great Britain: Solid victory

1. Introduction through gardening

The reception of the Linnaean works in England differed greatly from that in Holland. During his brief visit of 1736 to Britain Linnaeus had certainly succeeded in impressing for instance J. J. Dillen and Philip Miller, but this left no trace in print. The Linnaean generic reform, the sexual system and the insistence on purely diagnostic phrase names for species found no real echo in England until well after the publication of the *Species plantarum*. When it came, after 1759, it came quickly and convincingly.

The first half of the eighteenth century was not a period of great original botanical activity in Britain. The figure of Ray dominated the scene long after his death. His *Synopsis methodica stirpium britannicarum* was the main British 'flora'; the third edition (1724), edited and revised anonymously by J. J. Dillen, remained in general use until the publication of William Hudson's *Flora anglica* in 1762. Dillen (or Dillenius) was a German botanist, born in Darmstadt, who settled in England in 1721 and became professor of botany at Oxford. Dillen's work was highly respected by Linnaeus but does not form part of the Linnaean epoch. His *Hortus elthamensis* (1732) may have served as a prototype for the *Hortus cliffortianus*, but its significance in botany was negligible in comparison with that of Linnaeus's work.

The Dillen edition (1724) of Ray's *Synopsis*, however, does have a place in the Linnaean story because in 1754 Linnaeus's student Grufberg was given to defend a thesis, *Flora anglica*, in which all the plants of the *Synopsis* were listed in accordance with the Linnaean sexual system and binary nomenclature. Stearn (1957, p. 76), who gives a detailed account of the reception of the *Species plantarum* in England and of its influence on British botany, notes that even though the tract received immediate attention by The Royal Society, it seems to have been forgotten until late in the nineteenth

PETER COLLINSON, F.R.S., S.A.S.

Hinc, quæ Natura negabat
Visibus humanis Oculis ea Pectoris hausit.
Cumque Animo, et vigili perspexerat omnia Cura,
In medium discenda dabat.

Fig. 48

century. Linnaeus's *Flora anglica* was not a critical enumeration but a simple attempt at a concordance between the third edition of the *Synopsis* and the *Species plantarum*. Stearn cites Druce's opinion that this attempt was not very successful.

An interesting testimony with respect to the rather delayed introduction of Linnaeus's system and thought in England is given by Thomas Martyn in a letter to Smith (1832, 1: 507) written on the occasion of the publication of the *Selection of the Correspondence of Linnaeus* by Smith in 1821: "These letters show how dead botany was in England in the middle of the last century, when Collinson and Ellis, two men not professionally scientific, but engaged in commerce, were Linnaeus's principal correspondents! His system can hardly be said to have been *publicly* known among us till about the year 1762, when Hope taught it at Edinburgh and I at Cambridge, and Hudson published his *Flora*."

John Ellis (c. 1710–1776) and Peter Collinson (1694–1768) (fig. 48) were two amateur botanists and horticulturists. Ellis was a London merchant who imported many American seeds and plants, several of which reached Linnaeus, and who published some minor botanical papers. Peter Collinson was a woollen–draper and merchant at London, who had a garden and a herbarium and who was in close contact with several of the botanical celebrities of his day, including Linnaeus. Collinson also played a major rôle in plant introduction and as such helped to set the stage for the rapid development of British botany in the second half of the eighteenth century. One of Collinson's main correspondents was the North American botanist John Bartram (1699–1777); the correspondence between these two practical enthusiasts and admirers of Linnaeus was published by William Darlington (1782–1863) in his *Memorials of John Bartram and Humphry Marshall* (1849).

Ellis, Collinson and yet another London amateur–botanist, the physician John Fothergill (1712–1780), were only a few of a whole group of English horticulturists who made use of the new wave of botanical immigrants which reached Europe after the heydays (1680–1720) of the Cape plants.

Fig. 48. PETER COLLINSON; *b.* London, England, January 14, 1694; *d.* London, England, August 11, 1768; Woollendraper, amateur botanist and horticulturist who had a garden at Peckham until 1749, and then at Mill Hill. Correspondent of Linnaeus, Benjamin Franklin and Bartram; introduced many plants from North America into England [Engraving by Trotter; *Biohistorical Institute, Utrecht*].

This new wave of plant introduction, especially in England, was one of North American plants and shrubs. Many hundreds of new species reached the English gardens from North America between 1730 and 1790, and Linnaeus was very much aware of this. He received material from North America directly, from Kalm for instance, but he was especially fascinated by the great stream of novelties reaching England. His contact with the British horticulturists was close and preceded the swing of the professional botanists towards acceptance of the Linnaean reforms.*

North America was still very much a rich storehouse for European botany rather than a breeding ground for local botanical research. Within the limits set for this essay (1735–1789) only one significant taxonomic botanical publication appeared in North America itself: Marshall's *Arbustum Americanum* (1785, see also Ewan's introduction to the 1967 reprint). Walter's *Flora caroliniana* (1788), another important publication in the Linnaean style on American plants, appeared still in London. Gronovius' earlier *Flora virginica* (1739, 1762) was published in Leiden.

Humphry Marshall, Pennsylvanian horticulturist, compiled his *Arbustum* between 1780 and 1785, as a trade catalogue. The generic descriptions are translations from Linnaeus, and the place of each genus in the Linnaean sexual system is duly given. The book constitutes the modest beginning of the penetration of Linnaeus's ideas into American botanical literature. The main surge took place, however, after 1789, and is therefore not discussed here. Back then, to the mother country.

The first true Linnaean follower in Great Britain to make a contribution in print was the Irish naturalist Patrick Browne (1720–1790), who, significantly, had studied medicine and botany in Paris and, in this respect even more important, Leiden. He received his doctor's degree there in 1743 and came under the influence of Gronovius and van Royen. From 1746 until 1755 he stayed in Jamaica as a practising physician. Back in England in 1756, he published an impressive folio entitled *The Civil and natural history of Jamaica*. He follows, in general, the Linnaean system, although he does not use binary names; the citations from the *Species plantarum* are always of the phrase names only. Apart from following the sexual system Browne also attempted to make his phrase names purely diagnostic, and as such he showed himself a good follower of Linnaeus. Browne, however, was

* For a review of plant collectors in America as background for Linnaeus see especially Ewan (1970) and also Swan (1949).

[202]

not a slavish follower of the great master: in his general arrangement he places the 'imperfect' plants before the perfect ones. He states that this is in agreement with ancient custom, but also notes that it is more logical to start with the more simply organized plants which are, after all, closer to the minerals. Linnaeus and Browne corresponded with each other, and the former later acquired Browne's Jamaican plants. *Nomina trivialia* for the many new species described by Browne were proposed in two Linnaean dissertations: the *Plantarum jamaicensium pugillus* and the *Flora jamaicensis*, both of 1759, and in the tenth edition of the *Systema naturae* (vol. 2), also of 1759. Browne disappeared from the botanical scene after the publication of his great book. He remained interested in natural history, but left only some manuscripts of minor importance.

Browne's book was illustrated by the great botanical artist Georg Dionys Ehret (1708–1770), who illustrated so many of the mid–eighteenth century flower books. It was Ehret who made some of the drawings for the *Hortus cliffortianus* and who prepared the famous first illustration of the Linnaean sexual system (1736). He did illustrations for Weinmann's *Phytantoza iconographia* and for the Nurnberg botanist Trew (Treu).

Browne may have adopted much of the Linnaean method, but it cannot be said that with him the Linnaean influence became manifest in England. For this we have to turn to three truly English botanists: William Hudson, Philip Miller and John Hill.

William Hudson (1730–1793) was a British apothecary who published a *Flora anglica* in 1762. This *Flora* was fully based on the Linnaean method and used binary nomenclature for the species. It had everything a flora needed: clear diagnoses, citation of British literature, notes on habitat and localities, etc. This book replaced at last the third edition of Ray's *Synopsis* as the common British 'Flora.' Hudson stood at the beginning of a revival of the study of the British flora, which had been neglected in the previous decades in favour of the study of newly introduced plants, especially those from the American colonies. Stearn (1957, p. 78) tells of the stream of local floras unleashed by Hudson's book, the most notable being William Withering's *Botanical Arrangement of British plants* (1776, 1787, 1796), John Lightfoot's *Flora scotica* (1777–1778), Thomas Martyn's *Plantae cantabrigienses* (1763) and many more, all following the Linnaean pattern. As a direct result of this intense floristic activity we can see the publication of the magnificent folio by William Curtis (see W. H. Curtis 1941), the *Flora londinensis* (1775–1798)

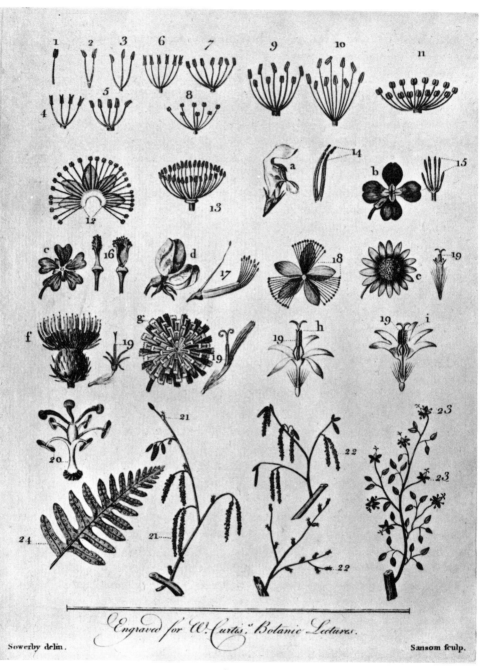

Sowerby delin.

Engraved for W. Curtis': Botanic Lectures.

Sansom sculp.

Fig. 49

(see Stevenson et al. 1961, Stearn 1969), and of the *Botanical magazine*, which was started in 1787. Curtis was also the author of a beautiful set of plates with text entitled *Linnaeus's system of Botany so far as relates to his classes and orders of plants* (1777) (fig. 49). With this young and energetic movement the Linnaean system gained a firm foothold in England which it kept until well into the nineteenth century. In the end a figure of the magnitude of Robert Brown was needed to break the Linnaean hegemony, which became stronger here than anywhere else outside Sweden.

One of the most influential books on the local scene in British eighteenth-century botany was Philip Miller's *Gardeners dictionary*. It was in these years that Britain assumed a definite lead in horticulture. The main factors responsible for this development were briefly mentioned above; here it may be pointed out that next to the literature on the local flora, it was through horticulture that the Linnaean influence obtained its grasp on British botany.

Philip Miller (1691–1771) (fig. 50 & 51) was the superintendent of the Chelsea Physic Garden. The rôle of this garden in British botany has been eloquent-ly described by William Stearn (1961). The Chelsea garden was for many decades the great centre of plant introduction and distribution in the British Isles, especially during Miller's long reign (1722–1770). Linnaeus visited him in 1736 and afterwards called him *Hortulanorum princeps*. In a period in which private gardening went through an almost explosive development and in which the demand for horticultural novelties was correspondingly pressing, it was quite natural for a semi–official institution such as Chelsea (which belonged to the Society of Apothecaries) to become almost automatically the center of British horticulture. Philip Miller's *Gardeners dictionary* provided ample illustration of this state of affairs in its many editions, between 1731 and 1768. "Edition by edition it reflected the progress of horticulture in Britain and recorded the new and rare plants introduced to Chelsea." Many of these new plants came from Leiden; but in the course of the years the percentage of direct introductions, mainly from the West Indies and North America, became more important. Miller adopted the Linnaean sexual system only as late as 1759, in the seventh edition of his *Dictionary*; the abbreviated version of 1754 (Stearn 1969, Stafleu

Fig. 49. William Curtis, *Linnaeus's System of botany, so far as relates to his Classes and Orders of Plants; illustrated by figures entirely new, with copious explanatory descriptions. Drawn up for the use of his pupils.* [London 1777]. Plate [2], Classes explained and illustrated by figures. *Reduced.*

[205]

MILLER.

De la société Royale de Londres
De l'Academie des Botanistes de florence.
Et Directeur du Jardin de Botanique
Des Apothicaires de Chelsea

Fig. 50

[206]

1969) still followed wholeheartedly the tradition of Tournefort and Ray, both of whom Miller seems to have known personally. The abridged edition, being 'post Linnaean' (that is, published after 1753), thereby became another of the many problem books of the early years of the Linnaean era. Many Tournefortian genera were validly published in it for the first time after the *Species plantarum* (see especially Dandy 1967). Miller was also extremely critical of the Linnaean generic reform, which had resulted in the lumping, splitting and renaming of so many of Tournefort's genera. In the 1759 edition of his *Dictionary*, however, he gave a review of the Linnaean system and adopted many of the Linnaean phrase names, although he did not yet adopt binary nomenclature. This was introduced only in the last edition published by Miller himself, the eighth, of 1768. With this event, coming soon after the publication of Hudson's *Flora anglica* in 1762, Linnaean nomenclature had gained its foothold in England.

One figure standing somewhat outside the mainstream of British botany must now be mentioned. John Hill (1716–1775), an apothecary by training and a man with a consuming interest in natural history in general, a prolific and somewhat acrimonious writer, was greatly ignored by his contemporaries, mainly perhaps because of some of his social idiosyncrasies. Stearn (1967) relates that he published some 76 works, of which at least sixteen deal with plants, among these being *The British herbal* (1756–1757) in one folio volume and *The vegetable system* (1759–1773) in not less than 26 folio volumes.

The *British Herbal* was anti-Linnaean. Hill makes many critical remarks with respect to Linnaeus's taxonomy and its innovations, and often brings forward the argument of 'nature' versus 'fancy' or 'dictated laws.' The book does not deal with native plants only, but describes many cultivated ones as well. The delimitation of his genera is often different from that of Linnaeus, and because of its early date the book is therefore still of nomenclatural importance. There were, of course no binary names in the true Linnaean fashion; neither were there any phrase names which were

Fig. 50. PHILIP MILLER; *b.* Debtford or Greenwich, England, 1691; *d.* Chelsea, England, December 18, 1771; gardener at Chelsea 1722–1770, *Hortulanorum princeps* (Linnaeus), author of the *Gardeners Dictionary* and many other botanical and horticultural publications [Reproduction of an engraving at the Royal Botanic Gardens, Kew, copy at *Conservatoire botanique de Genève*]. [? C. F. Maillet 1787 in French edition of Miller's Gardeners Dictionary, [see Milner 1906]. *Reduced.*

[207]

fully diagnostic. The phrase names were diagnostic only with respect to the species described in the book, and the result is that there are quite a few 'pseudo-binomials.' The book is listed in Art. 23 of the International Code of Botanical Nomenclature as a work "in which the Linnaean system of binary nomenclature for species was not consistently employed." In fact the book does not use the binary system at all; the biverbal names in the book are simply two-word phrase names. Dandy (1967) has also cleared up the nomenclatural status of Hill's names published in the *British Herbal.*

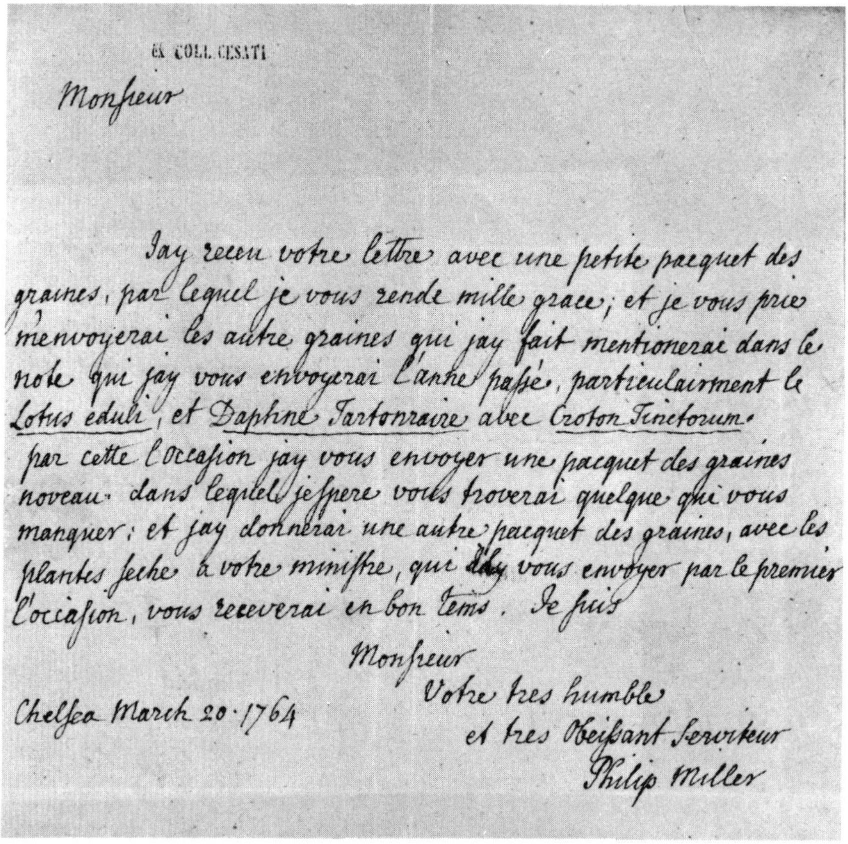
EX COLL. CESATI

Monsieur

Jay receu votre lettre avec une petite pacquet des graines, par lequel je vous rende mille grace; et je vous prie m'envoyerai les autre graines qui jay fait mentionerai dans le note qui jay vous envoyerai l'anne passé, particulairment le Lotus eduli, et Daphne Tartonraire avec Croton Tinctorum.
par cette l'occasion jay vous envoyer une pacquet des graines noveau. dans lequel je spere vous troverai quelque qui vous manquer; et jay donnerai une autre pacquet des graines, avec les plantes seche a votre ministre, qui vous envoyer par le premier l'occasion, vous receverai en bon tems. Je suis

Monsieur
Votre tres humble
et tres Obeisant Serviteur
Philip Miller

Chelsea March 20·1764

Fig. 51. Letter written by Philip Miller to Carlo Allioni (1728–1804) on March 20, 1764. Allioni was an Italian physician and botanist at Torino who corresponded also with Linnaeus, and who was one of the principal proponents of the Linnaean methods and ideas in Italy. [*Conservatoire botanique de Genève*]. *Reduced.*

Hill's criticism of Linnaeus was sometimes rather pungent, but this does not mean that he did not hold Linnaeus's writings in high regard. He had an open eye for the practical merits of the Linnaean system; this is evident from several of his other publications. In his '*Sleep of plants*' (1757a) for instance, issued in the same year as the *British herbal*, Hill prints a letter to Linnaeus and remarks:

"If our opinions have differed, 't is upon a single point; your arrangement of plants. In regard to that much greater article, the establishing their distinctions, and ascertaining their characters, I have always admired and reverenced you: to dispute your determinations then, were to deny the characters of nature. Free in the tribute of applause on this head, I have on the other been as open in my censures; equally uninfluenced by envy, and by fear. It is thus science may be advanced; and you will permit me to say, thus men of candour should treat each other." (See also Woodruff 1926, p. 431).

Hill's *British herbal* had a somewhat popular character, just as the *Gardeners dictionary*; however, both these books and the *Vegetable system* were sufficiently scholarly and technical to be of scientific botanical interest. The fact that they were written in English put them in a rather special position. Most of the floristic literature (an exception was for instance Withering's book) was still in Latin, but the horticultural writings as well as Hill's works were in the vernacular. These are the first signs in English botany of the waning of Latinity in the natural sciences, mentioned above (p. 174), a process fully in keeping with the eighteenth-century ideals of spreading knowledge and information as widely as possible. A similar movement was even more pronounced in France, where the 'big three'—Buffon, Adanson and Lamarck—all wrote in the vernacular. (Stafleu 1963, 1967, 1970). The use of Latin had the overtone—rightly or wrongly—of the exclusive; the vernacular met the requirement of the era for the easy diffusion of knowledge. It is mainly for this reason that Hill's *Vegetable system* is such an important work. First, however, a few words on two of Hill's other works.

In 1760 Hill published a *Flora britannica* which has been called (Jackson 1881, p. xxxvi) the first Linnaean flora of Britain. It indeed antedates Hudson's *Flora anglica* by two years; however, it was nothing but a new edition of the Dillenius edition of Ray's *Synopsis* in the order of the sexual system, but retaining the old names. It could hardly be taken seriously and had very little effect on British botany.

Even though Hill waited a long time before accepting the Linnaean system for his own works, he published on it as early as 1751, in the second volume of his *General natural history*, entitled *A history of plants*. This work, in the English language, was unsurpassed as a source of information on natural history and as a work of almost unbelievable labour. In it Hill discussed the Linnaean sexual system. In a later, more popular book, *Eden, or a compleat body of gardening* (1757), Hill states in the Preface "... at present, the system of Linnaeus is universally followed. No book on gardening has been written since this absolute change in the science .... Those who understand plants, now call them, universally and solely, by the names of this author .... We shall follow the system of Linnaeus, which we shall deliver completely, explaining his terms."

The *Vegetable system* is of great importance because it gave for the first time in the vernacular a comprehensive treatment of the plant kingdom, on a lavish scale and with coloured illustrations, adopting the Linnaean generic names and introducing binary nomenclature. The first volume (1759) is still in the old style, but from the second volume onward (there are 26 folio volumes containing 1546 full-sized illustrations) Linnaean binomials are used, although the sexual system is not followed. The title of the book is long and as characteristic of Hill as it is typical of his independent approach:

"The vegetable system. Or, the internal structure, and the life of plants, their parts and nourishment explained; their classes, orders, genera, and species, ascertained and described; in a method altogether new. Comprehending an artificial index, and a natural system. With figures of all the plants; described and engraved by the author. The whole from nature only."

Volume 5 contains "observations on a natural method, so far as it regards the connection of the classes." Hill's natural system was well worth studying, but his voice remained unheard. In the year in which he published his fifth volume (1763) Adanson published his *Familles des Plantes*, giving an extensive theoretical justification of the natural system. For a long time Hill and Adanson found no followers, standing as they were at the beginning of a new era. Hill was perhaps erratic and unconvincing, and theoretically less skilled than his contemporary Adanson (though hardly less erratic), but he was one of the first to rebel against Linnaeus's artificial system and essentialist classification.

2. *The Banksian era*

The times were not ripe for a new approach: on the contrary. The years 1759–1763 witnessed the almost undisputed victory of the Linnaean methods in England. Miller had adopted the sexual system in 1759, Hill used binomials in 1761, Hudson published a British flora with binary nomenclature in 1762. By 1763 the Linnaean system had become a feature of the British taxonomic Establishment and would remain so until Robert Brown. The rapidity with which Linnaean thought gained ground in England in the seventeen-sixties must be seen in the light of, on the one hand, the strong revival of floristic research, and on the other, the need for a practical system and nomenclature in a country with wide horticultural interests during a period of rapidly increasing plant introductions from many parts of an expanding empire. There was no direct reason to look upon Linnaeus as a representative of the past, as in France, where the Enlightenment swept away seventeenth-century theories; on the contrary: the new pragmatism of Linnaeus appealed strongly to the practical British. Perhaps they were more interested in growing their plants than in talking about them; a commendable attitude.

The phenomenon of the philosopher–naturalist of the Enlightenment was primarily French. French society was predominantly Catholic, in many respects still feudal. The government was in the hands of a small governing caste and strongly autocratic. The *philosophes* became the avant-garde of the much needed revolution; the change of ideas heralded a change in society. Holbach, the militant atheist, author of the *Système de la nature*, (1770), pointed out (quotation from Basil Willey 1940, chapter 9) "that in countries like England, and the other Protestant lands, where toleration exists, there are plenty of Deists and infidels, but very few atheists." The English had a bourgeois society originating from a reformation and a revolution which were firmly established and which needed no class or religious struggle to bring about a reasonable degree of tolerance. In the second half of the eighteenth century the French *philosophes* had to be world–changers rather than world–explainers (Willey), and they tended therefore to question every authority, whether political, social, religious or scientific. The British counterparts of the *philosophes*, as far as the naturalists were concerned, referred to themselves also as 'the philosophers' but they could better be called *curiosi*, because of the absence of a need for

FLORA at Play with CUPID.

Emma Crewe inv.ᵗ   S. Alken feeiᵗ

Fig. 52

[212]

militancy and the primary stress on inquisitiveness. The phenomenon of the *curiosus* belongs to a bourgeois society, with a faint metaphysical rather than a materialistic tinge; the *philosophe* has the same aims but is involved in a struggle to see certain primary conditions realized.

In England science and religion could remain in 'holy alliance' until the close of the century; in systematics the prevailing Linnaean taxonomy quite well fitted the pattern. The old creationist concept of nature was adhered to and the system was at the same time eminently practical. Nature was to be enjoyed; the old antithesis of man and nature was not questioned. Actually 'nature' was a Christianized demiurge pretty close to God, with laws of its own. Holbach's dictum that man, "faute de connoître la nature, il se forma des Dieux," is hardly relevant to the British naturalists of this era. Toleration in religious matters tended to increase religious liberalism, with the result that for many naturalists religion and interest in nature could easily remain only very loosely associated, the former being the thing to do, the latter the thing to enjoy. This pragmatic division of interest in British taxonomy is at the basis of the early dissociation of Linnaean taxonomy from its original hard–core creationism. The practical advantages of the Linnaean system were much more highly valued by British botanists than its philosophical, or rather metaphysical, background. The creationist varnish made it respectable, the empirical basis made it usable. Not all naturalists fitted that pattern: Joseph Priestley (1733–1804), for instance, the discoverer of photosynthesis, author of the *History of electricity* and friend of many French *philosophes* and British *curiosi*, was essentially a deeply religious man who sought a synthesis between the knowledge of nature and his Christian belief.

A totally different personality, also only loosely connected with the stream of ideas in systematics, was Erasmus Darwin (1731–1802), typically a *curiosus* but with a philosophical slant and a vivid imagination, but also a radical and freethinker. Darwin's curiosity and speculative mind led him to the concept of organic evolution. No wonder that Darwin—after

Fig. 52. "Flora at play with Cupid," frontispiece to Erasmus Darwin's *The loves of plants, with philosophical notes,* being the second part of his annotated poem *The botanic garden* [1789]. In the accompanying 'Advertisement' Darwin states: "The general design of the following sheets is to inlist Imagination under the banner of Science... While their particular design is to induce the ingenious to cultivate the knowledge of BOTANY; by introducing them to the vestibule of that delightful science, and recommending to their attention the immortal works of the celebrated Swedish Naturalist LINNAEUS." *Reduced.*

Two knights before thy fragrant altar bend,

Adored MELISSA! and *two* fquires attend.　　　60

MEADIA's foft chains *five* fuppliant beaux confefs,

And hand in hand the laughing belle addrefs;

Alike to all, fhe bows with wanton air,

Rolls her dark eye, and waves her golden hair.

Meliffa. l. 60. Balm. In each flower there are four males and one female; two of the males ftand higher than the other two; whence the name of the clafs "two powers." I have obferved in the Ballota, and others of this clafs, that the two lower ftamens, or males, become mature before the two higher. After they have fhed their duft, they turn themfelves away outwards; and the piftil, or female, continuing to grow a little taller, is applied to the upper ftamens. See Gloriofa, and Genifta.

All the plants of this clafs, which have naked feeds, are aromatic. The Marum, and Nepeta are particularly delightful to cats; no other brute animals feem pleafed with any odours but thofe of their food or prey.

Meadia. l. 61. Dodecatheon, american Cowflip. Five males and one female. The males, or anthers, touch each other. The uncommon beauty of this flower occafioned Linneus to give it a name fignifying the twelve heathen gods; and Dr. Mead to affix his own name to it. The piftil is much longer than the ftamens, hence the flower-ftalks have their elegant bend, that the ftigma may hang downwards to receive the fecundating duft of the anthers. And the petals are fo beautifully turned back to prevent the rain or dew drops from fliding down and wafhing off this duft prematurely; and at the fame time expofing it to the light and air. As foon as the feeds are formed, it erects all the flower-ftalks to prevent them from falling out; and thus lofes the beauty of its figure. Is this a mechanical effect, or does it indicate a vegetable ftorgé to preferve its offspring? See note on Ilex, and Gloriofa.

In the Meadia, the Borago, Cyclamen, Solanum, and many others, the filaments are very fhort compared with the ftyle. Hence it became neceffary, 1ft. to furnifh the ftamens with long anthers. 2d. To lengthen and bend the peduncle or flower-ftalk, that the

Woo'd

Fig. 53. Erasmus Darwin, *The Loves of plants, with philosophical notes*, part II of *The botanic garden* [1789]. *Reduced.*

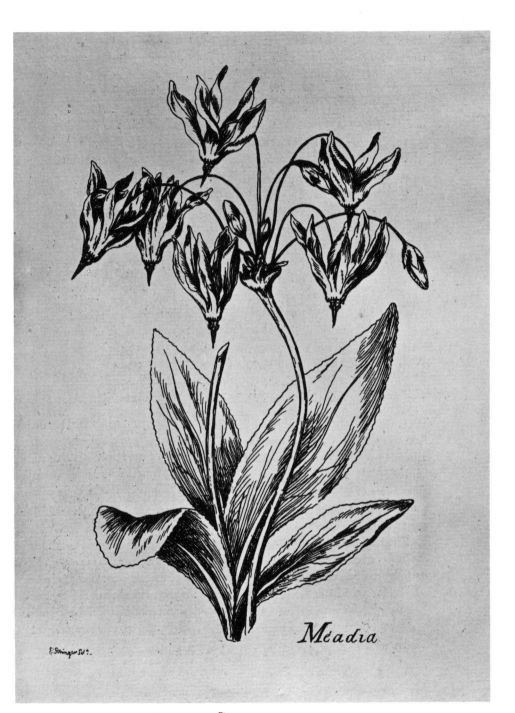

Méadia

Fig. 53

Hill—advocated, as one of the very few in Great Britain, the idea of a natural system of classification at a time when the Linnaean dominance was still almost absolute. Even so Darwin was one of the great promotors of the Linnaean ideas. His main botanical and zoological writings appeared after 1789. In that year, however, he published the second part of his great epic poem, *The botanic garden*. The part was entitled *The loves of plants* and dealt, of all things, with the Linnaean sexual system. This poem epitomizes the Linnaean cult in England and is unexpectedly pleasing, combining as it does elements of nature poetry foreshadowing Shelley and a didactic attempt at centering attention upon Linnaeus's writings, mixed with disguised criticism of religion. The poem is still worth reading, even though rather verbose at times.* One citation from the description of the sexual system:

> "Sweet blooms *Genista* in the myrtle shade,
> And *ten* fond brothers woo the haughty maid.
> Two nights before thy fragrant altar bend,
> Adored *Melissa*! and *two* squires attend.
> *Maedia's* soft chains *five* suppliant beaux confess,
> And hand in hand the laughing belle address;
> Alike to all, she bows with wanton air
> Rolls her dark eye, and waves her golden hair."

Even though the 'holy alliance' between religion and science in England had its parallel until the end of the century in an almost equally holy alliance between Linnaean thought and taxonomy, the last decades of the century witnessed developments which would ultimately break down this alliance. Unlike in France, where this breakdown was effected by a philosophy of nature, it came through empiricism in England. The contrast is of course not absolute: Linnaean thought caught on only superficially in France because it was introduced at a time when the *philosophes* were enmeshed in their struggle against authority. It caught on in England in the middle of the century because it provided such an admirable framework within which the knowledge assembled by the *curiosi* could be fitted. This knowledge increased rapidly because of the expansion of the British empire, mainly towards North America and the South Seas.

* For a catching picture of Darwin see King-Hele's recent commentary (1968).

The continuous stream of new plants which reached British Gardens from the North American colonies has already been mentioned. The development of these gardens themselves was part of the pattern of the bourgeois rural society in which the well–to–do lived in the country rather than in the towns. The garden of many a mansion deserved the epithet 'botanical'; there was a great demand for botanical novelties, a demand which was filled by itinerant plant collectors and by resident botanists in the colonies themselves. British gardens assumed a leading rôle in horticulture, and their rich collections provided a powerful stimulus to taxonomy.

The influence of the expansion towards the South Seas was perhaps even more profound. This expansion was not at once reflected in the composition of the collections of the botanic gardens, but rather in the holdings of the natural history cabinets. One figure, perhaps the archetype of the British naturalist *curiosus*, was intimately associated with this development: Sir Joseph Banks, 'spoilt child of fortune' (Beaglehole), the 'autocrat of the philosophers' (H. C. Cameron), traveller, collector, practical idealist, philanthropist, long time president of the Royal Society. The influence of Banks on British systematics (as on British natural science in general) during the closing decades of the eighteenth century and the early years of the nineteenth was such that the era could bear his name. Banks himself was not a taxonomist. It was not through his publications but through his personality and activities that he made his profound impact on the natural sciences. When Banks appeared on the scene, in the mid sixties, most of the activity in systematics was horticultural or floristic. Towards the end of his era the exploration of the South Pacific and the growth of the collections of living plants and herbarium material from that region, and from many other parts of the globe as well, had given birth to an advanced school of systematics. Banks and the scientists around him had the richest collections of their time at their disposal; their ideas had assimilated the mainstream of continental taxonomic thought, strengthening it and developing it further, and they thus founded the great school of nineteenth–century British systematics. At the beginning of the Banksian era British systematics included such knowledgeable horticulturists as Philip Miller, sympathetic floristic botanists like John Martyn and the reverend Lightfoot, a single imaginative personality such as John Hill; the end of the era had men like John Edward Smith and

[217]

Robert Brown, to mention only the most outstanding from a veritable galaxy of systematists.

The Banksian era was one of finding new horizons, of opening up the world and of the final abandoning of the Europe-centered view in systematics. The initial ideals were those of the Enlightenment: 'reason' and 'improvement of the human condition'; the cosmological philosophy was unitarian. The geographical as well as spiritual expansion after the end of the Seven Years' war (1756–1763) had its basis in these ideals of reason, primitive idealism, the finding of unspoilt human societies and the introduction of new natural products of direct benefit to man. The outcome, however, was an overthrow of exactly those ideals representing an essentially static, hierarchic, neoplatonic view of nature and society. The new emphasis was on enterprise, novelty and diversity. The picture of the world was no longer one of immutable, self-contained perfection, antithetic to change, but a dynamic one of creativity, of an open end to knowledge, and of the discovery of the intrinsic values of diversity. The movement is from neoplatonic philosophical uniformitarianism to romantic diversitarianism. The open horizons of the great Pacific South revealed the existence not of perfect primitive societies but of imperfect ones of infinitely diverse novelty. The discovery of the floras of Australia and New Zealand, more than of South Africa, profoundly influenced taxonomic thought.

British romantic empiricism, embodied for instance in Robert Brown, ultimately reached the same conclusions as the French philosopher-naturalists from Buffon and Adanson to Lamarck. This outcome was a vindication of the theoretical basis of biological systematics laid by the French taxonomic *philosophes*, replacing the scholastic classification of the past. Adanson and Buffon recognized diversity on the basis of relatively small practical experience, but with superior intuitive reasoning; a man like Robert Brown built his diversitarian view of nature on the basis of superior experience both from exploration and experiment, and discovered the new theory to be a fitting framework for his discoveries. The victories of empirical science and romanticism went hand in hand.

3. Joseph Banks

The life of Banks has been the subject of three major biographies. Maiden's

Sir Joseph Banks, the father of Australia, of 1909 is mainly an assortment of documents and extracts from journals stressing Banks' rôle in the settlement of Australia as well as his botanical activities. Edward Smith's *The life of Sir Joseph Banks* (1911) is a well written, factual account mainly based on the material at the British Museum (Natural History). The most recent study (1952) is by H. C. Cameron, entitled *Sir Joseph Banks, The autocrat of the Philosophers.* Cameron's book has the great advantage of being based on a maximum of original documents and letters and does full justice to Banks by placing him in the cultural and social cadre of his time, and by highlighting Banks's versatility in knowledge and interest and his commanding authority in scientific policy, as well as his failure as a scientist to publish the many results of his lifelong scientific activities. W. R. Dawson's *The Banks Letters* of 1958 presents an annotated calendar of the Banksian correspondence, an account which illustrates, more than any secondary publication could, Banks' central rôle in the natural sciences of his era. His diversity of interests and his ease in social contacts led him to correspond on a scope which could hardly have been surpassed by any other scientist (fig. 54 & 55).

In view of this ample documentation a brief outline of Banks's life will suffice, the more so since his influence and activities will be apparent in almost all aspects of this account of the Banksian era of British systematics. Joseph Banks was born on February 2, 1743, in London, the son of a wealthy member of the landed gentry of Lincolnshire. He went to school at Harrow and Eton, where his botanical interest was aroused when he was fifteen years old. A copy of John Gerard's *Herball* (1598) was his first guide. At Oxford (1760–1764) botany was still very much dormant, but Banks succeeded in obtaining some instruction from Israel Lyons, specially brought to Oxford from Cambridge for the purpose. In 1764 Banks settled in London; he had come of age and had entered upon his father's inheritance. He certainly was a 'child of fortune,' as Beaglehole (1955) calls him, though not necessarily a spoilt one. During these years at Oxford and London Banks must have repeatedly visited Philip Miller and the Chelsea Physic Garden. His enterprising spirit was not long in making itself felt: in 1766 Banks sailed for Labrador and Newfoundland on his first major expedition as a naturalist. The trip was made on a fishery protection vessel, H. M. S. *Niger,* which had sufficient freedom to enable Banks to make several collecting trips on land.

Fig. 54

Rauschenberg (1967) relates that in 1767 Banks, with Solander's encourage-ment, contemplated going to Uppsala to study under Linnaeus. He never did, however, and thus became the most successful of all of Linnaeus's *élèves manqués*.

During the trip to Newfoundland Banks had been elected a Fellow of the Royal Society, at the age of twenty-three. This honour brought him in direct contact with some of the leading scientists of his day, a contact which proved extremely useful when, in 1768, some of these scientists set out to organize an expedition to the South Seas to observe the transit of Venus of the third of June, 1769. The King placed the necessary sum at the disposal of the Royal Society and the Royal Navy was charged with the technical execution of the expedition. Banks, accompanied by Daniel Solander, artists and servants joined the expedition on the *Endeavour*, the first of Cook's great voyages. This expedition to the South seas shaped Banks's character and gave his life a definitive direction. The experience obtained in the years 1768–1771 on his epochmaking circumnavigation guided him in later life in all his scientific undertakings. The personal experience and the scientific results in data, collections as well as ideas, made Banks into much more than a gentlemen of leisure with a botanical hobby. Banks's character was such that this experience prepared him to become the undisputed authority in the field of science policy in later years.

Banks took no part in Cook's second voyage, even though this was his original intention; a combination of minor conflicts withheld him from participating. Johann Reinhold Forster and his son Georg went in his place. Banks made an excursion to Iceland in 1777 which turned out to be his last voyage. In 1778 he was elected president of the Royal Society, a position which he filled until his death in 1820; during those years Banks became the central figure of British natural science. He continued to enrich his collections, and his house at Soho Square contained the world's finest private herbarium and botanical library. Banks's librarians and curators were, in succession, Daniel Solander, Robert Dryander and Robert Brown. These names alone illustrate the importance of Soho

Fig. 54. SIR JOSEPH BANKS; *b.* London, January 4, 1743; *d.* Spring Grove, Middlesex, June 19, 1820; President of The Royal Society 1778–1820 [portrait painted by Benjamin West, engraved by J. R. Smith, engraving published 1 May 1788; *Biohistorical Institute, Utrecht*; original engraving at British Museum, Bloomsbury]. *Reduced.*

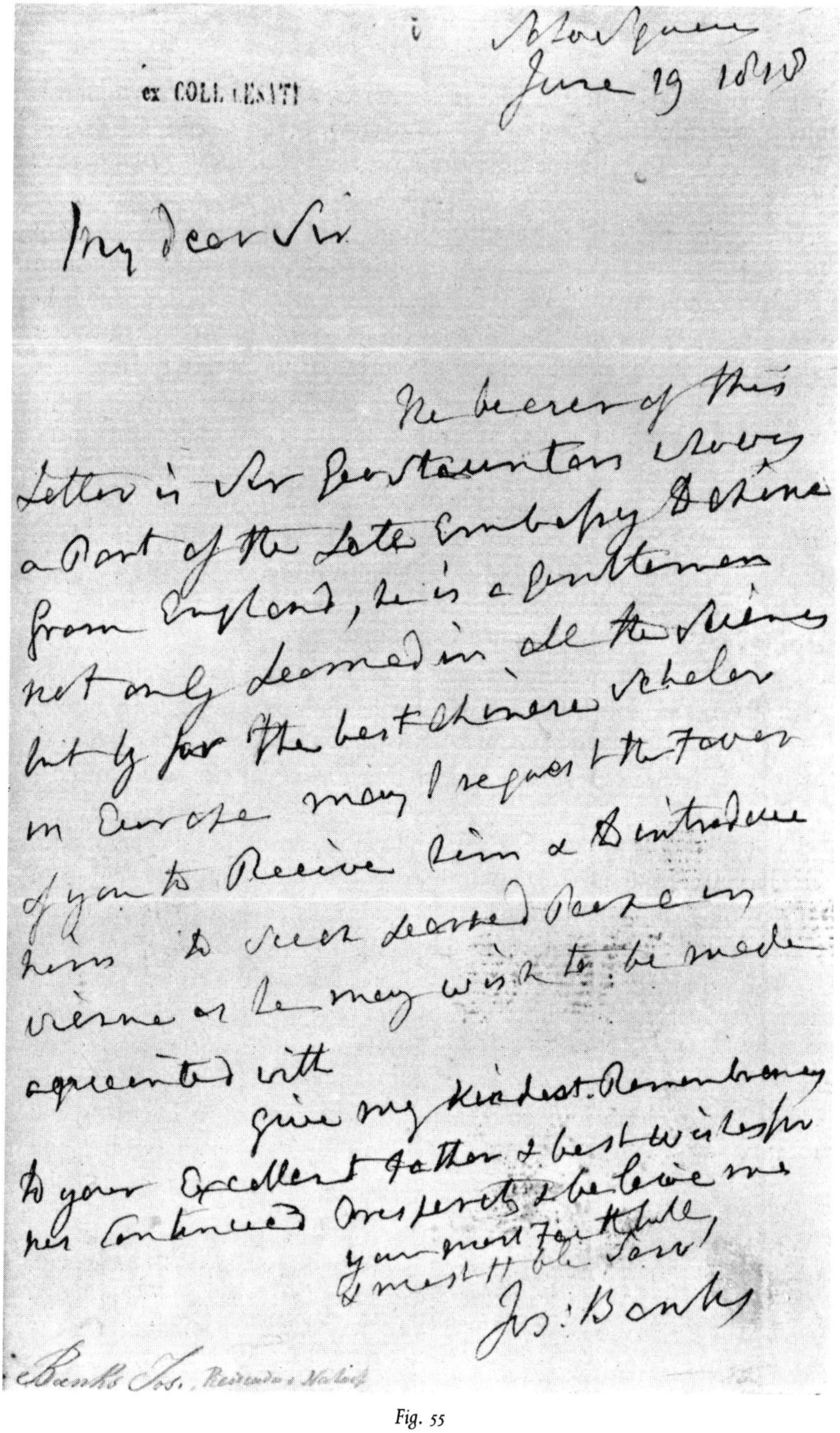

i   Soho Square
                     June 29 1810

My dear Sir

                    The bearer of this
Letter is Sir George Staunton a very
a Part of the Late Embassy to China
from England, he is a Gentleman
not only learned in all the Sciences
but by far the best Chinese scholar
in Europe may I request the Favor
of you to Receive him & to introduce
him to such learned Persons in
Vienne as he may wish to be made
acquainted with
                    give my kindest Remembrance
to your Excellent Father & best wishes for
his Continued Prosperity & believe me
                    your most Faithfull
                    & most H.ble Serv.t
                         Jos: Banks

Fig. 55

Square as a center of taxonomic research. Many expeditions were organized by Banks or through his influence; Kew gardens were placed under his supervision and became the repository for the thousands of living specimens of new plants introduced by Banksian collectors all over the world. Banks played a primary rôle in the preparations for the colonization of Australia. His impact on science was not restricted to Britain; his correspondence shows that his influence crossed national frontiers and even overcame the barriers of war. At his death in 1820 the world stood on the threshold of a new era. The Napoleonic disturbance overcome, science, technology and society rapidly found new roads. It was not the least of Bank's achievements that many of these new departures had been stimulated by his imagination and foresight.

4. The Voyage of the Endeavour

By the second half of the eighteenth century circumnavigation of the globe, though still rare, was no longer exceptional. Magellan's voyage of 1520–1522 around Patagonia through the Strait of Magellan towards the Philippine Islands and back to Europe around the Cape of Good Hope had become the protoype of several such enterprises. Furthermore, there were many trans–Pacific trips by the Spanish between the Philippines and Callao in Peru. During the seventeenth and early eighteenth century Dutch explorers like Schouten, Le Maire and Roggeveen (1721–1722) rounded Cape Horn on their way to Batavia. In the eighteenth century the British gradually became the great sailors of the world. The pattern of crossing the Pacific, however, was usually the same; after rounding Cape Horn the voyagers pushed up as rapidly as possible to the tropic of Capricorn, to pursue their voyage westward in the quieter tropical zones where they found more islands, food and fresh water on their way to the East Indies. The travellers coming from the West rounded the Cape of Good Hope and pushed through to Mauritius and Réunion (Ile de France and Ile de Bourbon) on their way to India, the Philippines or the Sunda Islands. Only

Fig. 55. Letter written by Sir Joseph Banks to the younger Jacquin on June 19, 1818. The letter introduces Sir George Thomas Staunton (1781–1859), writer on China, who was with Macartney's Embassy to China from 1798–1817, according to Banks "the best Chinese scholar in Europe." [*Conservatoire botanique de Genève*].

rarely did a ship stray towards the west coast of Australia; the South Pacific remained an unknown area. The stories of a Southland were numerous, but before the middle of the eighteenth century it was only Abel Tasman (1642–1643) who approached Tasmania from the west and who touched upon New Zealand.

During the years immediately following the Seven Year's war both the French and the British burst again towards the Pacific. This increased interest had many reasons, of which not the least was the expansionist drive of growing colonial empires. Nautical science had a deep interest in the Pacific, and furthermore there was always the urge for geographical exploration per se. The *Terra Australis incognita* was a tantalizing dream. Polynesia was known only very superficially. The Spanish domination of the Philippines had been broken in 1762 by the occupation of Manila by the British. The element of competition between the French and the British in filling the vacuum of knowledge, and of power, in the South Pacific was unmistakable.

Tahiti (Otaheite) was to play a great rôle in this wave of exploration. Pedro Fernández Quiros had discovered it as early as 1607, but this discovery had had no lasting impact. This impact came when Samuel Wallis, in the *Dolphin*, rediscovered it in 1767. Wallis and his men did little but recuperate and revictual at Tahiti. Scurvy had taken its toll on the Dolphin; the drinking water stank and salt beef and biscuits had been their fare. The island appeared to them as a dream come true. Even at that time the experience was not at all new; the Cape of Good Hope, Ile de France and Ile de Bourbon, for instance, had played a similar rôle for ages. Yet, the reports of the rediscovery of Tahiti had an electrifying effect on literate Europe. The stories fell on a ground prepared by the ideals of the Enlightenment. Primitive unspoilt society rediscovered; nature exemplified in its purest form. This shock of recognition of the realization of a dream must be taken with reserve. Tahiti was not the ideal country it seemed from that far distance and on the basis of this incidental story. Beaglehole (1955), in his introduction to the *Journals of Captain Cook*, analyses the psychological effect: "... Wallis had not merely come to a convenient port of call. He had stumbled on a foundation stone of the Romantic movement. Not as a continent, not as vast distances, was the ocean henceforth in common thought to be known. The unreal was to mingle with the real, the too dramatic with the undramatic; the shining light was to become a haze in which every island was the one island, and the one island a Tahitian dream."

The dream had its effect on science as well as on society. The story of Joseph Banks illustrates that this dream was a powerful stimulus in the development of taxonomic thought, insignificant as this element may have been in the full picture of that rapidly changing world of the late eighteenth century. The ultimate realization of the dream was the victory of the romantic movement in biological systematics; this romantic movement which could work a French revolution could easily draw biological scientists away from their superannuated concepts of stability, harmony and creation. An immediate result of the dream was an increase in exploration on better ships which were manned not only with sailors and marines but also with scientists and artists. This latter group became an element as indispensable to life on the ship and to the ultimate harvest of results as the marines were to keep the order and to provide safety against mishaps with natives who failed to act in accordance with the dream.

The pattern for these great scientific maritime expeditions was set by Bougainville and Cook almost at the same time. The British expedition, however, was to have the greater scientific impact, first because the number and quality of scientists and artists was greater, but also because they ventured definitely towards the South, bringing New Zealand and Australia into the picture.

The first great French voyage which was of importance to botany was that by Louis–Antoine de Bougainville (1728–1811). Sent out in 1760 by the government of Louis XV on a mission to hand back the Falkland Islands to the Spanish authorities, Bougainville received instructions to return via the Pacific and the Ile de France. Two ships were placed under his command, *la Boudeuse* and *l'Étoile*. A 'médecin–naturaliste' and an astronomer were added to the équipage; the naturalist was Philibert Commerson (1727–1773), who was accompanied by a single servant who later turned out to be Jeanne Barré, thus the first woman to embark on a circumnavigation of the globe. Bougainville's route was the traditional one. From Buenos Aires he rounded Patagonia through the Magellan Straits, then pushed up due North to the tropic of Capricorn and subsequently due west to the Society Islands. Tahiti was visited in 1768, claimed as French and named La Nouvelle Cythère, after the ancient refuge of sailors between the Peloponnesos and Crete, the Greek island of Kuthera, also the allegoric

The **SIMPLING MACARONI**.

Like Soland-Goose from frozen Zone I wander,
On shallow Bank's grow's fat., Sol······.

Pub. accor. to act by M Darly Strand July 13.ᵗ 1772

Fig. 56

homeland of love. It was, very appropriately, at this Nouvelle Cythère that Commerson's servant was discovered to be a female companion. Commerson made ample collections on Tahiti, some of which were used by Jussieu for his *Genera*, but which on the whole did not have the same direct impact on botanical science as the later collections made by Banks, Solander and the Forsters. Even as late as 1954 Merrill, in his study of *The botany of Cook's Voyages*, did not consult Commerson's collections to corroborate his important conclusions on the history of cultivated plants in the Pacific.

Commerson left the expedition at the Ile de France to continue his explorations in the Mascarene Islands. He died on the Ile–de–France on 13 March 1773, still attended by his faithful Jeanne. His botanical collections reached France with some delay and were put at the disposal of Antoine-Laurent de Jussieu, who found them of great importance for the further elaboration of his natural system. Jussieu's delimitation of families and genera was greatly helped by this superior material; it prevented him from repeating some of Adanson's errors due to insufficient information, and it strengthened him in his belief that such a diversity of forms was better dealt with by means of a natural classification than through the too rigid and simplistic Linnaean scheme.

Unlike Bougainville's voyage, which was still primarily strategic and political, with science admitted secondarily, Cook's Voyage was primarily

Fig. 56. DANIEL CARL SOLANDER (1736–1782), contemporary caricature, etching, ca. 1772. "The Simpling Macaroni is an etched whole-length portrait of SOLANDER, standing in profile to our right, holding in one hand a large flowering plant, and in the other a naturalist's knife, on the blade of which is written the maker's name, SAVIGNY. He appears to be speaking... It was the day of the Macaronis, who amused the town for a long season with published pictures of dandies and other eccentrics. BANKS and SOLANDER were, of course, lawful prey: with their renown in hiterto undiscovered trifles... The term signifies 'a compound dish made of vermicelli and other pastes, universally used in Italy. It came into England at the beginning of the last peace' (Macaroni and Theatrical Magazine, October, 1772). The word was introduced at Almack's and the subscribers came to be described as Macaronis. Originally aimed at luxury and extravagance, it eventually came to mean any person who exceeded the ordinary bounds of fashion and fell into absurdity in consequence. For more upon the Macaronis see *Annals of a Yorkshire House* (London, 1911) ..." (EDW. SMITH, The Life of Sir JOSEPH BANKS, London and New York, 1911, p. 176, who reproduces also a caricature of BANKS as "the Fly Catching Macaroni"). *Courtesy of the Trustees of the British Museum.* [Illustration and caption from Merrill, *Chronica botanica* 14: 184. 495, courtesy *Frans Verdoorn*; original at British Museum].

scientific in character. The members of The Royal Society wanted an expedition to the South Seas to observe the transit of Venus of the year 1769; Banks saw the opportunity for making it an occasion of botanical exploration as well. The memorial presented to the King by the Royal Society mentioned the astronomical observations as the main object of the expedition. The King granted the request, placed £ 4000.– at the disposal of the Society to defray expenses, and instructed the Admiralty to take care of the technical execution and to assume the overall responsibility. The Society and the Admiralty then granted Banks's request that "he also, together with his suite, being seven persons more ... together with their baggage, be received on board of the ship under the command of Capt. Cook" (Cameron 1952, p. 14). The costs of this botanical party were borne by Banks himself. Ultimately ten persons were admitted: Banks himself; Daniel Solander, the Swedish botanist, pupil of Linnaeus, in charge of the Sloane collections at the British Museum; the artists Buchan, Reynolds and Parkinson; the assistant naturalist Sporing, and four servants. Only four of these ten were to return: Banks, Solander and two of the servants.

"No people ever went to sea better fitted out for the purpose of Natural History. They have got a fine library of Natural History; they have all sorts of machines for catching and preserving insects; all kinds of nets, trawls, drags and hooks for coral fishing .... They have two painters and draughtsmen .... All this is owing to you and your writings." The 'you' here is Linnaeus, to whom the British naturalist John Ellis reported in a letter published by J. E. Smith (1821, p. 230).

The voyage of the *Endeavour* has been described and documented in extenso. The journals of Banks (1896) and Cook (Beaglehole 1955) are published, Merrill studied *The Botany of Cook's Voyages* (1954) in particular, Stearn (1969) has given a review of the botanical results; the further secondary literature is abundant (fig. 56). The general importance of the voyage was that it set the pattern for an intensive geographical and scientific exploration of the South and Central Pacific. Many islands were visited by various expeditions in succession, and some of them soon became among the botanically best-known parts of the world. This situation is in sharp contrast with the state of exploration of the continents: travelling on the high seas on relatively comfortable ships became safer and safer, especially when in convoy and with suitable detachments of marines. The intelligent use of antiscorbutics, mainly initiated by Cook, controlled the feared scurvy. The *Endeavour*, on a three year trip, suffered no deaths from scurvy. Cook's authority and Banks and Solander's keen scrutiny of the vegetable resources of the islands visited, together instituted a new marine diet which totally abolished one of the greatest hazards of long distance travel on the high seas. The relatively high losses eventually suffered by the crew of the *Endeavour* were through infectious diseases contracted on Java. Bernard Smith (1960) has pointed out that vessels "like Cook's *Resolution* [second voyage], despite her deficiences, combined the values of a fortress and a travelling laboratory. Land–travelling scientists had no hope of competing with the results of a Cook, a Flinders or a Dumont d'Urville." Travelling on board a ship had not only the great advantage of relative safety, it also provided ample opportunities to make collections and to bring them safely home. The South Pacific, Polynesia, the southern Atlantic and the Indian Ocean therefore became fields of extensive scientific exploration long before the Amazon, Central Africa, Siberia or even some parts of Europe and North America.

The *Endeavour* and its crew spent more than three months at Tahiti. The adjoining Leeward group of islands was called Society, in honour of the Royal Society, a name later adopted for the whole group including Tahiti and the other Windward islands. Banks and Solander made extensive collections, Parkinson made his drawings. In full keeping with the utilitarian ideals of the Enlightenment, but certainly also with the direct needs of food and hygiene, special attention was paid to the cultivated plants. As a result this first large collection of botanical material from Tahiti is of the greatest importance for the knowledge of the original flora, of the transport of plant species by man in the Pacific and, consequently, of the movement of man himself. Merrill (1954) has drawn attention to the great scientific importance of these early Tahiti collections. Solander collected, and described in manuscript, 260 lowland Tahitian species. This plant collection is now one of the most important documents pointing towards a settlement of Polynesia from the West, out of Malaysia.

After leaving Tahiti, Cook turned due South, to reach the fortieth parallel and to establish the absence of a land mass. He then turned west and hit New Zealand, both islands of which were then circumnavigated for the first time by Western sailors. The reception by the Maoris was not as friendly as on Tahiti: not all the primitive savages corresponded to the

[229]

ideals of natural man. Collections were made, the New Zealand flora was discovered, and again a first basis was laid for the knowledge of a new flora, one which would turn out to be even more different from anything known than that of Tahiti. After New Zealand the voyage was continued westward, Australia was hit, and, on April 19, 1770, Botany Bay was discovered, which remained for Banks perhaps the absolute highlight of his voyage. The profusion of plant life and the novelty of forms were such that Solander and Banks realized they had found an entirely new flora and, what was more, a vegetation and a climate which promised much for European settlement. The rest of the story is well known: the damage suffered on the shoals and reefs of the Queensland coasts, the repairs on shore in the mouth of the Endeavour River, the continuation of the voyage northward along the Australian coast, the reaffirmation of the existence of Torres straits separating Australia from New Guinea, the voyage home via Batavia, the Cape of Good Hope and St. Helena.

Banks and Solander brought home a rich herbarium, seeds for Kew, 955 coloured drawings and sketches of plants and animals, mainly from Tahiti, New Zealand and Australia, and ample manuscript material containing descriptions made during the voyage. Contrary to what might have been expected, very little of this material was published either by Banks or by Solander. Banks himself was too much engaged in other activities and was anyhow not the publishing type; even though a great letter writer, he was not an author. He left the tedious task of scientific description and evaluation to others, mainly to his companion Solander, who became his librarian and curator upon their return.

The botany of the voyage of the Endeavour was perhaps only a side issue; the undertaking as a whole, however, inaugurated a new era in scientific exploration. Never before had pure science been the primary object of such a voyage. With the Endeavour voyage the laboratory of the botanist had become almost global, even though still mainly maritime and coastal. The last unknown living flora, that of Australia, had been discovered and found to be richer than even the most enlightened botanists had dreamed of. The new riches had a profound effect upon the ways and means of dealing with such profusion: the inability of the old a priori systems to cope with the much–enlarged variety became evident, and a pragmatic approach became essential. In the beginning the Linnaean system still served such an approach just as well as it had served Linnaeus himself; most of the work done at first on the basis of the Banks and Solander collections was purely descriptive and presented in the Linnaean setting. This work remained for the greater part in manuscript. Solander, to whom Banks left the collections for study and publication, did not appear in print with a major publication during his lifetime. The renown of the collections assembled by Banks in his house at Soho Square, however, was such that it attracted many foreign scholars and visitors, and the Banksian herbarium and library thus became a main centre of taxonomic research, primarily descriptive and analytical rather than philosophical.

5. Kew Gardens and Soho Square

The appointment in 1759 of William Aiton (1731–1793), a pupil of Philip Miller, as head gardener by Princess Augusta of Saxe–Gotha, the Princess Dowager of Wales, marked the founding of the Kew botanic gardens. Augusta had united the properties of Kew House and Richmond lodge and, with the guidance of the botanophilic Lord Bute, wanted to establish a "physic or exotic" garden after the model of Chelsea. The laying out took place in 1760; nine acres were developed into a botanic garden arranged according to the Linnaean system. John Hill acted as special adviser, and in about seven years the number of species grown at Kew rose to 3.400 (Stearn 1961), as can be seen from Hill's *Hortus kewensis* of 1768.

After Princess Augusta's death, in 1772, her son George III took the gardens under his immediate care. Being not exactly an admirer of Lord Bute, the king put the gardens under the general supervision of Joseph Banks, known to him personally, who could not have hoped for a better chance to put one of his imaginative scientific schemes into effect. Banks looked upon Kew as the place to become "the great exchange house of the Empire, where the possibilities of acclimatising plants from one part of the globe to another might be tested and from which material for experimental work in any climate would always be available" (Cameron 1952, p. 63). This great conception far surpassed that of a merely curious collection of exotic plants; Kew gardens were to play a rôle in the development of the empire through the introduction of useful as well as ornamental plants from all parts of the globe, for the benefit of the home country as well as of the colonial settlements.

Banks had no plans to develop Kew in the same way as the Paris *Jardin du Roi*, which was a combination of a botanic garden and research laboratories with scientific staff. Kew gardens were to function only as a botanical garden, but then in a superior way; the accompanying scientific research for which a herbarium and library would be needed could take place in London, in fact during his lifetime mainly at his own house in Soho Square. Like Hill, Banks aimed at a summing up in book form of the plants grown at Kew. This summary was to become one of the most remarkable publications of eighteenth century British taxonomy, William Aiton's *Hortus kewensis* (1789).

Banks's personality and enterprise manifested itself perhaps most completely in the development of the Kew gardens. It has been estimated that during the time of his supervision (1772–1820) "about seven thousand new plants from overseas were introduced into cultivation in England, the majority through the exertions of Banks on behalf of Kew" (Turrill 1959, p. 23). Part of these introductions were the result of the activities of 'Kew collectors' sent abroad by or through Banks to collect living plants for the gardens and to make herbarium material for the collections at Soho Square. Some of the best known of these collectors were Francis Masson (1741–1806), who collected in South and North Africa, the Atlantic islands, the West Indies and North America; David Nelson (x–1789), who sailed on Cook's third voyage (1776–1780) and with Bligh on the Bounty, in an attempt to bring the breadfruit tree (*Artocarpus*) from the Pacific to Jamaica; A. P. Hove, who collected in India; Peter Good (x–1803), India and Australia, and George Caley (x–1829), Australia. Apart from these more or less official Kew collectors there were many other botanical explorers who sent living material to Kew. Archibald Menzies (1754–1842), who accompanied Captain Vancouver to South America, western North America and Australia, is but one example. Plants from eastern North America reached Kew either directly, e.g. through Masson, or indirectly, as for instance through John Fothergill and his American collector, William Bartram.

The growth of the Kew collections had to be accompanied by identification of the material and, if necessary, description of the new taxa. This task fell in first instance to Banks's librarian–curators, at first Solander and later Dryander and Robert Brown, but sometimes also to visiting botanists such as Gaertner, the younger Linnaeus, Charles–Louis L'Héritier and

[232]

Olov Swartz, or, especially towards the end of the century, to other British botanists, especially James Edward Smith. All this activity was centred around Banks's herbarium and library, both of which were among the richest of the period. Banks received material not only from his own collectors but from many other sources as well, British and foreign. He started out with his own Newfoundland collections and with those of the voyage of the Endeavour and of his trip to Iceland, and he added continuously to these by purchase of other herbaria, among them those of Paulus Hermann, Clifford, and Philip Miller. Part of the collections made by the two Forsters* on Cook's second voyage also came directly to Banks. Furthermore, numerous collections were obtained directly from collectors such as Loureiro, Alexander Russell, William Roxburgh, William Anderson, Olof Swartz. The list of collectors of the Banksian herbarium, which later became the basis of the general herbarium of the British Museum (Natural History), is a faithful mirror of almost all botanical exploration carried out between 1760 and 1820. Collections which did not reach Banks directly were acquired through colleagues abroad, and towards the end of the period there was hardly a botanical collector who would not have been proud to have some of his material incorporated in the Banksian herbarium.

The eighteenth century was the century of the natural history cabinets, the cabinets of the *curiosi* and the philosophers with their shells and monstrosities but sometimes also with quite extensive herbaria. Most of these 'cabinets' and collections, however, were mainly objects of collecting *per se*; very often the emphasis was on 'curiosities,' shells, fossils and monstrosities. Lasègue (1845), after discussing this background of 'curiosity' of most of the earlier collections, such as those of Gesner, Imperato, Petiver, Sloane, Seba, Clifford and Gronovius, correctly remarks that Banks's *Museum* was of a different nature: "Le Muséum si connu de Sir Joseph Banks, formé à Londres vers la fin du dix–huitième siècle, répondait à un autre ordre d'idées ..." The idea behind the Banksian collection

---

* The story of the activities of Johann Reinhold Forster (1729–1798) and his son Johann Georg Adam (1754–1794) on Cook's second voyage and in England, as well as in Germany, could fill a chapter of its own. Their rôle in the spreading of Linnaean thought, however, was modest. Their *Characteres generum plantarum* contained descriptions of many of the plants collected on the second voyage. It is thoroughly Linnaean but was unfavorably received by the British because of various non–botanical circumstances.

344.

Fig. B. Nux magnitudine paenum aucta longitudinaliter dissecta ut loculamentum lunatum ap=
pareat.

POLYGAMIA

MONOECIA.

paradisiaca. Musa *Linn. Sp. pl. 1477.1*

α.) *Maya* }
β.) *Fai* } *Insularibus Oceani Pacifici*

Hab. in Otaheite, Huaheine, Ulaietea, Otaha et
Ohiteroa.

Inter Principes Regni vegetabilis locum certissime
merentur Musae; si vel formam externam cum
simplex vel utilitatem consideres illas invenies
fere omnibus plantis palmam praeripientes. Et
expertissimus nostram in Insulis Oceani pacifici
cultam, Musarum nobilissimam pronunciare
Fructus Musae nullibi sapidiores (a nobis quote-
t.) vel pro gravi occasione melius adaptati
sunt.
Utut Incolis utilissima haec est planta, ita etiam
illorum cura magis commissa fuit quam ulla
alia, unde Varietates numerosissima pullulas-
verunt; ex his alia dulcissimos gerunt fructus,
quos condor uti bellaria comedere placet, alia
praebent fructus quos assare vel coquere opor-
tet et tunc ipso pane nequaquam inferiores
sunt. Diversis anni temporibus diversa varietates suos maturescunt, ut fere semper in
promtu suat; omnes vero culturae esse probles
vadet defectus seminum, illas itaque in species dispestere vanum erit in duas autem Fami-
lias omnes facile subdividi possunt, et hoc con-
sensu omnium Insulanis. Primaria Familia
ab Incolis vocatur *Maya*, altera *Fai*, prior
suppeditat fructus dulciores, posterior austeri-
ores et hi vix nisi cocti ad cibum vocantur.
Varietates maxime notabiles sequentes sunt.

α.) *Maya*.

1. Orhea.	15. Malamatahi.
2. Ehuevao.	16. Ahai.
3. E Sulita.	17. Taapeape.
4. E Sivahi.	18. Mamala.
5. Aletoa.	19. Etapua.
6. Aàa.	20. Oori.
7. Aivau.	21. Erenrai.
8. Ehumalai.	22. E Fawhili wheli.
9. Ehuapoto.	23. Palahatu.
10 Etorho.	**β.) *Fai***
11. Tayo urha.	1. E pautea.
12. E pute plute.	2. Ova.
13. E hauta.	3. Erhu rheva.
14. Rue rhoini.	4. Aa ili.
	5. E whala

Obs. Septendecim anteriores Maya, et duas priores
Fai,

Fig. 57

and library was indeed of another 'order': that of pure science. Banks collected with a strictly scientific purpose, neither to amuse nor to edify, but simply for the sake of research. Banks was the originator of the modern concept of a taxonomic research institute: a herbarium, a library, a scientific staff, a botanic garden, and direct contact with botanical exploration and plant introduction in general. This scientific idea fitted the early romantic movement; it had evolved from the ideas of the Enlightenment on nature, but it had outgrown the emphasis on direct utility and, even more, that on edifying pleasure. The Banksian concept of scientific botany was of individual exploration accompanied by pure research.

Most large herbaria go back to private eighteenth–century collections. In France we shall see the growth of the Jussieu collections and library which, by 1789, the year of publication of the *Genera plantarum*, were the richest in the country. Contrary to the Banks collections, however, those of the Jussieus primarily served their owners; they were not set up as a taxonomic research institution. The *Jardin du Roi* had in its 'botanical cabinet' some small collections, such as those of Tournefort and Vaillant, and it had been given the use of the Commerson and Dombey collections. The Jussieu herbarium was much richer and provided the actual basis for A. L. Jussieu's *Genera plantarum* of 1789. Lamarck wrote his extensive 'species plantarum' in the *Encyclopédie* also mainly on the basis of his own almost equally extensive collections.

In England there was only one such main collection, that of Banks, with, towards the end of the century, a good second in that of James Edward Smith. The herbarium collections at the British Museum were smaller; there was no special Department of Botany as yet (this was established later for the reception of the Banksian herbarium), although the Museum owned the important Sloane herbarium. By modern standards the Banksian herbarium, even though the largest of its time, was still of relatively modest size. Robert Brown reported on it to the trustees of the British Museum in 1834. It had not continued to grow after 1820, the year Banks died. The number of species in the 'arranged herbarium' (in ac-

Fig. 57. Page 344 of Solander's unpublished manuscript flora of Tahiti. Merrill points at the large number of banana varieties listed here. Banana thickets are still a conspicuous feature of the vegetation of Tahiti. [From E. D. Merrill, *Chronica botanica* 14: 344 (1954), courtesy *Frans Verdoorn*; original manuscript at British Museum (Natural History)] *Reduced.*

[235]

cordance with the Linnaean system) was then 23.400, and there were a suspected 5000 additional species in the 'unarranged' section, which included herbaria in book form, such as that of Paulus Hermann, as well as 1700 parcels of unsorted material.

The true value of the collection at the time was that it included, at any rate for the phanerogams, specimens of the great majority of described species, which made it an excellent tool for rapid identification and an unsurpassed basis for the publication of new taxa. The percentage of type specimens was much higher than in our more recent herbaria. Combined with this herbarium was a library of similar excellence. The contents of this library are known exactly through Dryander's catalogue of it, published in the years 1796–1800. All these treasures were cared for, in succession, by the three botanists who acted as curator–librarians, Daniel Solander, Jonas Dryander and Robert Brown.

Daniel Carl Solander, briefly mentioned earlier as one of the Linnaean pupils, was born in Piteå, Sweden, on February 19, 1733. He went to England in 1760 at the invitation of John Ellis and Peter Collinson, to remain there until his death. In the small circle of botanophiles in London of those years Solander must often have met Banks; Rauschenberg (1967) (see also Fries 1941) states that Banks and Solander met and became close friends in 1764, just after Banks left Oxford. In the years before the voyage of the *Endeavour* Solander was associated with the relatively newly established British Museum, possibly curating the botanical collections and library. Banks invited him to participate in the voyage as his chief naturalist. Upon their return the task of describing the collections fell to Solander (fig. 57). It is still difficult to assess the reasons why so little was published during Solander's lifetime; he left a considerable amount of manuscript, partly dealing with the plants from the great voyage, partly also with plants newly received from Kew or from other collections. Krok (1925, p. 655) has listed Solander's writings: this bibliography contains sixty–six numbers, but only four of these came out during his lifetime. The only significant paper of those four is *An account of the Gardenia*, published in 1763. Solander's manuscripts, however, proved to be a rich source to his successor Dryander, to the head gardener of Kew, Aiton (probably only indirectly, through Dryander), and to many other botanists, British and foreign, not directly connected with Soho Square. Conspicuous examples of foreign colleagues who benefited greatly from Solander's knowledge and manuscripts were, for instance, L'Héritier de Brutelle and Joseph Gaertner. A reference to a Solander manuscript is quite common in the botanical literature of the following decades; one species, *Ficus virginea* Hiern, was even published in the twentieth century on the basis of a (Banks and) Solander manuscript.

Solander's successor as botanist–librarian to Banks, Jonas Dryander, made extensive use of technical descriptions of new taxa drawn up by Solander when he edited William Aiton's *Hortus kewensis*. Many of the new species in the first two volumes of that work were actually recognized and described by Solander, whose failure to publish has been the subject of much comment. The manuscripts show that Solander was not at all idle, but that he limited himself to simple descriptive work. As a social figure he was well received and liked and the last twelve years of his life, spent in Bank's service at Soho Square, evidently went by as a pleasant whirlwind of social pleasures, curating duties and elementary taxonomic work. Linnaeus had no reason to be satisfied with this pupil who, in later years, never even answered his letters, and who also failed to make the material from the Endeavour voyage available to the great master. Linnaeus no longer travelled and therefore saw only a fraction of the treasures assembled by Banks and Solander on what was ultimately perhaps the most rewarding of all voyages made by any of his pupils. James Edward Smith (Corr. Linn. 2: 1–3) summed up Solander's achievements as follows: "It ought nevertheless to be remembered, that if the talents and liberality of this eminent man were not so directly useful ... they have been other-wise pre–eminently beneficial. They have proved the example and the spur of all that has been done for natural science, during half a century, in Britain; ... It was Solander who reduced our garden plants to order, and laid the foundation of *Hortus kewensis* of his friend Aiton. His instructions made everybody correct and systematic, and introduced Linnaean learning and precision ... Natural orders or affinities seem never to have entered into his contemplation. In nomenclature and terminology he was always classical and correct ..."

Rauschenberg's (1967) appreciation of Solander's inconspicuous but important rôle in British botany during the 1760's and 1770's seems eminently fair: "Although he published little and was dismissed by the generation who followed his own as an unambitious scientific gossip, in actuality he was well trained, was rich in experience, and pursued his chosen profession vigorously all his life. By any criteria, then, the first Cook voyage was staffed with a top–flight naturalist who was able to disseminate its findings because of his pivotal position in British science."

Solander arranged Banks's herbarium in accordance with the Linnaean system. His careful identification of many of the new plants, either living or preserved, which reached England during the second half of the century was still done within the framework of the eminently practical Linnaean classifications. Others, like for instance Joseph Gaertner, were to draw the further conclusions from the facts dutifully, if perhaps somewhat slowly, registered by this singular Linnaean pupil.

Jonas Carlsson Dryander, born in Göteborg, Sweden, on 5 March 1748, also a student from Uppsala, and perhaps of Linnaeus (Uggla 1945), became Banks's second botanist–librarian after Solander's death on 12 March 1782. He had finished his studies in Lund in 1776, had gone to England the next year, and had served as botanical assistant to Banks since 1778. Dryander must have been a less conspicuous figure than Solander. Much of his correspondence is left, but it deals mainly with the technical affairs around the Banksian collections. Dryander's great gift was bibliography, as is exemplified by his *Catalogus bibliothecae historico–naturalis Josephi Banks*, a monument of bibliography in natural history which has retained its usefulness up to the present. Dryander, as Solander had before him, greatly helped William Aiton with the preparation of the copy for the *Hortus kewensis*. The correspondence between Dryander and L'Héritier makes it clear that towards the end Dryander was practically in charge of this publication. Most of his own contributions are found in the third volume; however, in addition to these original descriptions Dryander's contribution was such that the fact that Aiton did not even mention him in his preface can perhaps be understood only if we assume that this preface too is mainly from the hand of Dryander. The book contains a wealth of detail and was the greatest contribution of its time towards creating order in the nomenclature and taxonomy of plants cultivated in British gardens either in the open air or under glass. For each species the date of introduction into cultivation in Britain is mentioned, data based on an extensive study of the literature in Banks's library, the Sloane herbarium and the Sloane manuscripts, all of which stood under Dryander's supervision. The arrangement is of course that of Linnaeus, and the book is therefore not so much a contribution to the principles of taxonomy as a compendium of taxonomic detail. Apart from the *Hortus kewensis* (Dryander also contributed substantially to its second edition, a contribution duly acknowledged by the younger Aiton) and the catalogue of the Banksian library, however, Dryander's publications are modest in content and number. He remained in charge of the Banksian collections until his death on 19 October 1810.

Dryander cannot have been a dull man, and he obviously had a good grasp of the history of biology. When writing to J. E. Smith (1832, p. 166) about some acquisitions for the library, he states, for instance, "Far be it from us to encumber the library with such an enormous quantity of nonsense as the collection of the works of Albertus Magnus ... of all dull books, the most dull are those of scholastic writers ..."

The third Banksian librarian–curator was Robert Brown (1773–1858), the only one to survive the great patron, but also the greatest and most original thinker among British botanists of the Banksian era. Brown was to prepare the road for the liberation of British botany from the Linnaean incubus (Gilmour 1944).

A focal point of the activities of British taxonomic botany in the last years of the century was The Linnaean Society of London, established 26 February 1788. Robert Brown, The Linnaean Society, and its first president, James Edward Smith, the proud owner of the Linnaean herbarium, however, are all beyond the period accepted for this essay. For England this is a somewhat artificial division. The year 1789 had not the same importance for England as it had for France, and the development of the Linnaean school in the British Isles went on long after that crucial date in continental European history. J. E. Smith's first botanical publication, a fascicle of *icones* and descriptions of plants preserved in the Linnaean herbarium, came out in 1789. The first volume of the *Transactions of The Linnaean Society* appeared in 1791. English botany was rapidly reaching a point at which Linnaean taxonomy became almost sanctified.

In France a totally different way of thinking had developed with respect to nature. The Enlightenment concept of nature differed fundamentally from the quietly creationist view prevalent in England. It was a new picture of the world and would help to defeat the ghosts of the past. Linnaean thought fitted the English pattern; it preserved the creationist concept of nature, but was at the same time eminently practical. No need was felt to use the knowledge of nature as a tool to bring about a social revolution; on the contrary, the emphasis was still on enjoyment and 'curiosity.' The parallel is not too far-fetched: France had a 1789 and England did not; the French quickly developed a natural system free from ancient extraneous values, but England remained Linnaean for at least two more decades.

8

Germany and Switzerland: Pros and antis

1. Background and the Rivinians

The picture of German botany in the Linnaean epoch reflects the political and social diversity of the country in the eighteenth century. Germany was a bewildering conglomeration of larger, smaller and minute states of all possible denominations, and its most notable feature was lack of internal communication. The notion of German eighteenth–century botany is almost as artificial as a class of the Linnaean sexual system. Politically the picture of Germany was coloured by the rise of Prussia as the dominant power in Central Europe, a position well established by mid–century. Prussia became "the great vitalizing nucleus of that conglomeration of territories which was neither Holy, nor Roman, nor an Empire" (Gershoy 1944: 9). This development, however, did not immediately entail a flowering of Prussian botany; in fact, the sciences played only a modest rôle in this semi–enlightened state. The real blossoming of botany in the German lands, in the widest sense of the word, took place in the independent Low Countries, in politically declining Austria and in the middle–Rhine region. Botany in Germany presents a heterogeneous picture all through the century, a picture composed of all the elements in which France, Sweden and the Netherlands had taken a lead, in combination with a strong strain of endemic plant taxonomy.

The Linnaean influence in Germany was not as outspoken and clear as in the Netherlands, Austria and England. On the contrary, Linnaeus's ideas penetrated slowly, taking root only in the later decades of the century and remaining ever in dispute.

The principal strain of endemic German taxonomy goes back to A. Q. Rivinus (1652–1723) and his *Introductio generalis in rem herbarium* of 1690. Rivinus was, in Linnaean terminology, a 'corollist.' He rejected the age–old basic split in the plant kingdom between trees and herbs and proposed a purely utilitarian system based on the structure of the corolla. His plant world was, of course, mainly that of the flowering plants. Those with perfect flowers were subdivided into plants with composite and with simple flowers. The simple flowers could be regular or irregular, and both these groups were subdivided on the basis of the number of lobes of the corolla. The system was simple because it was based on a character complex which is easily observed: the shape and the number of the elements of what is usually the showiest part of the flower. Rivinus did not pretend to propose a natural system; like his contemporary Tournefort, he just wanted a simple and orderly device to classify plants.

This Rivinian strain of thought was taken up by quite a few of the later German authors. One of the most outstanding, and one who at the same time made an honest effort to incorporate into it some of the Linnaean reforms, was Christian Gottlieb Ludwig (1709–1773), almost an exact contemporary of Linnaeus. Ludwig studied medicine in Brieg and Leipzig. He was engaged as a botanist to accompany J. E. Hebenstreit on an expedition to North Africa organized by the Polish government. This expedition, organized mainly to obtain a general knowledge of the natural products of North Africa, was one of the first purely scientific journeys of exploration. The party visited mainly Tunisia and Tripoli and studied the natural history and the antiquities of those countries. The collection made on this trip was preserved at Dresden but destroyed in the great fire of the Dresden Zwinger on 6 May 1849. This early travelling must have deeply influenced Ludwig and given him the lead over his home-staying, more philosophically inclined contemporaries.

After earning his doctor's degree at Leipzig in 1737 Ludwig had a hard time obtaining a scientific post, although he became an extraordinary professor of medicine at Leipzig as early as 1740. (The 'extraordinary,' then as now, referred in practice to the low salary.)

Ludwig had observed the pollination of palms and *Pistacia* in Africa and was from the beginning sympathetically inclined towards Linnaeus's emphasis on the rôle of sex in plants. His thesis *De sexu plantarum* of 1737 was followed by *Observationes in methodum Linnaei*, of 1739. Among these observations is a remark that there are many truly natural elements in the Linnaean natural system. *Lobelia* and *Jasione*, for instance, should have been put with the *Syngenesia* but are placed in the *Pentandria* because of their relationship with the *Campanulaceae* (Sprengel 1818, 2: 244). In his *Definitiones generum plantarum* (ed. 2 1747, here used; ed. 1 was of 1737) Ludwig adopts in general the Rivinian system for his higher categories, except that he makes the characteristic 'regular or irregular corolla' subordinate to the number of petals. In his generic delimitation he often follows the Linnaean reform, but he continues to use the old Tournefortian names. The 'definitions' are concise and to the point and differ from the Linnaean ones in that they admit vegetative characteristics. The third edition of this book, edited by Boehmer (1760), differed slightly with respect to the system of higher taxa but retained the Tournefortian nomenclature. Because of the early date of this book (after 1753) it contains the validation of a number of Tournefortian names.

Ludwig published also an *Institutiones historico–physicae regni vegetabilis* (1742; ed. 2 1757), in which he laid down his own *Philosophia botanica*. The book contains a key to all genera of the plant kingdom. In view of the use of the Tournefortian nomenclature, the 1757 edition is again important because of the validation of names abandoned by Linnaeus. The book (ed. 2) consists of 575 concisely worded paragraphs dealing with the whole of botany, including anatomy and nutrition. With respect to the Linnaean influence, in paragraph 252 of the second edition, discussing the *nomina trivialia*, Ludwig states:

"Cum characteres essentiales singulares difficile inveniantur, botanici non nunquam species, compendiario saepe nomine, ab accidentalibus etiam characteribus petito, insignire solent, haec vulgo recepta nomina Linnaeus in speciebus plantarum trivialia dixit et in margine non sine commodo disquirentium apposuit. Cum enim in nominibus generum inferiorum, nomina raro essentiam plantae exprimentia, sed saepe arbitraria admittuntur, forte etiam in speciebus compendiariae denominationes tolerandae erunt."

This may be paraphrased as follows: The essential character of the species, as expressed by the phrase name, is often difficult to establish. For this reason botanists often give short names to species based on accidental characteristics. Linnaeus calls these names 'trivialia' in his *Species plantarum* and puts these names in the margin, a practice which is quite convenient for the user. If we admit names of 'lower genera' [i.e. genera in the present sense] which express only rarely the essence of the plant and which are often arbitrary, we must admit such names also for species.

[243]

ALBERT DE HALLER, M.D. F.R.S.

W. Holl.

Fig. 58

[244]

In the next paragraph (253) Ludwig explains that there is no doubt that it will be possible to find for each plant a single essential or accidental character on which the trivial name can be based. The *Institutiones*, however, do not provide him with an opportunity to put this into practice.

Ludwig, like Linnaeus, is in several ways a representative of the past, and he shares with him a certain pragmatism in classifying. His concise definitions, the keys in his works, the artificial system, all betray the classifier rather than the biologist. His work duplicates in many ways that of Linnaeus, and it never caught on precisely because of this. Ludwig's active period ended around 1760; he did not produce a *Species plantarum*, nor did he introduce the binary system into Germany. The result was that his system of classification, in other respects so useful and clear, became superfluous. His last important botanical publication was the *Ectypa vegetabilium*, 8 folio fascicles (1760–1764) of plates of useful plants, produced by means of the technique called *Naturselbstdruck* (nature-printing).

2. Albrecht von Haller

The Swiss naturalist, poet and novelist Albrecht von Haller (1708–1777) (fig. 58), another almost exact contemporary of Linnaeus, was one of his most outspoken opponents in the German–Swiss world. Haller had relatively well-to-do parents and was given an excellent education. He studied medicine in various places and obtained a Leiden degree with Boerhaave. From 1736 until 1753 he was professor of anatomy, medicine and botany in Goettingen; later he occupied several posts in Switzerland.

Fig. 58. ALBRECHT HALLER (after 1749 von Haller); *b.* Bern, Switzerland October 16, 1708; *d.* Bern, Switzerland December 12, 1777; student at Tübingen 1723–1725, at Leiden 1725–1727, med. degree 1727, lector anatomy Basel 1728–1729, physician at Bern 1729–1734, town librarian Bern 1735, professor of medicine and botany at Göttingen 1736–1753, ennobled by German emperor 1749, prefect at Bern 1753, director of the salt mines in Roche, Vaud, 1758–1764.

"Huic lex summa fuit Naturae Voce doceri
Huic dominae doctas subdidit artis opes:
Ingenuus veri vel ad hoste nitentes amicus
Censor et erroris candidus ipse sui"

P. G. Werthof 1757

[Engraving by W. Holl: *Biohistorical Institute, Utrecht*].

[245]

Haller was an encyclopedic erudite, a poet, deeply religious, but also a good objective empiricist as far as the natural sciences were concerned.

Haller's most outstanding characteristics are perhaps his versatility and his immense erudition. His works on botany are only a fraction of what he wrote. In medicine and anatomy he produced important compilations, he was no mean poet, he published also on religion. Through most of these writings transpires a personality turned towards the past, essentially conservative, sometimes almost excessively religious, deeply sensitive, but also at times unexpectedly open-minded towards the natural world by which he was surrounded: searching for new evidence not in the statements of past authors, but by means of inductive research.

Botany was therefore only one of Haller's many occupations, and when judging his controversy with Linnaeus this should not be forgotten. The factual details of this controversy are not relevant here; they were reviewed most recently by Goerke in his biography of Linnaeus (1966). The two shared an inclination not to underestimate their own importance; both were easily disturbed by criticism. Even so, this great controversy cannot be reduced to a simple clash of difficult characters but must be seen as determined by more fundamental differences in biological outlook. Ironically both were, on balance, more much men at the end of an era than real innovators. Both made significant contributions to the progress of botany, although these contributions were entirely different. Linnaeus was the reformer of taxonomy and nomenclature as a general system of information. Von Haller, as a botanist, showed himself to be more biologically inclined, advocating extensive observation, description and experimentation.

Von Haller's botanical works are mainly floristic, almost exclusively dealing with Central Europe. His main works are an *Enumeratio methodica stirpium Helvetiae indigenarum* of 1742 and that great monument of plant description: the *Historia stirpium indigenarum Helvetiae* of 1768. In addition to these Swiss floras Haller published a third edition of Ruppius's *Flora jenensis* (1745), an *Enumeratio stirpium horti et agri gottingensis* (1753) and an important general work: *Bibliotheca botanica* (1771–72). Unlike Linnaeus, Haller travelled regularly and until late in life, mainly in Central Europe "wobei ihm seine Kurzsichtigkeit hinderlich im Aufsuchen, förderlich im Untersuchen war" (Jessen 1864). In the preface to his *Historia* Haller explains how he came to travel so much. By 1728 "I loved books and I was fond of a sedentary life.

[246]

I could, however, not hide from myself the fact that if I devoted my time to study uninterruptedly, my health would suffer greatly ..." (cf. de Beer 1953). He started out reconnoitering Switzerland on foot: "I described all the plants that I had collected, from their natural characters, as Boerhaave had taught us to do at Leiden." One of the first results of these journeys was Haller's poem *Die Alpen*, an early symptom of the romantic movement.

As a result of this continuous travelling Haller acquired an intimate knowledge of the flora of the Alps, a knowledge which profoundly influenced his biological outlook. The Alps, with their immense variety of habitats, exhibited to this excellent observer the one conspicuous aspect of plant life which escaped Linnaeus: variability. In many places (see Zoller 1958) in his works Haller advocates the study of all phases of the life cycle of plants, the value of detailed and critical description, the comparison of many specimens and even the need for experiments in cultivation. An interesting illustration of this attitude is Haller's statement in a letter to Linnaeus (17 October 1766) quoted by J. E. Smith (1821): "We cannot in all cases, say what is a species and what a variety; at least not without culture [sic] and observations." For further examples I must refer to Zoller's detailed essay on von Haller's botany (1958).

Haller had a keen eye for plant geography and ecology, undoubtedly again because of his intimate knowledge of the Alps. In his great Swiss flora of 1768 he draws the parallel between the altitudinal zonation of plants in the Alps and the zonation from north to south in the holarctic flora region.

One of the most important differences between Linnaeus and Haller lies in their attitude toward the fixity of species. For Linnaeus, this fixity was a dogma of no mean importance, a dogma based on refined observation of the role of sex in plants and of the nature of propagation. Haller had certainly no cause to reject creationism, but he showed a remarkable ambiguity in his beliefs in religion and his opinions in the natural sciences. It would go too far to call him a precursor of transformism; yet, with his open eye for the rôle of variability and for the difficulty in differentiating between varieties and species, as well as with his experiments to test specific limits by cultivation, Haller was a biosystematist avant–la–lettre.

Haller's impact on botany, however, was relatively modest. The reason for this is mainly his failure to grasp the importance of the binary system of nomenclature. He shared with Linnaeus the conviction that the specific names coined by their predecessors were confusing and lacking in diagnostic detail. Both Haller and Linnaeus attempted to give purely diagnostic phrase names to their species. Haller, however, did not recognize the importance of binary nomenclature for species; he considered the *nomina trivialia* to be imprecise and leading to wrong associations or ideas, obviously misjudging entirely their importance as simple code-designations. Consequently he very rarely used Linnaean binary names in his works. In this respect—as in many others—he was a man of the past. The Linnaean generic reform was totally unacceptable for him, and the sexual system, with its pragmatic aim, he rejected as superficial; instead, he adhered to the Rivinian system, bringing about some complications which did not exactly enhance the usefulness of his work. Of all aspects of the Linnaean reform Haller approved only, and with reservations, of the improvement of the specific phrases. He had no eye for the great advantages of simplicity and consistency which sprang from Linnaeus's works. His own taxonomy is involved and laborious, his systems are complicated, his nomenclature too complex for anything but a small flora (see also Stafleu and Westhoff 1968). As a result his work was greatly overlooked. His *Historia stirpium helvetiae indigenarum* would have had an enormous impact if he had used binary nomenclature; instead, it stood outside the main stream of eighteenth-century botany, and his emphasis on experimentation, observation and detailed description was lost because it was presented in an antiquated form.

Haller's most successful book, the *Bibliotheca botanica* honored the past; it is a critical bibliography, chronologically arranged and remarkably complete. Many of the entries contain brief critical evaluations. One of the most interesting is his diagnosis of Linnaeus's importance as a botanist. The entry—translated here somewhat freely—shows that notwithstanding former animosity—"laudatur et alget" (Berg 1965)—Haller's judgment was objective. It also proves again that his greatest strength was his feeling for history, his evaluation of the achievements of the past:

"In this year 1732 appeared the first work by Carl Linnaeus, a man who has started one of the greatest revolutions in botany and who has reached his goals almost completely. Highly gifted, sharp-witted, extraordinarily imaginative, systematically inclined, Linnaeus worked out a new plant taxonomy using his great intellectual powers and benefiting, especially during the later part of his life, from the stream of natural treasures which reached him from all corners of the earth. During his lifetime he had the satisfaction of witnessing the acceptance of his teaching by most of his contemporaries. It cannot be denied that through his efforts the separate parts of the plants are now much better described and defined than ever before and that the descriptions of today reflect nature much more precisely even though he created an almost new language for that purpose."

Haller was not a child of his century; the word 'progress' was no slogan for him. He regarded Linnaeus as a revolutionary, and it is doubtful whether he ever realized how much basic similarity there was in character and in mentality between himself and his great adversary. Even their life histories have much in common, from an important Dutch period in their youth to an old age dominated by fear of a *nemesis divina*. However, Linnaeus's achievements proved to be of lasting value; Haller's work, characteristic as it may be of the period, and despite its originality and generally high quality, had little impact on the development of science, mainly because Haller failed in one important aspect: communication.

One contemporary and countryman of Haller who had become a convinced Linnaean should be mentioned: Johann Gesner (1709–1770), a correspondent of Linnaeus who published only little during his lifetime but from whose letters (de Beer 1949) transpires the forcefulness of the Linnaean writings. Gesner, like Haller, had studied some time in Leiden, under Boerhaave, and also at Paris under Bernard de Jussieu. For some time he worked with Haller on an Enumeration of Swiss plants, which was published ultimately by Haller alone (1742), with a gracious acknowledgement to Gesner.

In his letter of 30 October 1748 Gesner writes: "All the time of which I speak [the early forties], your incomparable writings reached Switzerland. I saw what a desired reformation they brought about in botany and natural history, and how much the study would gain in brilliancy, completeness and finish, if it were imparted in accordance with your precepts." He set out to work at a 'History of plants' which he never finished: "I did not consider the choice of any method except your Sexual Method: than which I can find none fuller, truer or clearer, since it derives directly from the Laws of Nature herself ..." The plates of this work were indeed published, although posthumously, in 1795, under the editorship of C. S. Schinz. Two specimens of the eighty planned plates were sent to Linnaeus in 1763, and the latter confessed himself to be 'thunderstruck' by them.

[249]

Gesner's influence on botany was negligible. He published a *Phytographia sacra generalis et specialis* (1759–1773) and some smaller papers; the partial eclipse of this minor star by "the brilliance with which the star of Albrecht von Haller blazed over the whole of Europe "(de Beer 1949) was not wholly undeserved.

3. Regular and irregular Linnaeans

A more regular Linnaean line was followed in Germany (and in Russia) by Gleditsch (although with some rebellious elements), the Gmelins, and some of Linnaeus's own pupils, among them Schreber, Murray and Giseke. In Germany we also encounter the first signs of inductive work on cryptogams.

One of the most famous and socially successful German taxonomists of the Linnaean epoch was Leipzig–born Johann Gottlieb Gleditsch (1714–1786). Gleditsch, like Ludwig, had much in common with Linnaeus, rebelled against his dominance in his younger years, but ended his life as one of the staunchest supporters of the Swede in Germany. He studied medicine and 'philosophy' (natural sciences) at Leipzig. After some travelling and a medical practice in Frankfurt a.d. Oder, Gleditsch was appointed director of the botanic garden of the Academy of Sciences in Berlin and lecturer at the medical school. His entire published output was botanical or agronomical. He wrote, for instance, a *Methodus fungorum* (1753), an early and necessarily still primitive system for the fungi, and several treatises on economic botany; he also published a new edition (1780) of the *Philosophia botanica*. This edition differs from the original only in the further elaboration of the examples and comments, but not in any theoretical aspect.

Gleditsch's work on fungi showed some original features. He was, for instance, of the opinion that the air was filled with fungal spores which were not only inhaled by man with every breath but also ingested with almost every item of food or drink. The crucial work by P. A. Micheli (1679–1737) on fungal spores was known to him. Micheli had shown that such spores can be made to germinate and that they yield hymenia and even fruit bodies; Gleditsch repeated these experiments and added experiments of his own with lower fungi. However, work on fungi was in general still very primitive in the eighteenth century, and inductive, unbiassed research was rare. The best work on fungi of the era, from a systematic point of view as well as from a general biological standpoint is that of the Italian botanist and correspondent of Linnaeus, Micheli. Most widely followed, in systematics, was Linnaeus's division of the fungi into eleven genera, a division mainly based on the work of Dillen and accepted by a great majority of followers of Linnaeus. It was not until Persoon that a really new era for systematic mycology could start.

Gleditsch's most interesting theoretical work for the purpose of this essay is his *Systema plantarum a staminum situ* of 1764, an elaboration of a shorter treatise of 1749: *Système des plantes fondé sur la situation et la liaison des étamines*, published in the 'Histoire' of the Berlin Academy of Sciences. French was the language of the educated in the Prussia of Frederick the Great (1712–1786). Frederick's father, an extreme and unsavory pragmatist, had banished Latin from the list of his son's studies. Frederick found his own way towards Western culture and established relations with advanced French thinkers at an early age. His 'Anti-Macchiavel' was published in the Hague by Voltaire in 1740, the year he became king of Prussia. Frederick restored the Academy and made it resemble its French counterpart. He despised the German language and wrote and spoke French fluently; he was an accomplished (though dull) French author and a skilled musician; he considered himself one of the philosophers of the Enlightenment. It is against this background of utilitarian benevolence and enlightened despotism that one must see the many opportunities Gleditsch had to pursue an almost exclusively botanical and agronomical career. Gleditsch himself, however, was only very lightly touched by the Enlightenment and shows little or no appreciation of French botany of the second half of the century.

His system of plants founded on the insertion of the stamens is in fact simply a variation of the Linnaean sexual system, but without its emphasis on numbers. His main assumption is that the essence of the flower lies in the stamens and the pistils, that the calyx and the corolla are accidental parts serving only to protect the fructification, and that each part must be considered with respect to its 'species,' figure, number, situation, and proportion. Each of the four main parts of the flower can be considered from those five points of view, thus producing twenty different systems. Gleditsch states that he tried out all these artificial systems in order to discover which of them produced the highest proportion of natural entities. This procedure of writing out all the different systems with the object of finding the most natural one is strongly reminiscent of Adanson's similar attempt in 1763, with his 65 artificial systems.

Gleditsch found that none of his twenty systems was really satisfactory. "Cela ne m'étonna point; car c'est le sort commun, non seulement des methodes inventées par les botanistes, ...; personne que je sache n'ayant encore trouvé la véritable clef d'une methode naturelle pour les trois règnes de la nature."

From the twenty systems Gleditsch chose the one which looked to him most promising, that based on the position of the stamens in the various parts of the flower. Evidently the main division must be, as always, between perfect and imperfect 'flowers.' The plants with perfect flowers are then subdivided into those in which the stamens are inserted on the receptacle (*thalamostemones*), on the corolla (*petalostemones*), or on the calyx (*calycostemones*), or united with the pistil (*stylostemones*). The position of the stamens, says Gleditsch, is much more constant than their number or their proportion. This reliability of the main characteristics is of great didactical importance. The further elaboration of the classes in orders shows nothing remarkable, except that it is considerably less practical than the Linnaean sexual system, to which Gleditsch refers not even with a single word.

Gleditsch's system would have remained insignificant if it had not been taken up much later by one of the great rebels against Linnaeus, Conrad Moench. Gleditsch himself accepted the Linnaean generic reform and was, especially in later years, a supporter of much of what Linnaeus had said. Even so, his rôle remained modest: he was only one of the many who tried to find fragments of a natural method, and he was essentially more a classifier than a biologist.

Conrad Moench (1744–1805), not a Prussian botanist, but born in Kassel, became a rebel against Linnaeus only in his later years, under the influence of Gleditsch, Gaertner and Medikus. His *Enumeratio plantarum indigenarum Hassiae* of 1777 follows the Linnaean sexual system. In his later years, however, and especially after he had moved to Marburg in 1785, his anti–Linnaean leanings increased. In his *Methodus* of 1794, which falls outside the scope of this essay, he accepted the Gleditsch system, rejected the Linnaean generic reform and revived many Tournefortian names (Stearn 1966b, 1966, Stafleu 1967b): "The Linnaean genera, especially those made up of a large number of species (plants), are rather accumulations, so that each

[252]

one of them, after a study of its parts, will surely proclaim itself to belong to a different genus—unless one is talking merely about a superficial knowledge of the plants."

"Skilled observers of these matters know that not all the plants which are assigned to such genera agree with each other (i.e. are natural con-geners) in every respect. Who does not know that a description ought to be in conformity with nature? Or should one approve of a description which offers a form for which an example is non–existent?" (Translation John Heller).

In several ways the rebellion against Linnaean traditionalism by Moench was salutory. His narrower generic concepts were occasionally followed by others; however, in most instances they were never accepted. Nomen-claturally the book is still of importance because of the many new names; its taxonomic and general systematic value, however, is mainly historical.

We have encountered in Gleditsch a botanist who paid more than the usual attention to cryptogams. In general, work on the non–vascular cryptogams in the eighteenth century was primitive. Linnaeus's sexual system and its success show that the emphasis was heavily on the flowering plants. What was needed for the cryptogams, even more than for the phanerogams, was a simple unbiassed inductive approach, empirical research and more refined and cheaper optical instruments. We encounter growing empiricism everywhere after the middle of the eighteenth century, but the instruments would become more generally available only after the Napoleonic era. Three German botanists can be mentioned briefly because of their work on algae, fungi, and musci, respectively: S. G. Gmelin, J. C. Schaeffer and J. Hedwig.

The knowledge of algae especially remained primitive all through the eighteenth century. Well known early workers were Donati (1750) and Ginanni (1755); the latter denied the existence of sexuality in Algae. The term 'algae' in our present sense was not used before 1789; the only taxonomic work on this subject of any significance before that year was still entitled *Historia fucorum* (1768). The author of this first monograph of the algae was Samuel Gottlieb Gmelin, a German botanist residing in Russia and a member of a family which produced several interesting natu-ralists. The *Historia fucorum* was conspicuous because of its careful descrip-tions and its illustrations. The term *Fucus* covers, as with Linnaeus, a broad spectrum of algae and not our present group of Phaeophyceae.

In Jakob Christian Schaeffer (1718–1790) we meet for the first time in Germany that phenomenon so well known in England and France and so characteristic of the Enlightenment and its aftermath: the clergyman-naturalist. Schaeffer was a Protestant minister in Regensburg who had studied theology in Halle. His interest in natural history was that of an amateur but resulted in a considerable series of entomological and botanical (especially mycological) publications, mostly well illustrated. His first botanical publication was an *Isagoge in botanicam expeditiorum* (1759), a preliminary to his *Botanica expeditior* ('ready botany') of 1760. This guide to botany consists of an enumeration of all genera in tabular form, followed by extensive synonymy. The book brings little new but is interesting because it is one of the first German works in which the Linnaean generic reform, taxonomic as well as nomenclatural, is fully accepted. Lütjeharms (1936) considers Schaeffer's mycological work as a great step forward towards free inductive biological research, especially his *Vorläufige Beobachtungen der Schwämme um Regensburg* of 1759. Schaeffer made a special study of the fungus spores and points out similarities with pollen, but at the same time he stresses the absence of organs comparable with stamens. The fungal spores are therefore compared with asexual organs of reproduction in higher plants, such as bulbils. He rejects the thesis that fungi originate from mould. For him it is obvious that sexual reproduction is not the only means of propagation. The minute spores must be compared with bulbi: like the 'eyes' of potatoes, they contain a whole new plant. Schaeffer was well acquainted with Buffon's work and realized that the *omne vivum ex ovo* had its limitations: regeneration processes of lower animals, the growth of fragmented potatoes and the propagation of fungi by means of spores were seen by him as comparable processes which represented reproduction without a fertilization process. Schaeffer was an excellent observer and had all the makings of the biologist who could defeat the naturalist.

The founder of modern bryology, Johannes Hedwig, comes into this history because of the fundamental importance of his earlier works. At present his *Species muscorum* of 1801 is the starting point for the nomenclature of musci, but this work came out posthumously and contained in fact the result of a lifetime of excellent empirical and observational work. Hedwig was born at Kronstadt in Transylvania (now Brassó) in 1730, studied at Leipzig University, and remained for the rest of his life in Saxonia. During his medical training in Leipzig he became acquainted with the group of scientists which included Hebenstreit, Ludwig and Boehmer, mentioned above. After obtaining his degree in medicine in 1759 he moved to Chemnitz and started a practice. Florschütz (1960), in his introduction to a reprint of the *Species muscorum*, gives a review of Hedwig's development as a bryologist and outlines his chief scientific achievements.

Hedwig's interest in mosses was stimulated by J. C. D. Schreber who sent him some botanical books and a microscope. This microscope was a simple instrument, magnifying not more than fifty times. Hedwig himself, however, improved the instrument in the course of the years, and ultimately achieved magnifications up to 290 times. Refined microscopy very often depended still on the skill of the individual user to improve his instrument. The already reasonable microscopes known from the period were not mass-produced and were often beyond the reach of the amateur botanist.

With this superior skill, Hedwig succeeded in describing in great detail the organs of reproduction and sometimes also the processes of fertilization of some of the algi, fungi, bryophytes and pteridophytes. He published his results in his *Fundamentum historiae naturalis muscorum frondosorum* of 1782 and especially in his epochmaking *Theoria generationis et fructificationis plantarum cryptogamicarum* (1784, published at St. Petersburg as a 'Preisschrift').

Among his discoveries are that of the *antheridium*, which he compared with the anthers of higher plants; he depicted in great detail the asci of Ascomycetes, calling them sporangium and using the term *spore*, most likely for the first time. He also described archegonia, saw the germination of mosses from spores (which he compared with seeds) via a protonema, and remarked that a characteristic of plants seemed to be the repeated production of sexual organs rather than the one-time production characteristic of animals. The *Fundamentum* contains also the beginning of what was to become the *Species muscorum*, a treatment of the musci in which many new species and genera were for the first time accurately described and which may well be regarded as the first attempt at a natural system for the musci.

Hedwig published extensively, especially after he had become associated with Leipzig Univeristy. He was also deeply interested in the philosophical problems connected with the natural sciences, as is evident, for instance, from his translation of the works of Bonnet, which came out in Leipzig in four volumes between 1783 and 1785.

[255]

4. New ideas from the middle Rhine region

The middle Rhine plains, Württemberg, and Baden, which had once produced Brunfels, Bock, Fuchs and Cordus, produced towards the end of the eighteenth century several highly original botanists, Kölreuter, Joseph Gaertner and Medikus, of whom the last was perhaps the most violent anti–Linnaean and the most colourful personality, but whose ultimate contribution was the smallest of the three. Kölreuter and Gaertner, however, provided a new impetus to empirical deductive research and can be counted among the founders of biological systematics.

Joseph Gottlieb Kölreuter's (1733–1806) place in biology is more in general botany and in genetics than in systematics. However, his exemplary experiments and the clear results of his program of hybridization had great consequences also for systematics. Kölreuter was born in Sulz on the Neckar and started his experiments in hybridization in his native city. Some of his later experiments took place in Calw, Württemberg, in the garden of Acharius Gärtner, in St. Petersburgh, Berlin and in Leipzig. From 1764 onward Kölreuter was a professor of botany in Karlsruhe. He published the results of his experiments in a series of now classical publications: *Vorläufige Nachricht von einigen das Geschlecht der Pflanzen betreffende Versuchen und Beobachtungen,* and the first, second and third 'Fortsetzungen' of 1761–1766. In these papers Kölreuter published the objective protocols of his experiments as well as, separately, brief discussions of their importance. His whole approach was modern and scientific and is a fine example of objective inductive research unhindered by theoretical a prioris.

Kölreuter obtained his first fertile interspecific hybrids between species of *Nicotiana* (*N. paniculata* and *N. rustica*) and succeeded later in crossing successfully species of *Dianthus, Ketmia, Hyoscyamus* and *Verbascum*. He proved that hybrids were not necessarily exactly intermediate between the maternal and the paternal forms, but that there were hybrid swarms. He also proved that hybrid forms, over successive generations, changed back towards the parent plants upon repeated fertilization with the pollen of the mother or the father species. With these experiments Kölreuter proved conclusively that Linnaeus's hybridization theory had no foundation in fact. In a brief comment on a hybrid observed by Linnaeus he remarks that it would have been desirable "dass uns der Herr von Linnee eine umständlichere und mehr nach der Natur, als nach seiner abentheurlichen und wider alle Erfahrung laufenden Theorie von der Generation gemachte Beschreibung davon geliefert hätte." Kölreuter also made it clear that hybridization was possible at most between species belonging to the same family, but mainly between congeneric species. He also discovered the phenomenon of physiological dioecism and made important discoveries in flower biology, especially with respect to pollination by insects. It was only after Darwin, however, that the value of these early discoveries was fully understood.

Kölreuter was not convinced, or at any rate stated that he had seen no proof of the occurrence of hybridization in nature. His careful experiments, however, were the first step in the direction of biosystematics. Kölreuter tried to assess the limits of species by means of hybridization and drew attention to the phenomenon of variability. In a world still firmly convinced of the fixity of species, his experiments and careful reports were the first gusts of the wind of change.

Joseph Gaertner (1732–1971) (fig. 59) is another example of a German botanical author who had entered the empiricist era. His extremely thorough and detailed comparitive study of seeds, fruits and spores, *De fructibus et seminibus plantarum* (1788–1791), is an excellent example of that unbiassed approach to nature which was so characteristic of the biologists of the Enlightenment. The book is equally important because of its theoretical introduction and for its practical result: the opening up of an entirely new field of characteristics in systematic botany. Gaertner's *Carpologia* appeared only towards the end of his—too short—life. Gaertner evidently believed in a thorough preparation: from 1770 to 1788 he worked on the preparation of his text. He established contact with numerous travelling botanists and visited the important centers of botanical research and collections, Paris, Leiden and London. In the latter city he was warmly welcomed at Sir Joseph Banks's house at Soho Square, and the collections from the Endeavour were liberally made available to him. From Thunberg Gaertner obtained material from Japan and the Cape, from Jussieu and Cavanilles material from Spain and South America. His correspondents (see Stafleu 1969a) were too many to be listed here. The result was, however, that when the first fascicle of the *Carpologia*, as Gaertner himself often called his book, appeared in December 1788, it was immediately recognized as a major contribution to systematic botany. The book gives a wealth of detail, not only on the fruits and the seeds, but very often also on critical

Photozinkographie: J. Löwy, Wien.

Nach einer authentischen Silhouette.
Besitzer des Originals unbekannt.

Fig. 59. JOSEPH GAERTNER; *b.* Calw, Germany, March 12, 1732; *d.* Calw, Germany, July 1791; A German botanist, author of *De fructibus et seminibus plantarum* (1788–1791). [Silhouette of unknown origin, from I. Dörfler, *Botaniker–Porträts* no. 34 (1907)].

[258]

characteristics of the flowers of over a thousand genera. His structural analyses of many of the seeds and fruits still stand unsurpassed. Gaertner admired the work of Adanson and Antoine Laurent de Jussieu and had a similar inductive approach to nature. He recognized the endosperm (or perisperm; he obviously did not distinguish between the two), used the word 'embryo' for the young plant with its cotyledons, showed that the indehiscent dry fruits of labiates and other groups were not seeds, defined with precision the pericarp and made a distinction between spores and seeds in recognizing the absence of an embryo in the former. The term 'embryo' had been used before him by Adanson; it contrasted strongly with the previous usage of 'corculum seminis,' with its scholastic overtones.

The theoretical introduction to the *Carpologia* outlines the use of further sets of characters for the development of the natural system, fully in accord with Adanson's tenets of 1763. Gaertner stresses that the characters derived from the fruit and the seed form one set only and that ultimately classification should be based on a great variety of characters derived from all parts of the plant; he therefore can hardly be counted as a Linnaean. But neither was he anti–Linnaean; he simply sought a further expansion of our knowledge. With his characteristic modesty and high excellence of output, Gaertner was one of the most likable systematists at the end of the Linnaean era, heralding the coming of a new phase in biology with men like Robert Brown and A. P. de Candolle, who brought the final victory of empiricism. Unlike Kölreuter, however, Gaertner did not yet bring forward elements for the switch to a biological systematics in which variability and evolution play a major rôle.

The changes set in motion in Germany by men like Kölreuter and Joseph Gaertner were not isolated. Reference has been made repeatedly to the decisive influence of the botanists of the French Enlightenment in the turning of the Linnaean tide. In Germany they stood also at the beginning of other developments in biology, as exemplified by Goethe and his *Versuch die Metamorphose der Pflanzen zu erklären* (1790), by Christian Konrad Sprengel with his revolutionary *Das Entdeckte Geheimnis der Natur* (1793), starting–points for further typological–morphological, but also for further biological thinking. This phase in the development of German botany, however, belongs to another period in botanical history, that of the French revolution and Napoleonic Europe.

It is neither necessary, nor possible, within the scope of this sketch of the Linnaean influence, to give a full picture of German or German-influenced taxonomy. Many personalities have been left out of account or could be mentioned only incidentally. Their works, useful as they were for the increase of taxonomic knowledge, added little to the general picture of the evolution of taxonomic and systematic thinking. The Gmelins, Zinn, Trew, Schmidel, O. F. Mueller and Oeder (in Denmark), Ehrhart and many others all contributed to the growth of systematic botany, either by describing the plants collected during their travels, by giving inventories of their gardens, by providing local or regional floras, or by producing fine folio works with numerous illustrations, sometimes of great taxonomic as well as artistic value. It would also have been interesting to trace the influence of Linnaeus for instance in Denmark, with O. F. Mueller (interesting discoveries in cryptogams, see Lütjeharms 1936) and G. C. Oeder and their *Flora Danica*, or in Russia, where a whole group of botanists—often of German origin—worked, especially at St. Petersburg, and laid the foundations for the knowledge of the flora of the immense Russian empire. To do this, however, would lead me too far astray.

One figure, however, deserves a more than passing mention: Friedrich Kasimir Medikus, one of the most vociferous—and unsuccessful—opponents of the Linnaean reform, and again a man coming from that cradle of central European botany, the middle Rhine region. Medikus, although a contemporary of Joseph Gaertner, typically belongs to this Linnaean epoch because, in his reaction against Linnaeus, he sought support in the past rather than in the future. Although certainly touched in many respects by the French Enlightenment, Medikus' botanical world did not differ greatly from that of Linnaeus; yet the two men held entirely different opinions on taxonomy and methodology. Stearn (1961) has given a review of Medikus' activities and publications and has drawn special attention to his wholesale rejection of the Linnaean generic reform and return to Tournefortian nomenclature and taxonomy.

Friedrich Kasimir Medikus was born on 6 January 1736, at Grumbach, and studied with Johann Georg Gmelin at Tübingen. In 1759 he was appointed physician of the Mannheim garrison. Mannheim was the capital of the Pfalz, the Palatinate which, under the Elector Carl Theodor (1724–1799), was one of the most enlightened and French-oriented German micro-states. In 1766 Medikus spent some time in Paris, meeting the botanical celebrities of the period: Duhamel du Monceau, Bernard de Jussieu and Michel Adanson. Upon his return he was able to found a botanic garden under the sponsorship of the Elector and the then recently (1763) established *Academia Theodoro–Palatina*, and to devote himself entirely to botany.

Medikus was a sharp critic and a good observer but not at all inclined towards synthetic taxonomic thinking. His many publications overflow with critical, often almost spiteful remarks on the Linnaean system, but offer little in exchange. Still, they performed a useful function in showing inconsistencies and mistakes in the Linnaean system. One of the frequently recurring points of criticism is that Linnaeus neglected vegetative characteristics for generic delimitation. Medikus fully shares Tournefort's opinions in this respect and retains the latter's taxonomy as well as nomenclature. Much of Medikus' criticism was also directed against the incompleteness of Linnaeus's generic definitions, a circumstance caused by the latter's practice of basing these definitions on the type species and not amending them when further species were added to the genus.

Medikus published many excellent observations, especially on the Leguminosae, the Cruciferae and the Malvaceae. He published, for instance, *Botanische Beobachtungen* (1783–1784), *Theodora speciosa* (1786), *Ueber einige künstliche Geschlechter aus der Malven–Familie* (1877), *Philosophische Botanik* (1789–1791) and several articles in periodical publications. All these papers contain sharp, occasionally even unfair, criticism of Linnaeus. It sometimes seems as though Medikus' main purpose in publishing were to attack Linnaeus. The attacks did not go unnoticed and were countered, for instance, by the faithful Linnaean pupil Johann Beckman (Schmid 1937). More readable and balanced is the *Apologie* with which the first part of the *Philosophische Botanik* (fig. 60) ends. This *Apologie* and the introduction to the second part of the same book reflect in essence Medikus' taxonomic thoughts.

Medikus explains that after having tried for a long time to find a harmonious relationship between nature and the Linnaean system, he realized that no such harmony could be found and that it was not possible to improve it.

"Als Jüngling kam Linné nach Holland und entwarf sich da, oder vollendete daselbst sein Ideal einer neuen Methode. Es ist unglaublich mit welch hinreissendem Eifer er die herrliche Gelegenheit nutze, die daselbst aufgehäuften Schätze der Natur zu studieren. Gross und brillant war sein Eintritt in die gelehrte Welt, und sein *Hortus cliffortianus* spannte die Erwartung der meisten Botanisten damaliger Zeit ..." Why did Linnaeus not succeed in adapting his ideal to nature? After a few years he had to leave Holland and its botanical riches, to return to a place where he could study only a relatively small number of species of living plants. After 1738 Linnaeus dealt almost exclusively—says Medikus, and this is not altogether incorrect—with dried material. "Denn statt der lebenden Flora konnte er nur noch die todte studieren, und der muss das Kräuterreich nicht kennen, der den hohen Abstand einer lebenden Pflanze von einer durch Trocknung und Aufbewahrung verstümmelten Pflanze nicht fühlen sollte ..." Linnaeus did not realize this essential defect in his contact with the living world of plants. "... er fuhr mit eben dem Eifer fort die Kräuter-Kunde, aber leider auf eine ganz andere Art, und so wie die Astronomen die Gestirne, zu studieren" with the difference that the Astronomers knew that they could not visit their stars, but that Linnaeus, who could have travelled, thought this was superfluous. He sent his pupils to all corners of the earth, but stayed at home himself. Linnaeus had become a 'botaniste de cabinet,' one of those "Stuben-Gelehrten, die eben deswegen weil sie wenig Zeit zum Beobachten brauchen, und eine *ganz sonderbare Anlage zum Glauben haben*, desto mehr Zeit zum Schreiben übrig behalten ..." The decision, however, is not with authority but with nature.

Medikus then continues with a general criticism of Linnaeus's generic delimitation. He attacks especially the—in his opinion—haphazard way in which new species are added to genera without a change in the original generic circumscription. The result is a certain arbitrariness by which species are easily shifted from one genus to the other. "Daher war die ehemahlige Völker-Wanderung nur ein Kinderspiel gegen diese Pflanzen-Wanderung aus einem Genus in das andre; sie wird auch, solange das Linneische System besteht, ohne Ende seyn." Are the Linnaean genera really natural? Many of them are like mules, having 'art' as their father and 'nature' as their mother, showing the lack of reproductive capacity of the hybrid. Chaos before the first day of creation, must have been less than that of the genera in the sexual system. The real trouble is, says Medikus, that these genera are often neither truly artificial (that is in accordance with the tenets of the sexual system) nor natural, and this creates confusion. It will be necessary, for practical purposes, to work with artificial

Fig. 60. Title-page of F. K. Medikus, *Philosophische Botanik* [1789]. Both spellings Medikus and Medicus were used by the author.

Philosophische Botanik,

mit kritischen Bemerkungen.

Erstes Heft.

Von

den mannigfaltigen

Umhüllungen der Saamen.

Von

Friederich Kasimir Medicus,

Pfalz-Zweibrückischen Regierungs-Rathe, Direktor der Chur-
pfälzischen Staatswirthschafts Hohen Schule und der ökono-
mischen Gesellschaft zu Heidelberg, ordentlichem Mitgliede der
Akademie der Wissenschaften, und Vorsteher des Churpf.
botanischen Gartens in Mannheim ꝛc.

Mannheim,

in der neuen Hof- und Akademischen Buchhandlung

1789.

Fig. 60

genera, truly based on a consistent artificial system of characters of the fructification. At the same time one must try to delimit natural families by using all characters of the plants, the vegetative ones included. He makes a plea for further detailed observations, especially of the structure of the flowers and the fruits.

Medikus' criticism is therefore directed against two of Linnaeus's weakest points: his lack of knowledge of living plants, because of his refusal to travel and the inadequacy of the living collections at Uppsala, and the way he later incorporated new species in previously established genera. This criticism is not really fundamental. Essentially Medikus shares Linnaeus's basic opinions, such as the constancy of species, the need to base natural genera on the characters of the flower and fruit, the dubious nature of the natural system, etc. In the introduction to the second part of his *Philosophische Botanik* Medikus argues against those who think that similarities and relationships are the same: "Aehnlichkeiten und Verwandtschaften sind zwei himmelweit verschiedene Sachen." Many botanists tend to use these words as synonyms. The only relationship in the vegetable kingdom is that between the individual specimens which constitute a species. A natural system is therefore "ein Unding" as long as one thinks that similarity reflects relationship. If such a system is based on overall similarity ("Aehnlichkeit") and is called 'natural,' this is all right with Medikus, although to him it is just as artificial as the rest. There is no natural system; this is a chimaera ("ein Hirngespenst"). "In my opinion there is therefore no natural system, but only two major methods, both of which are artificial and both of which serve to facilitate learning. The first is the method by analogy, which rests on all characteristics which can be taken for all parts of the plants; the second is the method based on the fructification. The first one provides us with a general survey, the second one with certainty." Mixing these two methods leads to erroneous conclusions. The statement is remarkable because in its extreme pragmatism it foreshadows the twentieth-century opinions not only of authors like Gilmour and Walters, but also of many numerical taxonomists, who refuse to admit that there is a difference between the classification of animate and inanimate objects.

Medikus is a convinced nominalist: the only reality consists of the individuals linked by reproduction. Variability is ignored; there are no 'relationships,' only similarity and analogy, and each system is a human effort. Nothing is left of Linnaeus's essentialism, and what is substituted for it leads towards a pragmatic system of storage and retrieval of information but not towards the biological approach to the plant world as an ever–changing system with a history, a present and a future. The gradual growth of the realization that biological classification is somewhat more than the classification of inanimate objects went unnoticed by him. It is for this reason that Medikus, that witty writer and moderate observer, typically belongs to the Linnaean era.

Medikus works are like a mirror reflecting the Linnaean world of thought not without distortion perhaps, but in some details mercilessly showing up its *défauts de beauté*. J. Gaertner and Kölreuter moved decisively away from essentialist taxonomic thinking, coming closer to a biological systematics. The real impetus of this movement, however, came from France.

9

France: The birth of systematics

1. Provincial France

The picture of plant taxonomy in France differs in many respects from that in the surrounding countries. The Linnaean nomenclatural and generic reform was, in the end, as successful in France as everywhere else. The Linnaean sexual system, the species and genus concept, and in general the Linnaean essentialist view of nature, however were never fully accepted. On the contrary, in France we witness the birth of an entirely new view of nature and consequently of taxonomy: the biological view as opposed to the uniformitarian and essentialist notions of the past. This development was advanced mainly by biologists from the Paris region. For the spreading of Linnaean taxonomy in France, we have to look in first instance to the Provinces. In later years there developed in Paris, as well as elsewhere, a split between the Linnaean taxonomists and the followers of the natural system; this split, however, did not really become evident until after the Revolution and was, in many respects, determined by social and religious factors as much as by scientific opinions.

The ancient capital of French botany is Montpellier. Ever since the days of Rondelet, Montpellier has been a centre of taxonomic research and thought. Towards the end of the seventeenth century (in 1689) Magnol published his highly original *Prodromus historiae generalis plantarum*, in which he introduced the concept of plant families, with faint evolutionary overtones. Magnol's successor as professor of botany, Nissole, published only very little on botany. The next Montpellier botanist, however, François Boissier de Sauvages (1706–1767), became one of the staunchest supporters of Linnaeus in France.

Sauvages obtained his medical degree in Montpellier in 1726, spent some time afterwards in Paris and Leiden (with Boerhaave) to complete his medical education, and was appointed to one of the medical chairs at Montpellier as early as 1734. Sauvages was a prolific writer on many subjects, although mainly on medicine. His *Nosologia methodica* of 1763 was used by Linnaeus in his later years for his medical course. Sauvages' medical thought is described by his biographer Boisseau (1821) as 'un hippocratisme mystique.' Among his pupils were Commerson, Gouan and Gérard; but relations do not seem to have been very warm. In 1757 Commerson wrote to Gérard (Clos 1888) about the excellent qualities of Bernard de Jussieu as a teacher, adding: "il se plaît autant à faire éclore les jeunes talens que Sauvages à les étouffer. Le contraste est parfait."

Sauvages entertained a close correspondence with Linnaeus, although the men never met. Their mutual acquaintance with Boerhaave was the beginning of their contact; Sauvages states that it was Boerhaave who "voulut bien former entre nous cette liaison qui m'est infiniment précieuse." As a botanist Sauvages had only one claim to fame, his *Methodus foliorum*, published in the Hague in 1751. In 1743 he had published a *Projet d'une methode pour les feuilles des plantes* (not seen by me). The *Methodus* is an enumeration of the plants at and around Montpellier in accordance with an artificial system based on leaf characters. Its subtitle is *Methode pour connoître les plantes par les Feuïlles*. The main text is preceded by a letter to Linnaeus in which Sauvages gives his ideas on classification which, not surprisingly, coincide mainly with those of Linnaeus. His main theme is that classification must be practical and that nomenclature must be stable. Apart from having a method to identify plants on the basis of their flowers (the sexual system in this case), he stresses the need for a system which will enable the practical botanist and physician to know the plants from their leaves. It is evident, says Sauvages, that we cannot classify the plants by their medical virtues or other physiological characteristics, because we know too little of them. We must be guided by external characteristics and then only by the principal ones. If one pays too much attention to colours, fragrancy "etc.," like the illustrious Tournefort, the number of species grows to excess and the differences between insignificant varieties and true species disappear. "Laissons cet amusement aux Fleuristes et aux amateurs de papillons & des coquilles: l'Histoire naturelle a des bornes, si on détermine les espèces par les principes mécaniques, & c'est une obligation qu'on vous a de les avoir fixées."

Of course, in principle the method which "brings together the plants which have the greatest number of affinities" is preferable, but so far none of these natural methods has turned out to be as simple as the artificial ones. "Truly, what is the use of a botanical classification, if it does not facilitate for the beginners the knowledge of generic and specific names."

It is good to have different artificial methods because in some plants there may be no stamens, in others it will be difficult to determine clearly the nature of the calyx, etc. As long as the genera and species remain the same, it is good to have these different systems as so many keys to be used in different circumstances.

Sauvages continues to praise the nomenclatural reform because it has led to uniformity and stability and is fully in agreement with the changes in Tournefortian nomenclature proposed by Linnaeus.

The method by which the plants are known by their leaves is then explained in more detail. There are eleven classes based on position, shape and number, subdivided in 74 orders on the basis of number characters, sometimes also derived from the shape of the corolla, which is considered to belong to the leaves. The 1743 system was still based exclusively on the leaves in sensu stricto (fide Adanson 1763), but in the 1751 system several of the orders are based on characters derived from the corolla, which greatly diminished the value of the system for the identification of plants which are not in flower.

Sauvages' influence was very restricted. No later author ever took up his *Methodus foliorum*, except perhaps to criticise it. Two Montpellier students, however, who studied medicine while Sauvages was in office (they never referred to themselves as his pupils) were of greater importance for botany: Gouan and Gérard.

Antoine Gouan (1733–1821) became the doyen of Linnaean taxonomy in France. He was the first to introduce binary nomenclature in the country and to publish a flora which was almost fully Linnaean. Gérard, on the contrary, remained a 'Tournefortian' and became an advocate of the natural system.

Gouan received his early schooling with the Jesuits at the Collège de Toulouse (Amoreux 1822). He obtained his medical degree at Montpellier under the presidence of Antoine Magnol, son of the great Pierre Magnol. Sauvages brought him in contact by correspondence with Linnaeus. Gouan found in Montpellier little in the way of botanical material. He used Sauvages' copies of the Linnaean works, owned a copy of Tournefort's

LOUIS GÉRARD,

de Colignac, (Var).

1733 - 1819.

d'après le dessin de M^r. Letuaire.   Lith. d'E. Aurel, Toulon.

Fig. 61

Institutiones, found no herbarium to speak of at the University and a botanic garden which was not in the best possible shape. Gouan undertook the compilation of a catalogue of the garden, which Sauvages had arranged in accordance with the sexual system, as his first essay in botany; the resulting *Hortus regius monspeliensis* of 1762 was the first major French botanical publication using binary nomenclature. Sauvages' *Methodus foliorum* had already accepted the Linnaean generic reform; Gouan's catalogue was fully Linnaean in method and nomenclature. Gouan, in 1761, was not in charge of the garden but merely an assistant to one of the medical professors; it was only in 1768 that he succeeded Sauvages. In 1765 Gouan published the first regional flora in the Linnaean style: *Flora monspeliaca*. The only variation upon the Linnaean theme is the arrangement of the higher taxa, which is a mixture of Rivinus' system and the Linnaean sexual system. The main reason for this must have been a practical one: the book has no separate key to the genera and species, but the arrangement itself serves as such. By subdividing his classes on the basis of the corolla (e.g. *monopetali regulares*) in accordance with the Linnaean sexual system, Gouan succeeded in arranging the genera in much smaller groups than was possible with the sexual system alone.

Gouan had many pupils, several of whom attained fame as botanists: Gilibert, Dombey and Broussonet. He was in correspondence with almost all outstanding contemporary botanists; it was through his contacts with Haller that Gilibert was invited to come to Poland. Gouan lived to the age of 88, but his published output diminished gradually after his *Illustrationes et observationes botanicae of 1773*. His Montpellier school of taxonomists, however, produced several of the most important French Linnaeans.

Louis Gérard (1733–1819) (fig. 61), born in the same year as Magnol, was also a Montpellier student; however, his ideas went in an entirely different direction. After his studies Gérard was at first able to explore the Provence and to spend some time at Paris, with Bernard de Jussieu, before settling down as a physician at Toulon. His main botanical publication is the *Flora Gallo–provincialis* of 1761, which he dedicated to de Malesherbes, the enlightened statesman and protector of many of the *philosophes*. Gérard's close contacts with the group at Paris and with his fellow student at

Fig. 61. LOUIS GÉRARD; *b.* Cotignac, Var, France, July 16, 1733; *d.* Cotignac, Var, France, November 16, 1819; French botanist, author of *Flora gallo-provincialis* (1761). [Lithograph by E. Aurel after a drawing by Letuaire; *Conservatoire botanique de Genève*].

Montpellier, Philibert Commerson, as well as his more 'philosophical' inclination, made him take a very independent stand with respect to Sauvages' and Gouan's almost unqualified acceptance of the Linnaean system and reform. In his *Flora* of 1761 Gérard arranges his genera in 63 natural families and follows the generic and specific nomenclature of Linnaeus only in part; his specific names are mostly those of Linnaeus but he does not use trivial names. He was also in contact with Linnaeus by correspondence and was held in high esteem by the Swede, as is evident from the second edition of the *Species plantarum*, in which Gérard is mentioned with Haller, Gmelin, Allioni, Séguier and Scopoli as one of the *auctores reformatoris*.

Many of the original observations and new taxa of the *Flora gallo–provincialis* have not found acceptance in botanical literature simply because Gérard did not accept binary nomenclature. Gérard shares this fate with Haller, whose refined floristic knowledge also failed to obtain recognition only because of this technicality. Even in the eighteenth century it was important to use an efficient system of communication.

The natural system adopted by Gérard is evidently inspired by the Linnaean *Fragmenta* and Bernard de Jussieu's system, which will be discussed below. There are a certain number of families for which Gérard uses the same names as Linnaeus: *Piperitae, Gruinales, Contortae, Columniferae, Tricoccae,* to mention only a few. Others are different: the *Siliquosae* of Linnaeus (*Cruciferae*) are called *Tetrapetalae* by Gérard, the *Preciae* (*Primulaceae*) are *Rotaceae,* etc. An important deviation is the general order. Linnaeus, on purpose, put the cryptogams at the end because he started out from above and worked downwards. Gérard, however, evidently not hindered by non–botanical speculations, starts with the fungi, the algae and the ferns, and lets the monocotyledons follow. His dicotyledons start out with the *Compositae,* divided over three families: *Cichoraceae, Cinarocephalae,* and *Corymbiferae.* The apetelous groups, the *Tricoccae* and the Gymnosperms stand at the end; no special place is reserved for the *Ranunculaceae.* It is a pity that, like Linnaeus, Gérard gives no arguments for his arrangement and does not provide family descriptions. Furthermore, there is no key to the families. It is, therefore, understandable that notwithstanding its many interesting details and original thoughts, Gérard's attempt at a natural system went by unnoticed.

One 'Tournefortian' naturalist from the vicinity of Gouan and Gérard should be briefly mentioned: Jean–François Séguier (1703–1784) of Nîmes, the author of a very valuable *Bibliotheca botanica* (1740), a critical bibliography arranged by subject, and of a treatise on Italian plants, *Plantae veronenses* (1745–1754).

Séguier was a versatile and colourful personality, mainly interested in antiquity—after all: he was born in Nîmes and spent the greater part of his life there. Séguier studied law at Montpellier but picked up some botany as well; he travelled all over Europe with his Italian friend Scipio Maffei, visited Boerhaave, and spent some years with Maffei in Verona.

A Montpellier–trained physician and botanist of some fame was Jean–Emmanuel Gilibert (1741–1814), a pupil of Sauvages and Gouan, a convinced Linnaean, who was invited by Stanislas of Poland to develop botany at his University of Grodno. Gilibert stayed in Poland from 1775 until 1783 and afterwards served in various medical capacities in Lyon. While in Grodno, Gilibert published a *Flora lithuanica inchoata* (1781) which has achieved some notoriety because, even though it was Linnaean in design and method, it did not provide binary nomenclature. In his later years Gilibert, back in Lyon, published an extensive *Systema plantarum Europae*, with binary names, based upon Linnaeus's works. Gilibert published numerous other works, mainly compilations, which are at present of little value. He was a convinced Linnaean who repeated the Linnaean theses over and over again but added little of his own.

Other provincial French taxonomists who deserve brief mention are Pierre Joseph Buchoz (1731–1807) from Nancy, who produced numerous works which were mainly compilations; Noel Joseph de Necker (1730–1793) from Strasbourg, whose *Deliciae gallo–belgicae* of 1768 is fully in the Linnaean tradition, but whose *Elementa botanica* and *Phytozoologie philosophique* (1790) fall outside the scope of this essay; Dominique Villars (1745–1814) who wrote an excellent *Histoire des plantes de Dauphiné* in French (sic); and François–Joseph Lestiboudois, with his *Botanographie belgique* of 1781. Industrious and enthusiastic botanists; but their works, except for those of Necker, were almost exclusively floristic. The latter was a highly original naturalist whose *Traité sur la Mycitologie* (1783) contained many original observations as well as ideas. (See Lütjeharms 1936). The fungi, for instance, were considered a separate group of living beings, not belonging to either the animal or the plant kingdom but to the *regnum mesymale*, an idea again brought forward by recent authors such as Grant and Whittaker.

[273]

2. Botany in Paris in the eighteenth century

Botanical research in Paris during the eighteenth century was carried out mainly at the *Jardin du Roi* and, in later years, to some extent at the Trianon garden.

The full name of the *Jardin du Roi* was *Jardin royale des herbes médicinales*. Its early history (it was founded in 1635 as an establishment to promote pharmaceutical botany) is a chapter apart especially when we look at the directorship of Tournefort, who taught botany at the garden from 1683 until his sudden death in 1708. Tournefort was succeeded by Danty d'Isnard, who resigned in 1710. The director of the garden, Gui–Crescent Fagon (1638–1718), then appointed the 24–year–old Antoine de Jussieu to fill the place of the illustrious Tournefort.

Antoine de Jussieu was the first member of a family which would dominate plant taxonomy at Paris for nearly a century and a half. It is possible to speak of a Jussieu dynasty of botanists consisting of three brothers, Antoine, Bernard and Joseph, in the first part of the century; one of their nephews, Antoine–Laurent, mainly active during the revolution and its aftermath; and the latter's son Adrien, in the period of nineteenth–century restoration. All five Jussieus played an important rôle in botany, although the rôle of one, Antoine–Laurent, was undoubtedly much more extensive than that of the others. His achievements, however, cannot be dissociated from those of the others, especially his uncles, who prepared the ground for his career.

The family of the Lyonnais merchant Laurent de Jussieu (1651–1718) numbered sixteen children. Antoine, born 8 July 1686, was the first to show botanical interest, stimulated by the Lyon amateur botanist Jean–Baptiste Goiffon (1658–1730). Antoine studied medicine and botany at Montpellier under Pierre Magnol and obtained a degree in 1708. He wanted to continue his studies in Paris with Tournefort, but arrived there only a few weeks before the latter's death.

The professorship to which the young Antoine was called was not a fulltime job. The income was relatively low, and he was expected to earn his living with a medical practice. Antoine remained a practising physician during his whole life, but he found the time and energy to manage and develop the garden and to teach botany. He published some small memoirs and a new edition of Tournefort's *Institutiones* (1718) and trained some botanists, among them his two brothers Bernard and Joseph. Among the smaller publications of Antoine is one on the need to set fungi and lichens apart in a separate class, *Plantae fungosae* (1728).

Bernard de Jussieu (1699–1777) (fig. 62) the great teacher without whom Antoine-Laurent's work is unthinkable, made the journey from Lyon to Paris in 1714 at the invitation of Antoine. He finished his elementary studies in Paris and accompanied Antoine on travels through Spain and France. After this botanical initiation he followed his brother's example and took a degree in medicine at Montpellier, then a second one in Paris after his return in 1720. He was appointed *sous-démonstrateur de l'extérieur des plantes* on 30 September 1722, filling the vacancy created by the death of Sébastien Vaillant (1669–1722). In this position Bernard was charged with the teaching of field courses and the botanical supervision of gardens and glasshouses. As a teacher Bernard soon proved to be truly inspired, and nearly all subsequent mid- and late-century Paris botanists, such as Adanson, Guettard, Poivre, Duhamel, Lemonnier, Thouin, Claude and Antoine Richard, Bernard's brother Joseph de Jussieu, and his nephew Antoine-Laurent, can be said to have been his pupils. Many others attended his courses: Buffon and Malesherbes, and visitors such as Linnaeus, in 1738. All reports on Bernard mention his profound botanical knowledge and his great personal charm as a teacher. Linnaeus and Bernard de Jussieu kept up a lively correspondence, especially between 1736 and 1751 (published by Adr. de Jussieu, 1855). This correspondence, however, rarely touches upon the divergence of ideas between the two men: both write about new publications, new collections and new taxa.

Though he published little, his influence on French botany in the eighteenth century was unequalled. He wrote on *Pilularia*, *Lemna* (which he called *Lemma*) and *Littorella*, but never really sat down to put his teachings on paper. Through his Trianon system of 1759, however, we know Bernard as one of the great protagonists of the natural system. Louis XV was interested in horticulture and forestry and wanted a living collection of cultivated plants for his Trianon garden. Upon the recommendation of one of his amateur pupils, Louis de Noailles, Duc d'Ayen, who had an arboretum at Saint-Germain, Bernard de Jussieu was charged with the arrangement of the new Trianon garden. Another of de Noailles' protégés also appointed to the Trianon garden was the gardener Claude Richard (1705–1784). The latter's son Antoine (1735–1807) was sent out to collect plants for the garden

[275]

Fig. 62. BERNARD DE JUSSIEU; *b.* Lyon, France, August 17, 1699; *d.* Paris, France, November 6, 1776; French botanist at the *Jardin du Roi*. [Engraving of unknown origin; *Conservatoire botanique de Genève*].

in the Mediterranean area (1760–1764). Bernard wanted to have part of the garden as an *école de botanique*, illustrating a taxonomic system. This Trianon system, which was to play such a great rôle in the training of Antoine–Laurent and which is the basis of his *Genera plantarum* (1789), was dictated by Bernard in April 1759 to Claude Richard, to Michel Adanson, then his closest botanical associate, and to M. de Bombarde, a wealthy amateur botanist. The system consisted of an enumeration of genera arranged in un–named families (*ordines naturales*); it remained unpublished until 1789, when Antoine–Laurent inserted it in his book. The family names which appear in this version were added at a later date. The system was not accompanied by descriptions of the families, nor by any explanatory notes. Although different in some respects, it was in general not unlike the *Methodi naturalis fragmenta* published by Linnaeus in his *Classes plantarum*, in the *Philosophia botanica* and in various editions of the *Genera plantarum*. Here, too, we find a fragmentary and unexplained system which, on further analysis, proves to contain a great many groups that have stood the test of time. Practically nothing is known of the principles that guided Bernard in setting up this arrangement. The assumption made by later commentators that Bernard practised consciously the principle of the subordination of characters cannot be substantiated for want of relevant documents.

One of the earliest documents informing us on the genesis of Bernard de Jussieu's natural system is the thesis of Noël–Sebastien Blot (1747), described by Gidon (1934). From this thesis it becomes clear that Bernard's ideas were well crystallized by 1747 and that, at any rate in some cases, he actually used family names such as 'labiées.' One of Bernard's main guiding lines was the insertion of the various parts of the flower. However, characters derived from the vegetative parts were considered at the same level as those from the flower, and the Rubiaceae for instance are duly defined in Blot's thesis by, among other characteristics, their stipules. Actually the subject of the 1747 thesis was the analogy of medical properties existing between plants belonging to the same family, a characteristic feature of a system with a high predictive value.

The considerable library built up by Antoine and Bernard was placed at the disposal of other botanists, especially Michel Adanson, who used it extensively in the years 1759–1764, when he was writing his *Familles des plantes* at the house of the Jussieus. Adanson even lived in Bernard's house during those years, but had to leave this hospitable private botanical museum in 1764 on the arrival of one of Bernard's nephews. Another nephew, Antoine-Laurent, took up his abode in the house on the rue des Bernardins only a few months later, in 1765.

This change of members in the Jussieu household was symbolic: Adanson's star went down after 1764, that of Antoine-Laurent rapidly rose. Adanson had worked out his natural system during the years of his closest association with Bernard, although he always retained his independent judgment, and, above all, developed his original ideas in a truly philosophical way—philosophical, of course, in the eighteenth-century meaning of the word. Adanson tried in vain to persuade Bernard de Jussieu and Claude Richard to adopt his 'natural method' for the arrangement of the Trianon garden. The arrival of Antoine-Laurent ended the close relationship between Adanson and Bernard, although the two men continued to see each other at the sessions of the *Académie des sciences* and at the *Jardin du Roi*.

The Trianon botanic garden at Versailles never attained the same fame and importance as the Paris garden. The Trianon garden was virtually closed to the public: only a restricted number of *courtiers* had access to it —the *droit de regard*—and the place was not used for teaching. We know little of the actual state of the garden in the short period during which it was under the supervision of Bernard. Louis XVI, and especially his wife Marie-Antoinette, had other ideas, and in 1775 they ordered a horticultural rearrangement of the garden *à l'anglaise*. This rearrangement has often been critized, perhaps unfairly: Marie-Antoinette was not a scientist, but she loved flowers. We know this through her association with Redouté, and it is understandable that she preferred an arrangement for beauty to one illustrating rather obscure scientific opinions. From a horticultural point of view her Trianon garden seems to have been in excellent shape. It is doubtful whether the systematic arrangement of (part of) that garden ever really served a purpose; towards the end of Bernard's life it had probably become more of a curiosity. Still, Bernard's cedars can still be seen at the Trianon, undoubtedly offspring of the tree at the *Jardin du Roi* which had been brought to France by Bernard himself in 1727. Even today these historical trees in the Paris and the Versailles gardens are impressive monuments to the memory of the great botanist and teacher.

The third and youngest of the botanical triplets, Joseph de Jussieu (1704-1779), followed the footsteps of his brothers by entering medical training, this time at Reims and Paris. His destiny, however, lay elsewhere: he was invited to join—as a naturalist— the great French equatorial expedition of La Condamine, Godin, and Bouguer. This *Mission des académiciens du Pérou* (1735–1743), organized by the philosopher–statesman Jean–Frédéric Phély-peaux, Comte de Maurepas (1701–1781), a friend of the naval expert and bot-anist–horticulturist Duhamel du Monceau, was undertaken primarily to make astronomical observations at the equator. Maurepas, however, chose Joseph to accompany the expedition not only as a physician but also as a naturalist, with the specific task of collecting and sending home the im-portant natural products of the countries concerned. Joseph's adventurous life in South America is relevant to the history of taxonomy only because of the living and dried plant material collected by him and sent to Paris. His nephew recognized six new genera in these collections (e.g. *Cantua*). It is well known that Joseph played an important rôle in the early studies of *Cinchona* and that among the living specimens sent home were, for in-stance, plants of *Erythroxylon coca*. He returned to Paris only in 1771, his physical and mental condition having suffered greatly from the hardships of his South American years.

Bernard de Jussieu's nephew, Antoine-Laurent, born on 12 April 1748, the son of an elder brother of Antoine, Bernard and Joseph, arrived from Lyon in Paris in 1765 to finish his medical and botanical studies. Antoine–Laurent was undoubtedly the greatest and the most successful of the Jussieus.

Antoine de Jussieu died on 22 April 1758 and was succeeded by Louis–Guil-laume Lemonnier (1717–1799), a state physician, and later first court physi-cian to Louis XV.

Lemonnier was not a botanist by profession but just an enlightened amateur. The appointment—by Buffon—must have come as a surprise to Bernard de Jussieu, who had filled the post of sous–démonstrateur since 1745. Another good candidate would have been Michel Adanson (1727–1806), then just back from a stay of some years in Senegal. The reason why these two eminent botanists were bypassed by the king and his intendant Buffon was that the appointment was made mainly at the recommendation of Louis de Noailles, Duc d'Ayen, the amateur horticulturist and forester whose arboretum at Saint–Germain had inspired Louis XV to set up his Trianon Garden. De Noailles had known Lemonnier at Saint–Germain as a physician. The latter was with the French army on the Rhine in 1758 (the Seven Year's War was on) when the appointment was made. Upon his return to Paris Lemonnier offered the post to Bernard de Jussieu. The latter declined, much to the disadvantage of Michel Adanson, who would otherwise have been his logical successor as sous–démonstrateur. In this way Adanson, who would prove to be one of the most original botanical thinkers of the century, was in fact denied a career at the Jardin du Roi, a career which would have given scope to his work and facilitated the spreading of his ideas.

Lemonnier, brother of the famous astronomer Pierre Charles Lemonnier, became one of the most influential scientists in France mainly because of his combination of membership in the *Académie* (1758), his professorship at the *Jardin du Roi* and his court position. Even though he published little on botany himself, he did much to promote that science, and especially exploration. Lemonnier was also interested in physics; he studied the velocity of electricity and the electrical nature of thunderstorms. His medical duties did not leave him much time for his own research or even for teaching botany, but he found young botanists to replace him and to be sent on botanical missions abroad. He appointed Antoine–Laurent de Jussieu to teach for him at the Garden after 1770, when he was appointed *premier médecin ordinaire du roi* and had to reside permanently at Versailles. Lemonnier had a hand also in promoting the journeys of Michaux to the Levant, Aublet to French Guiana, Desfontaines to North Africa, and Labillardière to Syria and the Lebanon.

Through these expeditions Lemonnier was instrumental in enriching in no mean way the collections of living plants of the *Jardin du Roi*, the Trianon gardens and those of his friends in Montreuil. He also had a private herbarium (now in Genève) for which he received material from most of the expeditions in the organization of which he had been involved.

Among the amateur botanists connected with the Versailles court who had free access to the Trianon gardens was Antoine Duchesne, the provost of the King's buildings, an ardent amateur botanist, who, with his son Antoine–Nicolas (1747–1827), discovered in 1763 what appears to be one of the first spontaneous mutations observed in plants: a strawberry with simple leaves.

Another amateur botanist connected with the Versailles court was Chrétien-Guillaume de Lamoignon de Malesherbes (1721–1794), the state secretary of the royal house, director of the publishing trade, and president of the *Cour des Aides*, a fiscal court. De Malesherbes, one of the most famous and liberal French statesmen of the second half of the century, was an advanced aristocrat wholly taken by the ideas of the Enlightenment, and it was thanks to him that the *Encyclopédie* of Diderot and d'Alembert could be published in Paris without too much interference from the government.

De Malesherbes and Bernard de Jussieu were well acquainted with Jean-Jacques Rousseau (1712–1778), also an amateur botanist, whose *Essais élémentaires sur la botanique* (1771) were widely read and who attributed an important rôle to botany in his proposed educational reforms. Rousseau was a firm believer in the Linnaean artificial system, for didactic purposes. His *Essais* contain a popular account of Linnaean botany.

Other botanists at the court were Claret de la Tourrette (1729–1793), Henri–Louis Duhamel du Monceau (1700–1782), the Abbé Nollin, and the little-known M. de Bombarde (x–1766). The latter was one of the three people (Claude Richard, de Bombarde, and Adanson) who took down from dictation in 1759 the natural classification developed by Bernard de Jussieu for the Trianon garden. De Bombarde had a botanical library, as well as a botanic garden. The Abbé Nollin was the director of the king's nurseries. De la Tourette, a councillor at one of the fiscal courts, was for some time a botanical "courtier," but he spent the greater part of his life at Lyon. He was one of the recipients of Rousseau's letters on botany. Duhamel had been bypassed in 1739 for the appointment of director of the *Jardin du Roi*, a post given to Buffon. He was a remarkable man, an agronomist and meteorologist, holding the sinecure post of inspector of the navy, but mainly working on horticulture and forestry. His *Traité des arbres et arbustes* of 1755 was for many decades the standard work on French forestry.

This *Traité* illustrates strikingly the state of Paris botany around the turn of the century. The book is obviously written first of all for practical use, but the classification and nomenclature are of interest. The trees are treated in alphabetical order for practical purposes, but there is a chapter giving a general classification. The book was illustrated with the original woodcuts of the Valgrise edition of Matthioli, the blocks of which were in Duhamel's collection. The nomenclature is basically Tournefortian. This is not surprising: Tournefortian nomenclature was used at the *Jardin du Roi* until 1774, when Antoine-Laurent de Jussieu finally introduced the Linnaean names. Bernard de Jussieu, however well acquainted with Linnaeus, accepted neither the latter's nomenclature nor his generic reform. Duhamel admits that from a botanical point of view the Linnaean generic reform may

[281]

have its positive sides; accepted usage, however, has to prevail. He uses no binary names: his specific phrases are taken from the most common literature and are by no means fully diagnostic.

Duhamel's general system, which was not taken up by any later botanist to my knowledge, was a combination of the Tournefortian system and the sexual system. His three main classes are 1) trees with unisexual flowers, 2) monopetalous hermaphroditic trees, 3) polypetalous hermaphroditic trees. The subdivision is by the number of stamens. Since this system is perhaps not always satisfactory for use as a key to the genera, Duhamel added two artificial systems, one based on fruits and seeds, another based on the leaves. These artificial systems are nothing but simple keys.

Linnaean taxonomy made very slow headway among the Paris botanists. The most outstanding and active botanists of the seventeen fifties and sixties were Bernard de Jussieu, Duhamel and Michel Adanson, all convinced Tournefortians in nomenclature and, at least Jussieu and Adanson, strong proponents of a natural system. The Linnaean movement started in Paris considerably later than in the provinces, that is, after 1770.

One of the earliest purely 'Linnaean' authors residing in Paris was the picturesque Fusée Aublet (1720–1778) (fig. 63), a botanist and explorer who had studied botany, pharmacy, and chemistry at Montpellier and Paris. Through his association with Bernard de Jussieu he came into contact with the group of enlightened magistrates, courtiers and authors which included Malesherbes, Rousseau, d'Holbach, Bombarde, le duc d'Ayen and several others. D'Holbach opened "his purse and his library" to him. Bombarde received much of his material later sent home from the colonies and of Bernard de Jussieu he writes: [he] "je ne crains point de l'avouer ... étoit ma bibliothèque, & presque la seule." Aublet's vocation, however, was more adventurous: in December 1752 he left Paris on a mission to Ile-de-France (Mauritius) to establish a central pharmacy and a botanic garden. Upon his return early in 1762 he was offered a similar opportunity to go to the island of Cayenne, French Guiana, where he stayed from 1762 to 1764 as *apothécaire–botaniste*. During these years Aublet botanized assiduously on the French Guiana mainland. He assembled a sizeable herbarium which he brought home to Paris in 1765, after a brief stay at St. Nicolas (Haiti). Again in association with Bernard de Jussieu, Aublet spent the following years working on his material and writing his *Histoire des plantes de la Guiane françoise* (1775; fig. 63 & 64) (see also Lanjouw and Uittien 1940). The preface to this book contains a detailed autobiography, which is alas one of the very few sources of knowledge about Aublet.

There are signs that Aublet's activities in Guiana were very limited because of his steadily deteriorating physical condition. He himself says "Tous les momens que me laissoient mes devoirs étoient consacrés à la recherche des plantes, & à les décrire avec tout le soin possible sur le lieu même…" It is possible (as was not unusual at the time) that part of his Guyana material was collected by native collectors. Life in the tropics took a heavy toll of Aublet's physique. This was perhaps also due to side-effects of his progenitive activities: during his last years in Paris he alienated the more sophisticated part of botanical society by claiming to have left three hundred descendants in the French colonies. Something of these circumstances transpires through the words in the preface in which Aublet describes the hardships of the life of a plant collector in the tropics. They should undertake this only "après s'être assuré qu'ils ont une forte constitution, une santé parfaite, aucun vice héréditaire ou acquis [sic], une fermeté d'ame, une ardeur & une résolution à toute épreuve, de la gaieté dans l'esprit, de l'adresse, des sens exquis…"

Aublet's further words on the conditions under which a naturalist worked in the French possessions are almost exactly identical to those of Adanson with respect to his Senegalese years: the scorn of the other settlers, the absence of chances of financial reward, the hard–boiled mercenary attitude of his 'colleagues.' In addition to that there are the hardships of trying to botanize in the tropical jungle with its—at that time—almost unknown hazards.

On his return to Paris in 1765 Aublet tried to retrieve the material sent home by him since 1752. The result was disappointing; most material had disappeared, mainly because de Bombarde had died and his collections had been dispersed. The plants from Guiana were almost the only material left to work with.

The *Histoire* of 1775 is written, characteristically, in French and in Latin "in order to make the work more generally useful and to make its use

Fig. 63. Frontispiece of Fusée Aublet, *Histoire des plantes de la Guiane françoise* [1775]. The author's portrait appears on the oval inset. *Reduced.*

Fig. 64. Title–page of Fusée Aublet, *Histoire des plantes de la Guiane françoise* [1775], 'arranged according to the sexual system.' *Reduced.*

[283]

1. *Palmier maripa*.
2. *Regime de maripa, et Fruit détaché*.
3. *Palmier comon*.

4. *Grappe du regime de comon*
5. *Grappe du regime d'avoira*.
6. *Fruit du Palmier bache détaché*.

7. *Regime du Palmier zaguénete*.
8. *Cierge triangulaire*.
9. *Cierge octogone*.

Fig. 63

O

HISTOIRE
DES PLANTES
DE
LA GUIANE FRANÇOISE,

RANGÉES SUIVANT LA MÉTHODE SEXUELLE,

AVEC PLUSIEURS MÉMOIRES

Sur différens objets intéressans, relatifs à la Culture & au Commerce de la Guiane Françoise, & une Notice des Plantes de l'Isle-de-France.

OUVRAGE ORNÉ DE PRÈS DE QUATRE CENTS PLANCHES EN TAILLE-DOUCE,

Où sont représentées des Plantes qui n'ont point encore été décrites ni gravées, ou qui ne l'ont été qu'imparfaitement.

PAR M. FUSÉE AUBLET.

TOME PREMIER.

À LONDRES, & se trouve À PARIS,

Chez PIERRE-FRANÇOIS DIDOT jeune, Libraire de la Faculté de Médecine, Quai des Augustins.

M. DCC. LXXV.

(1775).

Fig. 64

easier for all European nations of which the scientists and even the *curiosi* know at any rate one of these two languages."

Aublet handsomely acknowledges Bernard de Jussieu's help in writing the book: he had verified the descriptions, drawings and engravings and checked the synonymy, "enfin il a bien voulu conduire la plume de l'Auteur, pour rendre les détails des plantes dans les termes de l'art, consacrés par les botanistes modernes."

For these reasons it is remarkable that Aublet's book is fully Linnaean both with respect to taxonomy (the sexual system and the generic delimitation) and to nomenclature. It contains the description of not less than 400 new species as well as of new genera, among which are several of wide distribution, such as *Vochysia*, *Ocotea* and *Pouteria*. It still is the basis for the study of the flora of the Guiana region. Aublet—not quite in the Linnaean tradition—accepted several vernacular names, for instance *Vochy* (now *Vochysia*), as scientific generic names. Later authors, more faithfully Linnaean and Latinist, such as J. C. D. Schreber and G. A. Scopoli, thought it their duty, or prerogative, to replace these 'barbarous' names with more conservatively coined ones in due Latin form; as a result an undue and unnecessary amount of synonymy arose out of Aublet's book. A further result was that there are now not less than 27 references to Aublet in the list of *nomina generica conservanda*.

Aublet's names often have priority over those in general use coined by less unorthodox Linnaeans (e.g. *Vouapa* Aublet would be the correct name for *Macrolobium* Schreber if the latter had not been conserved).

Another Linnaean at Paris was Charles-Louis L'Héritier de Brutelle (1746–1800). I have described his life and work elsewhere in some detail (1963a) and limit myself here to a brief outline.

L'Héritier was a Paris magistrate, also of the circle of Malesherbes and Rousseau, whose social principles made him an advocate of far-reaching reforms and thus one of those who paved the way for the French revolution. As a botanist L'Héritier was a self-made man, an ardent amateur and a fervent Linnaean. As a scientist he made his way to the highest ranks of the *Académie des Sciences*, and became one of the staunchest supporters of the Linnaean school in France.

L'Héritier was a judge at the *Cour des Aides*, one of France's oldest law courts, acting as the supreme fiscal Court of France. This court, headed by Malesherbes waged a veritable war against high government officials with unscrupulous tax–collecting practices. L'Héritier served on this court from 1775 until the early days of the revolution.

As a botanist L'Héritier was not at all philosophically inclined: his preference for the Linnaean method was based on its great practicality. His greatest interest lay in describing new plants from faraway regions, caught as he was by the fascination of discovering and describing the immense diversity of phanerogams: "publier les plantes nouvelles, non figurées ou mal connues, voilà quel est mon but."

The collections arriving in Paris from the great French expeditions such as that of Bougainville and Commerson fascinated L'Héritier, *magistrate and botanist*. He was keen on locating new plants, either as herbarium specimens or grown from seed or cuttings in the arious gardens. The fact that the Commerson collection had been entrusted to Jussieu, who took a very long time before publishing on it, annoyed L'Héritier, and by a variety of means, orthodox and less orthodox, he tried to get hold of new plants. He described them at first in his great broadsheet work *Stirpes novae aut minus cognitae*, Paris 1784–1785 [1785–1805]. L'Héritier had obtained the services of a Belgian artist living in Paris, Pierre–Joseph Redouté, for the illustrations. It was l'Héritier who actually discovered the latter's interest in plant illustration and who gave him the thorough botanical–analytical training which, together with his artistry, was the basis of Redouté's later phenomenal success as one of the greatest flower painters of all ages.

L'Héritier was obviously attracted to Sir Joseph Banks and his collections at Soho Square. He was introduced to Banks by P. M. A. Broussonet (1761–1807) and started writing to him in 1783. From this correspondence and from other sources it becomes clear that relations between the Paris botanists were strained and that they jealously guarded their secrets until publication. When L'Héritier, through a decision by Buffon, was charged with the elaboration of the plants collected by Joseph Dombey in South America, he feared that his work might not remain undisturbed. He moved overnight to London with the Dombey plants in order to write them up in the relaxed atmosphere of British botany, with the best possible collections (Linnaeus and Banks) and libraries freely available for consultation. For details of this involved and romantic affair I must refer to my above–mentioned publication (1963a), and especially to Steele's *Flowers for the King* (1964). L'Héritier's stay in Paris resulted in the publication of his *Sertum anglicum* (1788; i.e. 1789–1792), a gesture of gratitude toward English botany and botanists: "The celebrity of her gardens brought me to England, and especially that herbarium of Linnaeus, famous for its excellence and erected to the immortal fame of that outstanding man as well as for the continued study of botany."

"I dedicate and offer in a special way this list of her plants to the English nation. For praise ought to redound to its source ..."

Jean Baptiste François Bulliard (1752–1793), called Pierre Bulliard, was another picturesque outsider whose works represented the Linnaean tradition in Paris. Bulliard was a descriptive naturalist, little given to theoretical or methodological meditations, but an industrious and skilled draftsman and floristic botanist. His main vocation was hunting and shooting

Fig. 65. ANTONIO JOSÉ CAVANILLES; *b.* Valencia, Spain, January 16, 1745; *d.* Madrid, Spain, May 10, 1804; Spanish botanist at Madrid; director of the Madrid botanical garden 1801–1804. [Photographic reproduction of a silhouette owned by the Cavanilles family, published by E. Reyes Prosper, *Dos noticias historicas del immortal botánico y sacerdote hispano-valentino D. Antonio José Cavanilles,* Madrid 1917 [copy at *Conservatoire botanique de Genève*]. *Reduced.*

and his first, now famous, printed work was the *Aviceptologie françoise,* a general treatise "of all the tricks that can be used to catch the birds of France."

The six volume *Flora parisiensis* (1776–1783), now a rarity, had descriptions and plates (by Bulliard himself) of 640 taxa, "rangés suivant la méthode de M. Linné," but actually in alphabetical order: "mais l'ordre Alphabétique comme le plus commode et le plus à portée de tout le Monde constitue l'arrangement de chaque Cahier" (frontispiece). The Linnaean system was outlined in a separate introduction.

During the publication of this major semi-popular work Bulliard must have started thinking about an elaboration of it on a national scale: From 1780 until his death he published, in fascicles, his enormous *Herbier de la France* (13 volumes) containing 602 plates, with—especially in the beginning —extensive descriptive engraved captions, the figures themselves often colour–printed. The book, which is a bibliographer's nightmare (see Gilbert 1952), treated essentially three series of plants; the *plantes vénéneuses*, the *plantes médicinales* and the *champignons de la France*. The last series in particular was noteworthy because of its many excellent pictures and descriptions of fungi. Bulliard's empiricist outlook is perhaps best expressed by the quotation from one of his works with which Gilbert (1952) opens the biography and bibliography of this great hunter and naturalist: "Du simple, du laconique et du vrai, c'est ainsi que je m'explique." Bulliard's death, like that of L'Héritier, is surrounded with mystery. Even Gilbert has not succeeded in establishing with certainty whether Bulliard met his death while botanizing, by a stray bullet from a hunter (the traditional family view), or simply in Paris by illness. The traditional view has its charm: he who had discovered how to "mislead and surprise" the birds, died in harness.

During the last years before the revolution a Spanish clergyman, Antonio José Cavanilles (1745-1804) (fig. 65 & 66), was actively engaged in botanical studies in Paris, Cavanilles' approach to botany was very much like that of L'Héritier: he was primarily interested in describing new taxa, and for this the Linnaean methods provided him with the best frame–work. While in Paris he published the first eight of his ten *Monadelphia classis dissertationes*. Cavanilles' main botanical activity, however, was still to come. He returned to Madrid in 1789 and there he published his main work, the *Icones et descriptiones plantarum* (1791–1801). Spanish systematic botany received a tremendous impetus from the exploration of the South American continent by travellers such as Ruiz and Pavon; but this impetus, with the accompanying development of more sophisticated systematic botanical work, made itself felt only after 1789.

It will be clear from the above that the true Linnaeans in the Paris region were small in numbers and mainly outsiders. The botanical establishment (also divided internally) was non-Linnaean before 1789, even though most

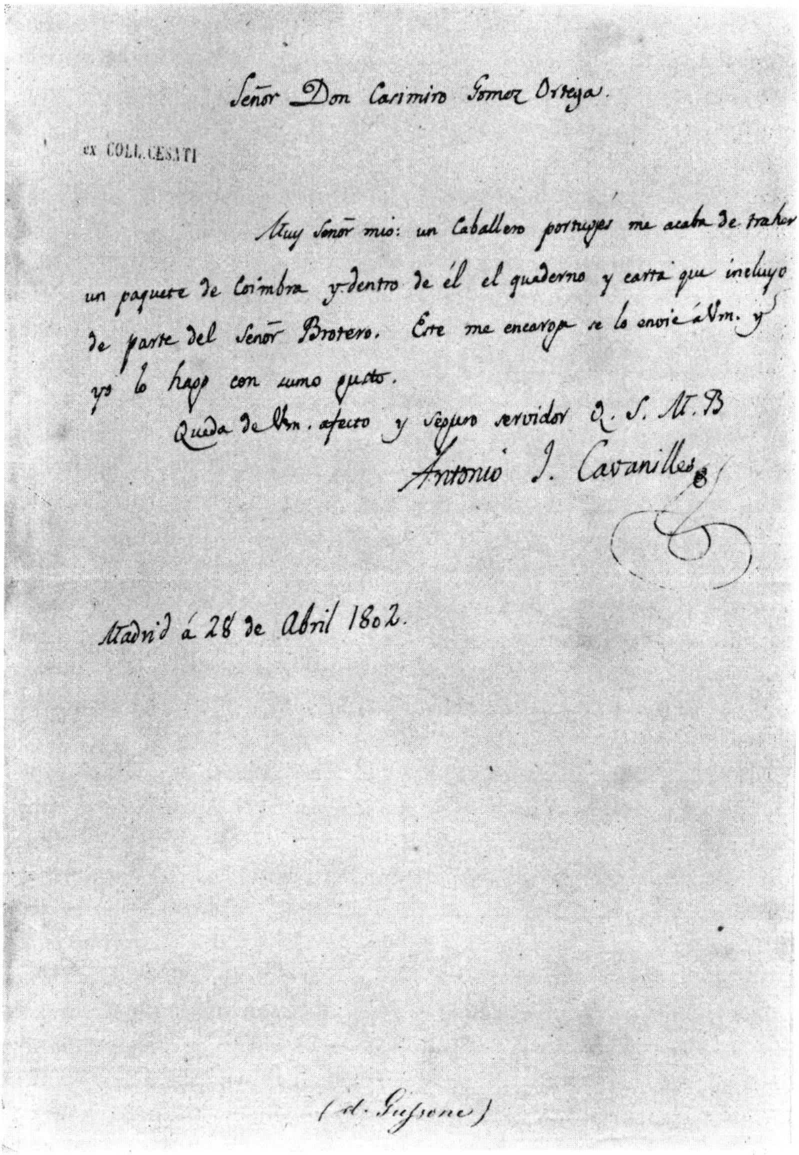

Señor Don Casimiro Gomez Ortega.

Muy Señor mio: un Caballero portugues me acaba de traher un paquete de Coimbra y dentro de él el quaderno y carta que incluyo de parte del Señor Brotero. Este me encarga se lo envie á Vm. y yo lo hago con sumo gusto.

Queda de Vm. afecto y seguro servidor Q. S. M. B

Antonio J. Cavanilles

Madrid á 28 de Abril 1802.

(d. Gussone)

Fig. 66. Letter written by A. J. Cavanilles to C. Gomez Ortega on 28 April 1802 [*Conservatoire botanique de Genève*]. *Reduced.*

of its members accepted Linnaean nomenclature. An interesting swing in the public appreciation of Linnaeus took place after the revolution when, on 23 August 1790, a bust of Linnaeus was erected in the Jardin des Plantes under the great cedar tree planted by Bernard de Jussieu*. On 9 August 1790 L'Héritier wrote to J. E. Smith that all 'orthodox naturalists' would celebrate the occasion of Linnaeus's birth. The date of birth was perhaps not exact, but these happenings show that with the Revolution the teachings of Linnaeus had somehow gained in prestige among at least among some of the Paris botanists.

However, so far we have dealt with only a few of the French botanists. A number of others, among whom Adanson, Jussieu and Lamarck are the most conspicuous, approached systematic botany differently, firmly objecting to the still–growing tendency to accept the Linnaean sexual system. Their entire attitude towards systematics and towards nature was different, and it was this attitude that led to the establishment of biology as a modern discipline. For this development we turn first to the birth of biology through the Enlightenment.

3. The biology of the Enlightenment: Buffon

THE BIRTH OF BIOLOGY

Towards the middle of the eighteenth century we see the victory of the ingenious and simple method of classification of plants developed by Linnaeus. However, classification is not yet systematics; a key is not a mo-

---

* The initiative came from the *Société d'Histoire naturelle de Paris*, among whose members were most of the above–mentioned botanists but not Jussieu and Adanson. The first and only volume of the *Actes de la Société d'Histoire naturelle de Paris* (1792) contains a folio-size engraving showing the bust of Linnaeus under the cedar tree. The accompanying text describes the proceedings in some detail. "Le 23 d'Auguste 1790, la seconde année de la liberté française, à sept heures du soir, l'association des Naturalistes, dont le but est d'honorer la mémoire des Grands Hommes qui ont avancé les progrès d'Histoire Naturelle, en plaçant leur buste dans le Jardin des Plantes, a inauguré solennellement le buste de Charles Linnaeus, Suédois, après avoir arrêté que ce buste en plâtre seroit remplacé le plutôt possible par un buste en bronze, afin que cette image de Linnaeus fût impérissable comme sa mémoire et ses ouvrages, et consacrât éternellement les sentimens d'admiration de ceux qui le lui ont élevé."

nograph. What about the multiple affinities, what about the major task of systematics to present a picture of the structure and possible origin of the diversity of the animal and vegetable world? Practical need had temporarily drowned the voices of those who were more philosophical, who were happy to know the names but who expected more of systematics than pure diagnostic classification, who wanted to describe rather than to define. The second half of the century witnessed a strong reaction in this respect, mainly in France. The basis of this reaction was the gradually growing conviction that ultimately a system based on overall affinity would give a better picture of the structure of the world of plants. We have seen again and again, with Linnaeus, his followers and his adversaries, a groping toward a natural system. As long as the pragmatic need for a key was felt more heavily than the need for a better overall picture, the natural system had no chance. A fully unbiased approach to nature, free from essentialist aprioris, was the first need for the next step on the long road from classification to systematics. It was not by chance that this step was set in the country leading Europe in one of the greatest spiritual and social movements of western civilization.

The birth of modern biology, the life sciences with their own methods and criteria, took place in France during the eighteenth and early nineteenth century. This process was one of the many benificial results of the Enlightenment, the great movement by which the human mind, and especially the sciences, were liberated from the tutelage of tradition, revelation and theological speculation. The importance of this movement in paving the way for modern society is well known. Progress, reason, tolerance and liberty were to replace stability, revelation, authority and asceticism. Such changes also required a new concept of nature, free from the extraneous elements which had influenced philosophy, religion and science for so many centuries. The mechanistic view of nature which was so characteristic of the sixteenth and seventeenth centuries was replaced by a concept of nature which recognized the specific identity of biology. The laws of life were no longer regarded as simply those of mathematics. A living organism was no longer seen as an animated machine (with supra-natural animation), but as an entity in time and space, characterized by processes such as growth and development, having a history as well as a mechanism.

It is significant that the word 'biology' is a product of the early nineteenth century. It was used for the first time almost simultaneously by the German Treviranus and the Frenchman Lamarck in the first years of the new era. Lamarck used the word 'biologie' for the first time in print in December 1801, in the preface to his *Hydrogéologie*. In this remarkable work, which I have discussed in some detail elsewhere (1971a), Lamarck states in the preface:

"Une bonne *Physique terrestre* doit comprendre toutes les considérations du premier ordre, relatives à l'atmosphère terrestre; ensuite toutes celles du même genre, qui concernent l'état de la croûte externe de ce globe, ainsi que les modifications et les changemens qu'elle subit continuellement: enfin celles de la même sorte, qui appartiennent à l'origine et aux développemens d'organisation des crops vivans. Ainsi toutes ces considérations partagent naturellement la physique terrestre en trois parties essentielles, dont la première doit comprendre la théorie de l'atmosphère, la *Météorologie;* la seconde, celle de la croûte externe du globe, l'*Hydrogéologie;* la troisième enfin, celle des corps vivans, la *Biologie*."

We find here the first definition and use of the word 'biology': a theory of living organisms. Lamarck never wrote his *Biologie* as such, but it was in many respects replaced by his later *Philosophie zoologique* (1809). A few months after Lamarck, in the year 1802, the German botanist G. R. Treviranus published the first volume of his book *Biologie oder Philosophie der lebenden Natur*.

Even though the word 'biology' was thus born with the nineteenth century, the first statement of the concept goes back to Buffon.

Lamarck's work epitomized an evolution started by several of the greatest French scientists of the eighteenth century: Buffon, Diderot and Adanson. These three pathfinders cleared the road for biologists such as A. L. de Jussieu, Daubenton, Lamarck, and to some extent also Cuvier, to work out a new, biological systematics.

The overwhelming increase of factual data during the sixteenth and seventeenth centuries had forced natural scientists to concentrate upon systematizing knowledge in order to master the great profusion of nature. They used the Aristotelian methods of logical division and classification to deal with this huge amount of detail. Very often first priority had to be given to the definition and the naming of objects, rather than to attempts to describe nature comprehensively. The 'systems' and 'methods' of classification had a clearly pragmatic and hence usually rather arbitrary and artificial basis. The great pragmatist Linnaeus stands at the end of this development. He served natural history by systematizing its body of data; the order thus created enabled others to proceed from classification by definition towards systematics by description.

The seventeenth century had seen great progress in scientific ideas and concepts, but mainly in the physical, mathematical, and astronomical sciences. Objective registration of facts, experiments, and unbiased co-ordination of the facts and results of experiments into a scientific picture of the universe was already characteristic of the century of Newton and Leibniz. The application of these methods to the life sciences, however, took place mainly in the course of the eighteenth century.

The enormous diffusion of knowledge in the field of natural history in the eighteenth century and the great popularity of everything concerned with nature were features of a changing social pattern: the coming of the Enlightenment.

The essence of the Enlightenment is to be found in the success of its ideas: the ideas themselves were not new but had gradually pervaded the minds of scientists and advanced philosophers since the days of the Renaissance, which had seen the great reaction of the human mind against the medieval domination of mere authority. The fifteenth, sixteenth, and seventeenth centuries saw a steady growth of independent thinking, a growth mainly among scientists and philosophers, rather than among the educated classes as a whole. The success of the Enlightenment was the general acceptance of the basic freedom of the human mind to carry out a rational analysis of all phenomena, whether worldly or unworldly, physical or spiritual, natural or social, philosophical or religious. The sweeping success of this opening of the human mind, of the acceptance of reason instead of belief, was accompanied by a broad interest in all natural sciences. Nature was one of the key-words to this success, because nature stood for objectivity, was accepted as exemplary, and provided the essential basis for judging the world and its institutions. The other keywords were reason, humanity and tolerance.

THE ENCYCLOPÉDIE AND THE NATURALISTS

The great carrier of the ideas of the Enlightenment was Diderot and d'Alembert's *Encyclopédie*. This great work (36 volumes, 1750–1780), is now perhaps more often admired than consulted. The difficulty lies in finding the article headings under which the most significant new ideas were published. One has to read the article 'Genève' to understand how opposition by the Church nearly broke down the royal privilege granted to d'Alembert of publishing the book itself, and why the early volumes were outlawed, though not withdrawn. (The analytical index in the last two volumes is a good guide to the important articles.) The rôle of nature was of primary importance in the philosophy of the Enlightenment, and this importance is reflected by the *Encyclopédie*. Louis Jean Marie Daubenton (1716–1799) did most of the early botanical and zoological articles. In his article *Botanique* he gives a profound critique of the 'spirit of the systems' which dominates the discipline and puts forward a view which is a succinct exposé of what will later be called the natural system. The encyclopedia contains also many detailed descriptions of genera (in later volumes e.g. by Adanson), with Latin names and full synonymy hardly ever listed in the technical literature.

In several of the general articles (botanique, méthode, and histoire naturelle, not signed but presumably by Daubenton) the argument is put forward that the 'nomenclateur' (the diagnostic biologist, the one who classifies) puts a brake on independent progress. The picture of nature must consist of complete descriptions, not solely of the so-called important characters, but of all of these, external as well as internal. The 'systems' based on arbitrary characteristics were mostly misleading and did not do justice to the great diversity of nature.

"Dans le siècle présent la science de l'*Histoire naturelle* est plus cultivée qu'elle ne l'a jamais été; non-seulement la plûpart des gens de lettres en font un objet d'étude ou de délassement, mais il y a de plus un gout pour cette science qui est répandu dans la public, & qui devient chaque jour plus vif & plus général."

Daubenton goes on to show that this interest is clearly shown in the rapidly-increasing number of *cabinets d'histoire naturelle*, and remarks that this contrasts favorably with the *cabinets de médailles* and the cabinets filled with *machines de physique expérimentale* of an earlier period. Another interesting emphasis is on the study of *living* plants and animals:

"On ne connoîtra jamais une nation par la lecture de la meilleure histoire que l'on en puisse faire, aussi–bien que l'on avoit vécu parmi cette nation,..." "Il en est de même pour l'*Histoire naturelle* ... les systèmes les

[295]

plus ingénieux ne donnent pas une idée aussi juste des productions de la nature que la présence des objets réels ..." "Pour entendre & pour juger ces systèmes ... pour s'y représenter le tableau de la nature, il faut avoir vû la nature elle-même." The conclusion is that the systems and descriptions, based as they are on human conventions, are but unreliable guides which must be left behind as soon as one has acquired "assez de lumières pour se conduire soi-même."

It is not the place here to sketch even briefly the history and importance of the *Encyclopédie*. A rich literature exists on the book and its authors*. Publication was possible because some 5000 'souscripteurs' paid 956 pounds each. An amateur botanist known almost exclusively as a statesman was most influential in protecting the enterprise against the reactionary attacks: the director of the book trade, de facto the super-censor, Malesherbes. Also important was the sympathy of Mme. de Pompadour. Great articles are those on 'histoire,' 'esprit' and 'imagination' by Voltaire, 'goût' by Montesquieu, 'chémie' by the famous baron d'Holbach, articles on music by Rousseau, on philosophy by de Condillac. The book brought together an extremely influential, though controversial group of the most liberal spirits of the age; it moulded the intellectual climate and paved the way for the revolution. The theoretical dissertations on biology published by Buffon (who himself did not participate in the *Encyclopédie*, although he promised an article on 'nature'), Daubenton and Adanson are reflected in many of the articles. Diderot himself, especially in his *Pensées sur l'interprétation de la nature* of 1754, was clearly influenced by the thoughts of these biologists: "The abstract sciences have occupied the best minds for too long. Words have been multiplied endlessly, but factual knowledge has lagged behind ...Unfortunately, rational philosophy is much more concerned with comparing and combining facts already known than with collecting new ones." (Translation by Cassirer, 1951; see also Rostand in Berr 1952).

The *Encyclopédie* is imbued with this new spirit of collecting new facts and using them for the benefit of mankind; authority and tradition are rejected in the name of 'progress,' which manifests itself through the natural as well as the economical and social sciences. Its importance for biology has so far been little stressed; its publication reflects, but was itself instrumental in bringing about, the new developments in biology, and more

* See, for instance, Ducros 1900, Grosclaude 1951, Berr 1952, Charpentier 1967, Lough 1968.

especially the evolution from diagnostic classification to descriptive systematics.

The broad interest in the natural sciences on the part of all who made up that literary-minded society of eighteenth-century France is also reflected in the gradual increase of science items in such fashionable journals as the *Mercure de France* and the *Journal encyclopédique*, and even in the thoroughly conservative anti-Voltairian, anti-encyclopedist *Année littéraire* of Elie Fréron (1718–1776). These literary journals were all concerned with physics and biology as well as politics, philosophy, and belles-lettres, and reviewed the pertinent literature extensively. The more scientific *Journal des sçavans*, which had appeared since 1665, was extremely popular and widely read: so popular that pirated editions appeared abroad, closely following the Paris original. The *Journal encyclopédique*, that remarkable journal published from 1756 to 1793 in Bouillon, away from the Paris censor, was at the time the most fashionable and independent, but also one of the most widely read 'literary' journals that accompanied the encyclopedist movement. Its very extensive treatment of, for instance, Buffon's and Adanson's works is typical of its character and indicates a general interest in the more scholarly books on biology as well.

The words 'nature' and 'natural' have their own special meaning in every phase of human culture, and as such the terms are very difficult to define. In the Enlightenment the terms were used in relation to man or to human institutions or to patterns of thinking. In this respect 'natural' was used in opposition to 'supernatural,' the natural really meaning the rational, that which is open to reason, the supernatural standing for what is above reason or even contrary to reason. Deference to the natural implies distrust of the traditional and especially of the traditional patterns of thought. This 'naturalism' is found in the eighteenth century in theology as well as in philosophy: in theology it had already led in the seventeenth century to the phenomenon of deism and the denial of the possibility of revelation; in philosophy it led to free thought and liberal thinking.

This twofold aspect of 'naturalism,' the theological and the philosophical, is characteristic of the natural scientists of the Enlightenment. It was often dangerous to take sides with the philosophical rationalists and to deny revelation, but one could easily indulge in open and free research in biology ('natural' history), so long as one did not draw the all-too-obvious conclusions. A remarkable feature of many biological publications, and

[297]

especially of the thriving popular books, was the lip service paid to certain theological opinions, the most generally found one being the statement that all research revealed the wisdom of God in creation. The eighteenth century is also still the century of the clerical scientists: according to Mornet (1911), about half of the authors who then published on natural history in France either belonged to the Roman Catholic clergy or were Protestant ministers.

The great attention paid to nature by non–scientists, especially with regard to biological and sociological phenomena, shows the liberalizing influence of science on the human mind in the eighteenth century. With 'nature,' that 'new' source of truth, that unspoiled reality which could be invoked to attack established authority, natural history became popular to an unsurpassed degree. This popularity was also evident in an important aspect of natural history which is lacking in the physical sciences: the possibility of making collections. I have discussed this above when mentioning Joseph Banks: the century was one of collections, of natural history cabinets and private herbaria. The discovery of new countries produced an influx of new material from overseas: travelling and reading about travelling was en vogue. Collecting items from overseas, from faraway unspoiled and natural countries, was part of it; besides such great collectors as George Clifford (1685–1760) in Holland, Sir Hans Sloane (1660–1753) and Sir Joseph Banks in England, René–Antoine Ferchault de Réaumur (1683–1757) in France, there were many who collected on a smaller scale. Many of those collections constitute the foundation of present-day institutional collections. The importance attached to these collections is shown in the full title of Buffon's *Histoire naturelle, générale et particulière, avec la description du Cabinet du Roi* (vol. I, 1749) (fig. 67). The Cabinet du Roi was the museum counterpart of the *Jardin du Roi;* Buffon was director (intendant) of both of them. Another sign of the popularity of collections and natural history cabinets is the steady stream of catalogues describing them that came from the press in the later part of the century. Hérissant (1771, p. 51) cites not less than five such catalogues for the year 1763 alone. Collecting plants was relatively easy and a very popular pastime: Jean–Jacques Rousseau (1712–1778) compiled a considerable herbarium (*cf.* Jansen 1885, and Lanjouw et Uittien 1940), and so did many of the other *philosophes*. "Det är nu a la mode att hafva Natural samlingar" (it is now fashionable to have natural history collections), wrote Clas Alströmer (1736–1794) on 30 January 1763 to his teacher

HISTOIRE
NATURELLE,
GÉNÉRALE ET PARTICULIÈRE,
AVEC LA DESCRIPTION
DU CABINET DU ROY.

Tome Premier.

A PARIS,
DE L'IMPRIMERIE ROYALE.
M DCCXLIX.

Fig. 67. Title–page of Buffon, *Histoire naturelle, générale et particulière, avec la description du Cabinet du Roy.* [1749]. The title mentions explicitly the description of the collections of the royal natural history cabinet which was part of the combination of botanic garden and natural history buildings entitled *Jardin du Roi,* now the *Muséum d'Histoire naturelle.*

Carl Linnaeus (Fries 1909, p. 69). Next to the general predilection for collecting, interest in natural history was promoted by the literary journals and by popular books such as *Le spectacle de la nature* by Noel–Antoine Pluche (1688–1761). This book was found by Mornet in 206 out of 500 catalogues of private libraries in eighteenth–century France. According to P. Rousseau (1945, p. 298), it was more widely read even than the works of Voltaire. The book was published in nine volumes from 1732 onward, and new editions of the first volumes were already in demand long before the last ones appeared. The second edition of volume one appeared in 1733 and was pirated that same year in Utrecht. Translations appeared in many languages and its success was enormous, to be equalled only seventeen years later by Buffon's *Histoire naturelle*. Pluche was a clergyman who taught at the Collège de Reims and who was later director of the Collège de Laon. He was relieved of his duties because he refused to adhere to the Unigenitus bull, which played such an important part in the internal struggles of the Roman Catholic church in France between the Jansenists of the clergy and of the parlement and the Jesuits. The subtitle of the *Spectacle de la nature* is *Entretiens sur les particularités de l'histoire naturelle, qui ont paru les plus propres à rendre les Jeune–Gens curieux, & à leur former l'esprit* (fig. 68). The part dealing with plants (part 2, vol. 2) deals mainly with horticultural and sylvicultural botany "laissant donc aux savans le soin de former des [familles] par des divisions exactes, & par des traités qui embrassent tout …" This popular book was of great importance in lending prestige to natural history and promoting this science among the members of the established classes. Gradually its ideas pervaded social thinking as well, as became evident in the later activities and publications of the encyclopedists. Books and journals like these, together with the craze for collecting, brought about a situation in which knowledge of natural history was a "must" for every educated person, and through which social institutions felt the influence of the 'new look' in human thinking.

Fig. 68. Title–page of the volume containing 'botany' of *Le spectacle de la nature* part 2, vol. 2 [1752] by the Abbé Pluche. The author's name is absent from the title–page. This is not the first issue or edition; the Pluche publications were frequently reprinted and re-issued.

LE SPECTACLE

DE

LA NATURE

OU

ENTRETIENS

SUR LES PARTICULARITÉS

DE

L'HISTOIRE NATURELLE,

Qui ont paru les plus propres à rendre
les Jeunes-Gens curieux, & à leur
former l'esprit.

SECONDE PARTIE.

CONTENANT CE QUI REGARDE
les dehors & l'intérieur de la Terre.

TOME SECOND.

A PARIS,

Chez la Veuve ESTIENNE & Fils, rue S. Jacques,
à la Vertu.

M. DCC. LII.

Avec Approbation & Privilége du Roi.

Fig. 68

[301]

BUFFON

From the above analysis of the rôle of nature in the world of ideas of the 'philosophers' and 'encyclopedists,' it will be clear that the so necessary change from classification of mere objects of natural history to biological

Fig. 69. GEORGES–LOUIS LECLERQ, COMTE DE BUFFON; *b.* Montbard, France, August 7, 1707; *d.* Paris, France, April 16, 1788; director of the *Jardin du Roi* 1739–1788. [Portrait by F. H. Drouais at the age of 54, engraved by C. S. Gaucher, an VII, for the Sonnini edition of Buffon, *Histoire naturelle*, Paris an VII (1799)–XIII (1805)].

classification was initiated by the natural philosophers of the Enlightenment. Buffon and Diderot changed the concepts guiding the study and understanding of nature fundamentally. Life and its phenomena (but not its origin) had been thought to be understandable through physics or, even better, through mathematics. The Cartesian concept of nature was mainly abstract; none of the factual objects in nature ever reached the perfection

[302]

of mathematical thought. A living creature was a machine, understandable in terms of physics, and of which the history consisted simply of one single act: creation.

The historical element, the consciousness of time as an intrinsic element in the understanding of life, was absent from this concept of nature. The birth of biology consists in the realization by the scientists that life must be described in terms of processes as well as status quo; that living beings have an existence in time, and not in space alone. Historical knowledge of facts and processes became a second fundamental source of knowledge in describing the living world. This historical knowledge, in its widest sense, constitutes, with the physical knowledge based on timeless mathematical abstractions, the basis of biology. From now on a timeless definition of essentials is no longer sufficient; life must be described as a phenomenon in space and time. The Greek and Renaissance view of nature was timeless. Relatively few authors had ever tried to define a species concept at all, let alone one that included the rôle of time. Aristotle considers fecundity in animals as a specific character (Agassiz 1962, p. 209). Linnaeus (Phil. bot. no. 157) states that we count as many species as there were created in the beginning. He mentions the law of generation which accounts for the production of identical unchanging forms, but that is as far as time goes. In George–Louis Leclerq, comte de Buffon (1707–1788) (fig. 69), we encounter, however, a biologist of exceptional insight, almost free from traditional thought and religious scruples, a highly intelligent though somewhat speculative mind, exquisitely original and in many ways far ahead of his time.

Diametrically opposed to Linnaeus and often completely misinterpreting his merits and intentions, seldom taking the trouble to describe carefully and sort precisely the great multitude of facts, Buffon managed to formulate thoughts which were strikingly original, and which foreshadowed great developments.

Buffon's aim was to write the epic history of human knowledge of nature. In his *Histoire naturelle* he gave a synthetic account of natural history, putting it in the great perspective of further development of human knowledge and adding new thoughts, often of a speculative nature, thus provoking reactions and stimulating research. Buffon's artistic temperament, combined with a lucid mind and an encyclopedic knowledge, produced one of the great masterpieces of biological writing.

Buffon was well aware of the fact that the success of his ideas depended upon their presentation. In his 'Discours' of 25 August 1753, upon his admittance to the *Académie française*, he states:

"Les ouvrages bien écrits seront les seuls qui passeront à la postérité: la multitude des conoissances, la singularité des faits, la nouveauté même des découvertes ne sont pas de sûres garans de l'immortalité; si les ouvrages qui les contiennent ne roulent que sur des petits objects ... ils périront ... Ces choses sont hors de l'homme, le style est l'homme même ...."

"Le sublime ne peut–être que dans les grands sujets. La poésie, l'histoire et la philosophie ont toutes le même objet, & un très grand objet, l'Homme et la Nature. La philosophie décrit et dépeint la nature; la poësie la peint et l'embellit .... l'Histoire ne peint que l'homme."

In this quotation the word *philosophie* is used characteristically in the sense of 'describing and depicting nature.' The 'philosophy' does not lay down the rules in accordance with which nature must be studied—such as for instance in Linnaeus's *Philosophia botanica*. On the contrary, it is primarily the description of nature itself: the philosopher "parlera des loix de la Nature, des êtres en général, de l'espace, de la matière, du mouvement & du temps ..." A fundamental change: the natural scientist studies movement and time.

The first volume of the *Histoire naturelle*, published in 1749, consists of two parts: a 'premier discours' on the way to study and treat natural history, and a second one on the history and theory of the earth, the *Théorie de la terre*. These discourses are followed by nineteen articles documenting the theory of the earth. One of the most conspicuous features of this theory was its emphasis on geological time as shown by the climatic changes of the past and by the distribution of fossil animals related with those changes.

The discourse on the methodology of the study of natural history is still well worth reading. Buffon's nominalist attitude is evident; he accepts no a priori elements of knowledge, he believes only what he sees, and even then he stresses that his conclusions are simply his own and open to change, and in no way a revelation of objective truth.

"You must start by seeing a great deal; you must also look with an open mind ["presque sans dessein"], because if you consider the facts only from a certain point of view in a certain order, in a certain system, even if you have chosen the best way, you will never obtain the same comprehensiveness of knowledge as you will attain if you let your mind march alone from the beginning, reconnoitre, find its way without help and form for itself that first chain which represents the order of its ideas."

One of the first things one discovers in this way is that, looking at all creatures, down from the most perfect to the simplest, one sees only a gradual change, no abrupt divisions. These inconspicuous changes are the great work of Nature; one recognizes them in all their aspects, dimensions, shapes, movements and generations alike.

A general system is therefore impossible. "La nature marche par des gradations inconnues, & par conséquent elle ne peut pas se prêter totalement à ces divisions ..." Buffon takes botany as an example. Numerous systems have been created and all of them are defective. One system destroys the other, but each is found to "suffer the common fate of all systems based on arbitrary principles." It is just as foolish to judge the difference between plants on the basis of their leaves alone, or on their stamens, as to try to know the difference between animals only on the basis of their skin or their organs of reproduction; "and who does not see that this knowledge is not science, that it is at most a convention, an arbitrary language, a means of communication, but one from which no real knowledge can be obtained?" No wonder that Buffon became known as the *ennemi des systèmes*.

Buffon sharply criticizes Linnaeus and his attempt to overthrow Tournefortian nomenclature and taxonomy. The genera of Linnaeus, based as they are on the fructification only, unite plants which no one else so far had united. "N'est-ce pas se jouer de la Nature & de ceux qui l'étudient?" This reform is presented with the appearance of a mysterious order and clothed in Greek and botanical erudition, and it is for this reason alone that the method has found some acceptance. The main error is that 'la marche de la nature' is ignored. The differentiation is by nuances, and it is only by trying to judge the whole on the basis of an arbitrarily chosen part that divisions appear.

The *Théorie de la terre*, as well as the second volume of the *Histoire naturelle*, contained several statements on the history of the earth which offended the Jesuits of the *Faculté de Théologie de Paris*. The offensive thoughts had nothing to do with biology per se but were, first, a statement on the gradual nature of geological changes (Buffon's concept of geology was essentially uniformitarian), and then several statements on the relativity of the concept of 'truth' in the natural sciences. "We can believe that there is something outside ourselves, but we are not certain of it ..." Buffon was forced to withdraw several of these statements. The fourth volume of his work contains the letters exchanged between Buffon and the theological faculty in which the latter spell out the offensive paragraphs and in which the former reaffirms his belief in Scripture. Buffon was not made to be a martyr: he preferred to play the game quietly. Buffon's view of the time–dimension of nature, as expressed in his *Histoire naturelle* (quoted in a translation by Cassirer 1951), is as follows:

"Just as in human history one consults documents, examines coins and medals, and deciphers ancient inscriptions in order to determine the revolutions and epochs in the intellectual life of man, so in natural history one must search the archives of the world, unearth the oldest relics, collect remnants, and unite all signs of physical changes which are traceable to the various ages of nature into one corpus of evidence. This is the only way to determine any fixed points in the infinity of space and to leave behind a few milestones on the unending pathway of time."

Buffon's act of introducing time in the study of nature cannot be dissociated from that general phenomenon which characterized the Enlightenment and which was the great discovery of the eighteenth century: 'progress.' All around him the philosophes heralded the new confidence in the future of humanity. In the sixteenth century the scientific Renaissance restored to science confidence in itself, confidence in the achievements of the present rather than of a classical past known only through books. In biology this century reinstated independent observation. The mathematical–physical development of the seventeenth century cleared the ground for independent research in other realms of the human spirit; the eighteenth century, combining confidence and science, looked to the future: the creed was 'progress.' No progress, of course, without time-consciousness. Scientific history was born with Voltaire, scientific biology with Buffon, Adanson and some of their contemporaries. These developments are unthinkable without the general social and psychological movement of breaking the charm of orthodoxy, revelation and authority, of banishing the belief that civilization degenerated from an (imaginary) golden age. Francis Bacon—and many others—had already stated that we stand on the shoulders of our predecessors, but as with so many of Bacon's aphorisms, the impact of this idea had been negligible. The Enlightenment brought the general breakthrough of ideas and attitudes of isolated seventeenth-century thinkers. The great step forward was the new mental attitude which pervaded all human life, including the sciences. In biology

[306]

this consciousness of progress, this looking at life as a creative process rather than as a prefabricated machine, led to a desire for a better knowledge of all phenomena in all their phases of existence.

Description was the password, description not only of single elements which were thought to be of special importance and which served for diagnostic purposes only, but description of all aspects of the processes and forms of life. Buffon looked upon individuals as the only fixed elements in space and time and regarded every grouping of them as man–made. In this respect he was purely nominalistic. When describing the living beings of today, however, he found another point of fixity: the sterility barriers between the species (Hist. nat. 4: 384–386):

"C'est donc dans la diversité caractéristique des espèces que les inter-valles des nuances de la Nature sont le plus sensibles & le mieux marqués; on pourroit même dire que ces intervalles entres les espèces sont les plus égaux & les moins variables de tous, puisque'on peut toujours tirer une ligne de séparation entre deux espèces, c'est à dire entre deux successions d'individus qui se reproduisent & ne peuvent se mêler ... ce point est le plus fixe que nous ayons en Histoire naturelle, toutes les autres ressem-blances & toutes les autres differences que l'on pourrait saisir dans la com-paraison des êtres, ne seroient, ni si constantes, ni si réelles, ni si certaines ..."

Buffon attributed a physical identity to an individual species because it is the total sum of all individuals which form a reproductive community. This physical identity is the only fixed point in systematics; it gives the spe-cies a natural existence which, in principle, cannot be attained by any of the higher taxa. Elsewhere he states: "Les espèces sont les seuls êtres de la Nature" (Hist. nat. 13: i). With respect to systematics, he holds that lines of separation exist in nature only between the species, because of their biol-ogical reality (interfertility); all other dividing lines between, for instance, genera, families, orders, are unreal, not constant, uncertain.

In a way Buffon is therefore the founder of the biological species concept avant–la–lettre. His historical view, however, also led him to formulate the early beginnings of the theory of evolution.

Comparative anatomy reveals a common plan in the organization of groups of animals. The species may now be too far apart to hybridize, but we may ask whether this was always the case? Could presently allied but independent species not have arisen from common ancestors? If systematics has a meaning at all, what other can it be than community of origin, true genealogical relationship? (Buffon used the word genealogy, not phylogeny, which did not exist at the time.)

After pointing out that it is possible to distinguish 'families' in nature, more or less in conformity with the families of man, Buffon states in his chapter on the donkeys (Hist. nat. 4: 382) that, granted such families exist:

"... on pourra dire également que le singe est de la famille de l'homme, que c'est un homme dégénéré, que l'homme & le singe ont eu une origine commune comme le cheval & l'âne, que chaque famille, tant dans les animaux que dans les végétaux, n'a eu qu'une seule souche, & même que tous les animaux sont venus d'un seul animal, qui, dans la succession des temps, a produit, en se perfectionnant [sic] & en dégénerant, toutes les races des autres animaux."

When he wrote the fourth volume of the *Histoire naturelle*, Buffon had just been compelled by the church authorities to re–affirm his belief in special creation, because of earlier similarly unorthodox views. He had to pay lip service to these ghosts of the past and continued with supreme irony, unsurpassed in biological literature (p. 383):

"Mais non, il est certain, par la révélation, que tous les animaux ont également participé à la grâce de la création, que les deux premiers de chaque espèce & de toutes les espèces sont sortis tout formés des mains du Créateur ..."

On the other hand: "On peut glisser dans un in–quarto des opinions qui, dans une brochure, feraient scandale" (Buffon in a letter to Charles de Brosses).

Buffon's great difficulty was of course that he had no experimental proof of new forms arising through hybridization or mutation; a few years later, his compatriot and follower Adanson had actual mutations before him (e.g., the single leaflet variety of the strawberry obtained by Duchesne) and could pursue with more vigour the admittedly speculative concepts of Buffon. It should also be realized that Buffon's definition of species, cited above, in which the sterility barriers play such an important rôle, can also in part be taken as anti–evolutionary. His ideas on evolution were extremely general; he advanced no theory about its mechanism and there is nothing to suggest that the Buffonian species could not 'degenerate' in some other way than hybridization, e.g. by mutation. Buffon's writings contain contradictory statements; it is important, however, that even within the context of such contradictions various new ideas make their appearance.

I have paraphrased Buffon's opinions as we find them expressed mainly in the fourth volume of his *Histoire naturelle*. In other places of his book Buffon partially withdraws some of his most daring statements, or rephrases them more cautiously. This was due to outside pressure and does not detract from their intrinsic value. Buffon formulates some fundamental biological concepts. He is modern because:

1. he formulates the biological species concept avant–la–lettre, even though he has only a vague notion of populations;

2. he exposes the nominalist character of genera and of taxa of higher categories (Linnaeus considers genera as 'natural,' that is 'real' or 'created,' but shares Buffon's opinion on the higher groups to some extent);

3. he explicitly introduces the time–element in systematics;

4. he formulates the idea of phylogenetic relationship, although the word he uses is 'degeneration.' He does this mainly by recognizing that the present fertility barriers between species may not always have existed, and that common structure can be understood only in the light of common ancestry.

Enough to show that Buffon, the dandyesque and supercilious criticiser of Linnaeus, the difficult, often arrogant leader of the group of biologists at the *Jardin du Roi*, produced a book in which the ideas are so advanced that it still makes fascinating reading. His *Histoire naturelle* is of the greatest importance not only for the history of biology, but also for an understanding of the way the mind of the born scientist works:

"Sa découverte essentielle a été la Nature. Il lui a appliqué à la fois sa vision du vrai, son pouvoir à démêler, sa capacité à expliquer, sa propension à la synthèse, avec deux instruments incomparables: la clarté et l'enchaînement de la pensée ..." (R. Heim, in 'Buffon,' 1952.*)

The introduction of the historical element by Buffon was of the greatest importance for the evolution of biology as an independent science. In the first place, this introduction heralded the modern view of nature. As mentioned before, nature had so far been timeless; if there was change, this change was cyclical, never directed to a different ultimate result. 'Progress' and 'development' were new elements in the picture of nature, elements which would later be called evolution. (See e.g. Collingwood 1945).

* For recent studies on Buffon see also the other articles in Heim (et al.), *Bvffon* (1952), Guyénot (1941), and Roger (1963).

A further consequence of Buffon's views was that for the first time biological knowledge became dissociated from physics. Biology evolved from natural history. Scientific method in physics was dominated exclusively by mathematics; historical knowledge in combination with mathematical analysis in sensu lato is characteristic for modern biology. Definition of timeless 'essentials' was no longer sufficient; life should be described in all its phenomena. In Cassirer's words (1951): "there is in the making a transition to a conception of nature which no longer seeks to devise and explain becoming from being, but being from becoming." We might also say that biology moved from 'definition' to 'description.'

Buffon was the outspoken enemy of all 'systems' because they are based on definitions only. Accepting the principle of continuity, he furthermore denied the existence of all barriers, except those between species in certain phases of their existence. Here again we meet the duality between discrete entities and continuity, but this time on a purely biological basis. An enormous step forward, but one which went by almost unnoticed for lack of empirical proof. But while his attack upon the dogma of the constancy of species remained unsuccessful, Buffon did succeed in fertilizing the minds of his compatriots Adanson, Daubenton, and Lamarck. A. L. Jussieu was far less influenced by him. Daubenton, mainly a zoologist, was briefly mentioned above in connection with the *Encyclopédie*, but must be left out of further account here. I have discussed Adanson's, Jussieu's, and Lamarck's works and ideas extensively in other publications (1963, 1964, 1971a); a brief note on these formidable opponents of Linnaeus is, however, in order. Together they symbolize the coming of the end of the Linnaean era, even though their main contribution to systematic botany, a natural system built upon inductive principles and, in Lamarck's case, the foreshadowing of an evolutionary explanation of biological diversity, would be generally accepted only in the nineteenth century.

4. Consolidation of the natural system: Adanson, Jussieu, Lamarck

MICHEL ADANSON

Unlike his contemporary Linnaeus, Michel Adanson did not have the benefit of being in the limelight of the history of botany almost from the moment of his first publication. On the contrary, Adanson's work was neglected by generations of botanists and had little direct impact on the work of others. Adanson's claim to fame, although he published two books and several shorter treatises, is based on only one book: the *Familles des plantes* of 1763, written in French (with a difficult personal orthography) and characterized as much by its advanced taxonomic theory and practice as by its ultraconservative nomenclature. It was this nomenclature, in principle based on absolute priority and fully rejecting the Linnaean reform, which was mainly responsible for the doom of oblivion which struck the book.

The *Familles des plantes* presented for the first time a logical plea for an attempt at a natural classification on the basis of inductive research, free from the aprioristic harness of essences and priorities, but typically eighteenth century: open–minded and rational. Adanson's view that a plant taxonomist must have a personal knowledge of a tropical flora marked a difference with his great contemporary. Previously taxonomists had worked mainly with Western European and Mediterranean plants; the world, however, was much wider and had much that was new in store for the inquisitive naturalist who would go out and see for himself. The plant taxonomist had to see his plants alive, whether in the field or grown by himself in his garden. He should conduct experiments on hybridization and also study the variability of the offspring of plants from the wild in cultivation. The constancy of species was not an item of faith; at most it could be a fact, but perhaps it was not a fact at all. New taxa might arise through hybridization and mutation. A thorough knowledge of the plant world would be reached not by diagnostic systems which are merely artificial keys, but by a study of all features of the plants in all phases of their development and by a careful analysis and comparison of their detailed descriptions.

When describing nature there was, for Adanson, no place for Aristotelean–Thomistic 'systèmes' which were improvisations on metaphysical themes rather than scientific studies of formal and genealogical relationships.

Buffon's picture of the living world, says Adanson, would imply that the only reality is a constant stream of individuals, changing and merging and without definite divisions between them. In the last instance there would then be only one universal being. This, however, is not acceptable. It may well be that nature is one and undivided with respect to the supreme being; it is certainly divided for us, "et cela sufit." These three words ("and this is sufficient") show Adanson's modern approach. It is all good and well that there is divine or conceptual unity: what matters is the picture presented to the human mind, to human reason. This essentially nominalist attitude enabled Adanson to search for the discontinuities in nature, or at any rate for the various situations in nature in which changes are abrupt rather than gradual.

On this basis, but otherwise fully in agreement with the ideas expressed by Buffon on the artificiality of the various 'systems,' Adanson started his search for what he called 'the natural method.' The first volume of his *Familles des plantes* contains a detailed and critical account of methods and principles of plant classification. This important theoretical work was the first of its kind; it is of great importance for the understanding of eighteenth-century systematics.

Adanson accepted Magnol's concept of the natural families and elaborated on this theme for families as well as for genera. 'Natural' meant here: 'as encountered in nature.' He did not single out any characters a priori, but made an inventory of as many characters and affinities as possible. The inventory was a series of 65 artificial arrangements of the genera, each based on a single or on a few characters. From it Adanson derived his 'natural method,' which was the prototype of all subsequent natural systems in botany. We would now describe it as a system based on a great many characters and character-complexes, with a high degree of information. Adanson refused to admit a priori weighting of characters, but evaluated them a posteriori, after careful comparison and consideration. Burtt (1966) has proposed to call this process 'intrinsic' weighting of characters, as opposed to the 'extrinsic' weighting on the basis of extraneous a priori arguments such as 'essence,' 'naturalness,' etc.

Adanson kept himself as free as possible from traditional thought and was therefore flatly opposed to the Aristotelian–scholastic systematics of Linnaeus. However, it would be wrong to see Adanson only in his reaction to Linnaeus; his importance, like that of Buffon, went much farther and was in a way autonomous. He turned classification into systematics.

The step was still only a first one. Adanson was deeply interested in the fossil record but could do little with it; understandably so, if we take into account that he was mainly concerned with phanerogams. He shared Buffon's ideas on the origin of species by hybridization; in addition, he was the first to speak of the rôle of hereditary mutations in the process of speciation.

Adanson's general concept of nature was in sharp conflict with prevailing Christian essentialism and creationism. In his published writings he expresses himself only indirectly in this respect; in his copy of Linnaeus's *Systema naturae* of 1766 he wrote (Nicolas 1963):

"Le tout universel n'a pu être qu'un ensemble simultané incrée et éternel de toute éternité qui n'a pu être créé, il n'y a que la raison et l'imagination humaine qui créent, quoi? Des idées et qui inventent et perfectionnent les machines."

Adanson produced no autobiographies like his Swedish colleague, nor has he had the benefit of what seems almost like an orgy of studies making him a national hero. Adanson lived to become a forgotten man; when he died, on August 3, 1806, he was already, in the eyes of his colleagues, more a curious relic of a distant past than a representative of living science. This feeling of distance and of estrangement pervades the first published document on Adanson's life: Cuvier's *Éloge* of 1806. His manuscripts, library and herbarium remained in the hands of the family and became available for scholarly research only after 1960. A curious coincidence was then responsible for an Adanson revival which led to a re-evaluation of the man and his work, two hundred years after the publication of his main work. A number of twentieth-century taxonomists interested in the application of statistical and numerical methods to plant taxonomy adopted for their movement the name 'Neo-Adansonian' on the grounds of a supposed parallel between some of Adanson's ideas and their 'numerical taxonomy.' At the same time, and quite independently of the Neo-Adansonian movement, the great majority of Adanson's manuscripts and books came on the market and were acquired by some public institutions. Adanson's private copy of the great *Encyclopédie*, heavily annotated with critical remarks as well as autobiographical details, came to Dakar and stimulated J. P. Nicolas to write the first critical biography of the French taxonomist. The botanical books and manuscripts went to the Hunt Botanical Library in Pittsburgh, which then staged a great Adanson symposium (1963) and published a number of papers in a two-volume work entitled simply 'Adanson,' edited by G. H. M. Lawrence. The opening paper of this work is an abbreviated version of the unpublished biography of Adanson by Nicolas.

Michel Adanson (fig. 70) was born on 7 April, 1727, in Aix-en-Provence.

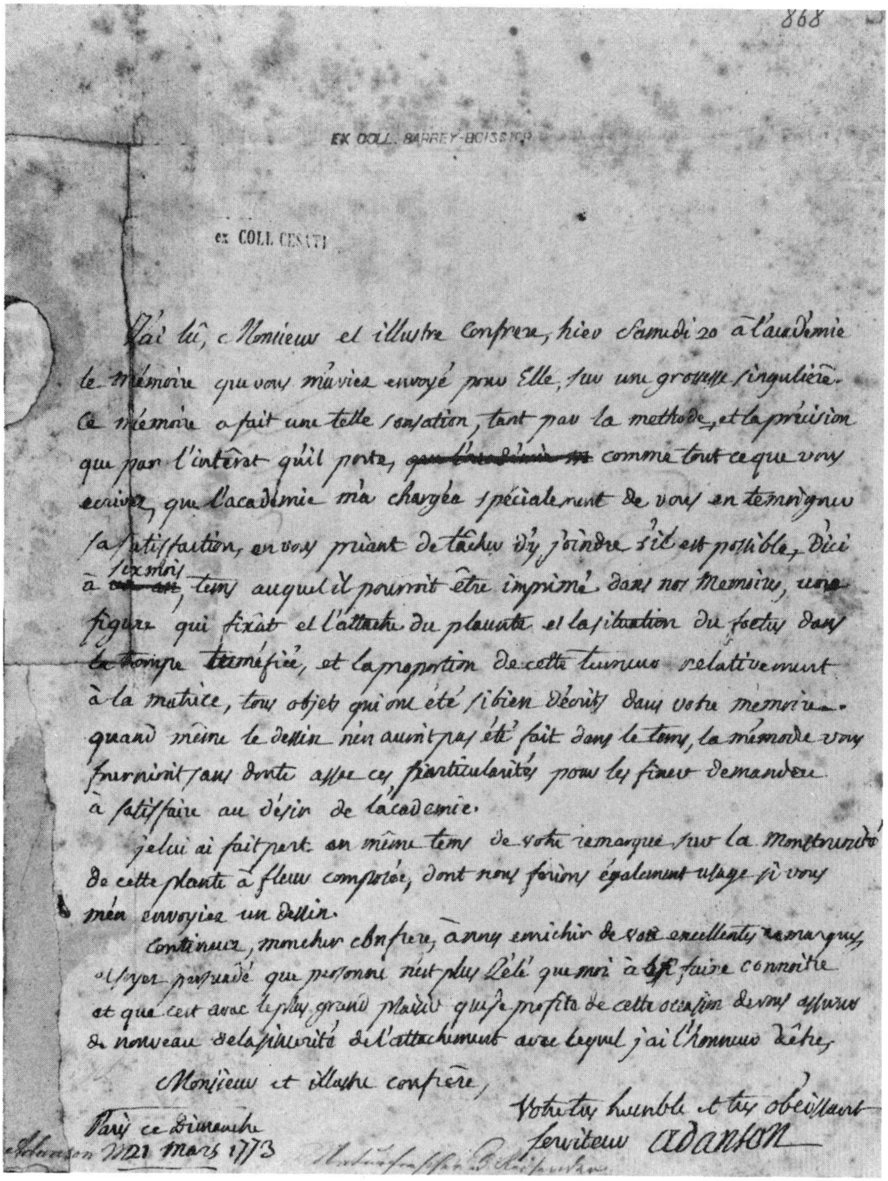

868

EX COLL. BARBEY-BOISSIER

ex COLL CESATI

J'ai lû, Monsieur et illustre Confrere, hier Samedi 20 à l'academie le memoire que vous m'aviez envoyé pour Elle, sur une grossesse singuliere. Ce memoire a fait une telle sensation, tant par la methode, et la precision que par l'interêt qu'il porte, ~~[illegible]~~ comme tout ce que vous ecrivez, que l'academie m'a chargée specialement de vous en temoigner sa satisfaction, en vous priant de tacher d'y joindre s'il est possible, d'ici à ~~[illegible]~~ sexmois, tems auquel il pourroit être imprimé dans nos Memoires, une figure qui fixât et l'attache du placenta et la situation du foetus dans la trompe petrefiée, et la proportion de cette tumeur relativement à la matrice, tous objets qui ont eté si bien décrits dans votre memoire. quand même le dessin n'en auroit pas été fait dans le tems, la memoire vous fourniroit sans doute assez ces particularités pour les faire dessiner à satisfaire au desir de l'academie.

Je lui ai fait part en même tems de votre remarque sur la Monstruosité de cette plante à fleur composée, dont nous ferions egalement usage si vous m'en envoyiez un dessin.

Continuez, mon cher Confrere, à nous enrichir de vos excellentes remarques, et soyez persuadé que personne n'est plus zelé que moi à les faire connoître et que c'est avec le plus grand plaisir que je profite de cette occasion de vous assurer de nouveau de la sincerité de l'attachement avec lequel j'ai l'honneur d'être,

Monsieur et illustre confrere,

Votre tres humble et tres obeissant serviteur Adanson

Paris ce Dimanche 21 mars 1773

Fig. 70. Letter from Michel Adanson to A. von Haller, dated March 21, 1773 [*Conservatoire botanique de Genève*]. *Reduced.*

He attended the Collège Sainte–Barbe in Paris, undoubtedly a school of some quality. Religion, classical languages and philosophy were the main subjects of secondary education, and everything shows that the substance of this knowledge was not wasted upon Adanson, although it is equally clear that his interest in natural sciences gradually awakened and stimulated his protest against much that was taught. Between 1744 and 1746 Adanson followed lessons at the Collège Royal and the Jardin du Roi, becoming acquainted with Réaumur, Bernard de Jussieu, Daubenton and—undoubtedly, although there is no direct proof—Buffon. He was introduced to the Duc d'Ayen, Louis de Noailles, who, as has been mentioned, had a well–stocked garden and arboretum at Saint–Germain, and with Pierre Barthélémy David, one of the directors of the *Compagnie des Indes*. Through David, Adanson was able to obtain an administrative position for some years at the trading post of the *Compagnie des Indes* in Senegal. He left for Africa in 1748 and remained there until 1754.

Adanson's Senegalese voyage, made as a young man in his formative years, played a rôle in his life which can be compared with that of the stay in Holland for Linnaeus. Both men set out to acquire new knowledge, convinced as they were that their home countries did not provide sufficient background for their formation as botanists. Both returned to their homes before reaching maturity, but with their mental concepts formed. The substance of their experiences, however, was as different as their personalities.

Adanson's Senegalese years shaped his character and provided him with a biological field experience which would guide him throughout his life. The practice of tropical botany showed him that the existing systems were of only very limited use in classifying the wealth of new forms, and that they were worthless in obtaining an insight into biological relationships.

"En efet, la Botanike semble chanjer entièrement de face, dès qu'on quite nos païs tempérés pour entrer dans la Zone torride: ce sont toujours des Plantes; mais elles sont si singulieres dans leur forme, elles ont des attributs si nouveaux, qu'ils éludent la plupart de nos Systèmes, dont les limites ne s'étendent guère au–delà des Plantes de nos climats... Il suffira de ... faire remarquer, qu'il i a entre les tropiques des païs immanses où l'on ne trouve aucune plante de certaines familles qui semblent réservées à l'Europe..."

"Ces diverses remarques, en me démontrant l'utilité des voiajes, me prouvoient de plus en plus la nécessité de considérer les Plantes d'une façon toute nouvele. Je crus donc qu'il faloit me dépouiller de l'ancien préjujé en faveur des systêmes & des idées qui en sont la base & qui bornent nos conessances, & qu'il faloit chercher dans la nature elle-même son Systême, s'il étoit vrai qu'ele en eût un …" (Familles des plantes 1: clvij; orthography of Adanson).

These years profoundly influenced the young botanist, who found himself in a different world, faced with seemingly endless difficulties. Through the evident inadequacy of the existing artificial methods and of those he had himself invented (following the custom of the day, when every botanist created his own system), he came to realize that their basic scope was too narrow. From one extreme he went to the other: if the systems were inadequate because their base was too narrow, he would use the broadest possible one. The flora of the tropics was so entirely different that he discovered entire plant families which were new to him or of which he had known only a few members, such as the palms; on the other hand, some families of plants that are very common in Europe, such as the Umbelliferae, were conspicuously absent from west tropical Africa. Being a child of an era in which the concept of 'nature' was all–important, he became convinced that one had to look for a classification in nature itself. Nature's course had to be followed in science; such a course would lead to the universal method in botany, just as it would lead to all universal knowledge in science itself. Abandoning one's own ideas in favor of the universal truth was evidently necessary: the various personal ideas in botany had led to nearly as many systems as there had been botanists. These old systems were misleading and distorted the picture of nature as if it were seen in a distorting mirror, a mirror given a bias by the human mind. Unbiased observation alone would reveal the master–plan of the universe. Adanson's ideas were not confined to botany alone: it was in these lonely years in Senegal that he conceived the notion of an universal encyclopedia in which all phenomena were to be described from the point of view of this philosophy. Every object or fact in every sphere of knowledge was open to analysis and description along these lines, and it would thus be possible to describe the structure of the universe.

Adanson relates that already in Senegal, backed by the conviction that it was necessary to take all parts into account, he had started to describe all plants that he met in all their parts. All those descriptions he put together in lists, omitting the common features and thereby singling out their differences. "It was by looking at all those descriptions combined that I found that the plants arranged themselves naturally in classes or families that could not be systematic [artificial] or arbitrary because they were not based on only one or a few parts which might change in some respects, but on all parts, so that the disappearance of one of those parts was compensated by the addition of another part."

On 18 February 1754 Adanson was back again in Paris: rich in experience, bringing more than five thousand specimens of plants and animals and a great many manuscripts, biological as well as other, varying from notes on the geography of Senegal and maps of the area to a dictionary of the Ouolof language. He began at once to write up his experiences and findings. The result was the *Histoire naturelle du Sénégal, Coquillages*, of 1757, containing a general account of his journeys and of the regions visited, followed by a treatment of mollusks. This zoological monograph deals not only with the hard shells found in the collectors' cabinets but also with the organs of the living animals as observed alive in the field. He applies for the first time his system of overall affinity, showing how simple it is to draw up a number of systems all based on one or a few characteristics, but that it is preferable to use combinations. According to Monod (1961), the method shows that the young zoologist (he was 30 at the time) was still "*à la recherche* d'une méthode," but that the result, for the time of writing, was considerable. A very interesting feature of the *Coquillages* is that Adanson used binary nomenclature for species of mollusks one year before Linnaeus's starting–point book for zoology, the *Systema naturae* ed. 10, appeared. The specific nomenclature proposed here for mollusks was further worked out in the *Familles des Plantes* and differs from that of Linnaeus in two important respects:

1. The first species of a genus, i.e. the type species, carries the generic name only (uninomial) without a species designation.

2. Additional species of a genus, which in principle could be shifted to other genera, have binary names consisting of the generic name and an epithet which is a noun of the same character as the generic name.

In 1758 Adanson was appointed *Censeur royal* by Louis XV at the instigation of Malesherbes, then director of the printing trade, who used such sinecures carrying a small salary to help his scientific and literary protégés. In the meantime Adanson had started the preparation of his *Familles des plantes*, the plan of which he presented to the *Académie* in his maiden speech delivered soon after his appointment as *adjoint botaniste*, replacing Fougeroux de Bondaroy. During his sojourn in Senegal Adanson had been appointed a corresponding member of the *Académie Royale des Sciences*, under the sponsorship of F. de Réaumur. Now his appointment as *adjoint botaniste* definitely set him on the road to a career at the Academy, a career which Adanson needed badly because he had no other opportunity to fill a scientific position. The Academy posts carried small salaries or 'pensions,' and it was mainly on this income that Adanson lived his frugal life.

The *Familles des plantes* appeared in 1763 (volume 2) and 1764 (volume 1) and was favorably received by the contemporary French literary press. The year 1763 was undoubtedly Adanson's most glorious year. After this book he published a lengthy study on the Baobab, called *Adansonia digitata* by Linnaeus, a study which is much more than a monograph of the then monotypic genus; it is a critical treatise on the Malvaceae. He prepared several reports for the French government on the development and exploration of French Guiana and Senegal in which he showed himself to be a man of vision: his proposals for increased travel and exploration, for the right plants to grow and animals to breed, for interchange of products between the colonies instead of with the mother country only, all have a distinctly advanced flavor. Needless to say that these reports fell on barren ground.

In 1764 Adanson, who had lived in Bernard de Jussieu's hospitable house in the Rue des Bernardins since his return from Senegal, had to move to a house of his own. Two Jussieu nephews were arriving from Lyon to take up their abode with Bernard. I have already mentioned above that this move was symbolic: one of the nephews was Antoine–Laurent. From 1764 on Adanson's published output becomes negligible, even though his manuscripts prove that his activity remained the same. The reason for this great change to non–productivity remains obscure, notwithstanding the recent biographical studies. Adanson was a member of the Academy, and as such in contact with his colleagues. His requirements were modest and he could spend all his time on his scientific work.

He never worked for money; on the contrary, he turned to experimentation and compilation with increased vigour. He grew melons, barley and grapes, in order to study their varieties in cultivation. He became more and more interested in the biological nature of taxa. For some time he believed that he had witnessed mutations and that species could change. Later he withdrew these statements and ascribed the monstrosities and the other changes which he had recorded to ecological circumstances. He coined the word 'mutation,' but had evidently no clear insight into the nature of this phenomenon; like Buffon and so many others, Adanson was only groping, feeling his way towards a new concept of taxa. With all his industry he never equalled the refined, elegant, exact and illustrative experiments of Kölreuter.

Adanson's importance for botany after 1763 is relatively small; for a detailed description of his life during the long years in which he produced manuscripts but not publications I must refer to Nicolas (1963). Much of Adanson's energy went into an attempt to publish an universal encyclopedia which he had planned during his Senegal years. This encyclopedia of natural history was to describe the universe and all human knowledge of it in the same way as his *Familles des plantes* described the vegetable world. Nature was an unbreakable whole, and the book should present an integrated picture of this whole. It was impossible to publish it in parts: Adanson requested the Academy to give its sanction to its publication. It seems, however, that by the time the scheme was presented to the Academy (1775) the manuscripts were of a very uneven quality. Some were extensive and worked out in the smallest details; for others there were only empty covers. Even so, the amount of work done by Adanson at that time impressed the rapporteurs deeply. The project, however, was so chimerical that no definite support was given. In later years Lamarck and others wrote what comes closest to Adanson's dream, perhaps without the synthetic element which he had in mind: the *Encyclopédie méthodique* published by Pancoucke.

In the meantime, however, Adanson contributed over 400 articles to Diderot's *Encyclopédie*. These articles, evidently based on the manuscript annotations for his own undertaking, appear in the first two volumes of the supplement to the *Encyclopédie*. Neither these articles nor the botanical contributions to other volumes by other botanists have ever been adequately studied; a cursory glance shows that together they consitute an important chapter in the botany of the Enlightenment.

The later decades of Adanson's life were difficult. His position in the Academy assured him a reasonable income until the revolution, but the gap between him and the younger generation of botanists widened. Gradually Antoine-Laurent de Jussieu, more practical than Adanson and also perhaps somewhat easier in his relations with colleagues, assumed a leading rôle. The revolutionary years were very difficult until the Academy was reorganized as the *Institut de France* and Adanson was reelected. Even at his advanced age, Adanson was a diligent member and attended most of the meetings of the Académie des Sciences. He died on 3 August 1806.

Adanson had shown to be a formidable opponent of the Linnaean reform. In his *Familles des Plantes* he had rejected Linnaean binary nomenclature, the generic reform and the sexual system. It is not the place here to enter again into his arguments, but as an illustration I quote here the entries under 'Linnaeus' in Adanson's subject index to the first volume of his book:

"LINNAEUS; ses ouvrajes	25
Ses 3 métodes universeles systématikes,	xxix
Sont très inférieures à cele de Tournefort,	xlij
Nombre de plantes qu'il a conu,	cxvj
Rejete la voie de comparaison dans l'étude des plantes	cxxix
Ses changemans de noms anciens,	cxxxij
N'ont pas été reconus par les botanistes qui tienent le 1er rang,	cxxxiv
S'attribue la découverte de l'enroulement des feuilles,	cxxxv
Et des Nectères,	cxxxvj
Et des grènes des Mousses,	cxxxvj
Sa synonymie n'est pas par-tout exacte,	clj
Ses 20 volumes sur la Botanike sont la plupart des réformes des précédens,	cxliv
Ses dogmes sont remplis de paradoxes,	clj
Ses genres étrangers sont très-fautifs,	Page cxcvj"

Never before, and rarely after, did a botanical subject index contain such incisive and to-the-point criticism; even so, the result was negligible. Adansons's work fell into oblivion; Linnaeus's '20 volumes on botany,' even though they were 'mere' reforms of what had been discovered by others, appeared at a time which was ripe for them. Adanson's plea, in itself excellent and fully justified, for a natural system and an inductive approach in botany would have been better received if he had accepted the positive merits of Linnaeus's reforms as a simple system of information storage and retrieval; instead, through his complete denial of the positive achievements of Linnaeus Adanson maneuvred himself into a position not unlike that of Haller. Success for the natural system was possible only on the basis of the Linnaean generic reform and nomenclature. That he realized this was one of the great merits of Antoine-Laurent de Jussieu.

ANTOINE–LAURENT DE JUSSIEU

The botanist who reaped the harvest of what had been sown by Linnaeus, Bernard de Jussieu, Gérard, Adanson and several others was Antoine–Laurent de Jussieu, the fourth member of the Jussieu dynasty of botanists and, undoubtedly, the most significant one. Jussieu lacked perhaps the originality and philosophical inclination of Adanson, but he was certainly his match as a taxonomist. His eminent practical sense made him successful where Adanson failed. At the time when Jussieu came into the picture it was already less necessary to take a stand with respect to Linnaeus. The important practical achievements of the Swede, embodied in his nomenclatural and generic reform, were generally accepted; his generic nomenclature and binary names for species were almost universally used. The time was right to combine the practical advantages of the Linnaean epoch with the new approach offered by the natural system.

Antoine–Laurent de Jussieu was born on 12 April 1748, the son of an elder brother of Antoine, Bernard, and Joseph: Christophle de Jussieu (1685–1758). Christophle was a pharmacist at Lyon with profound botanical interest who had, for instance, Fusée Aublet among his pupils. In 1765 Bernard invited Antoine–Laurent to finish his studies in Paris, and to live with him in the house on the rue des Bernardins. He stayed there with the rapidly aging Bernard until the latter's death in 1777; during these twelve years Antoine–Laurent's career was made and his future provided for. The daily contact with his eminent teacher profoundly influenced him, as is clear from his *Genera plantarum* (1789), as well as from the reverence with which Antoine–Laurent used to speak of his uncle in later years.

The seventeen–year–old Antoine–Laurent, who had just finished secondary school in Lyon, started the study of medicine at the Paris medical faculty. In 1770 he obtained his degree as medical doctor after submitting a thesis on the comparison between animal and vegetable physiology: *An oeconomiam animalem inter et vegetalem analogia?* Soon after his final examination, Lemonnier, Antoine's successor as professor of botany at the *Jardin du Roi*, invited Antoine–Laurent to act as his deputy, mainly in giving the botany course at the garden. The choice of Lemonnier, court physician to Louis XV and amateur botanist of very moderate repute, as Antoine's successor, worked to the disadvantage of Bernard de Jussieu and Michel Adanson. With the appointment of the much younger Antoine–Laurent to fulfill virtually all the duties of the professor of botany, the prospect of a teaching career was finally closed to Adanson. Antoine-Laurent had found the right niche from which to develop his unusual gifts: in this he was a lucky man. His career was therefore in sharp contrast with that of the tragic figure of Adanson. It would be wrong, however, to regard this chain of events as a series of acts of nepotism; the development must be judged with more feeling for the subtleties of the mutual relationships of botanists and courtiers and for the personalities involved. It remains a pity, however, that the influences which promoted the gradual evolution of Antoine-Laurent into a great scientist quenched the hopes of that other man, however different—and difficult—he may have been. Antoine-Laurent never seems to have realized the tragic aspect of the course of events that led him to the top of his profession; at any rate he was never great enough to pay a tribute in writing to his older and harmless rival, whose contribution to taxonomic science was of the same magnitude as his own.

The talents of Antoine-Laurent soon became evident in his first botanical publication, the *Examen de la famille des Renoncules*, submitted to the *Académie des Sciences* in 1773 and published in 1777. This early publication, in which the author develops his general ideas from a profound study of a single family, reminds one of the analogous first paper by Adanson on the *Malvaceae*. Both authors gave the essence of their natural methods in these early papers: Adanson stressed the multiplicity of characters and the need to take them all into consideration, while Antoine-Laurent—taking this more or less for granted—emphasized the difference in value or weight of these characters.

Almost simultaneously with the presentation of his *Examen*, early in 1773, came the election of Antoine-Laurent to the *Académie des sciences* as *adjoint-botaniste*, in place of Adanson, who was promoted to the rank of *associé-botaniste*.

Antoine-Laurent's second paper was presented in 1774: *Exposition d'un nouvel ordre de plantes adopté dans les démonstrations du Jardin royal*. This paper (published 1778) deals mainly with the criteria used to circumscribe Jussieu's classes, and less with those used for what would ultimately become of greatest importance in the *Genera plantarum*, the delimitation of the families.

From 1774 until 1789 Antoine-Laurent published very little. These years were used for the thorough study of the genera and families of the angiosperms that was indispensable for the writing of his book. In 1776 the king entrusted to Antoine–Laurent the herbarium of the late Philibert Commerson (1727–1773) for study and publication. We have seen above how Commerson accompanied de Bougainville from 1766 to 1769 on his voyage around the world. The rich Commerson collections (the original set at Paris numbers 30.000 specimens) were of basic importance for Jussieu's preparatory work for the *Genera plantarum*. Commerson's field notes were handed to Jussieu in 1784; he published 37 of Commerson's new genera, duly attributing them to their spiritual father, and based another 15 genera on Commerson material. Among the Commerson genera validated by Jussieu are several important taxa such as *Hortensia, Bougainvillea, Colletia, Hebe, Securinega* and *Hura*.

The king's decision to put the Commerson herbarium in the hands of Antoine–Laurent was not entirely to the liking of some of the other Paris botanists, especially since it was so long before the results of the study were published. This must have been the reason why a few years later, in 1786, the rich collections made in South America by Joseph Dombey were assigned by the king through Buffon to the outsider L'Héritier de Brutelle for study and publication, rather than to the botanist at the royal garden. The transfer of the Commerson herbarium to Jussieu caused the latter to get in touch with Sir Joseph Banks (1748–1820) in order to avoid duplication with Banks's work on the collections made by himself and Solander during Cook's first voyage (1768–71). The two botanists entertained a regular exchange of specimens, but also showed signs of "green fever" to get elected as members of foreign academies. Banks was elected foreign member of the French Academy of Sciences in 1787, but Jussieu, who had applied for election as Foreign Associate of the Royal Society as early as 1787, had to wait until 1829 before that honor was bestowed upon him.

Another of Jussieu's correspondents was Sir James Edward Smith (1759–1829), who sent him information on the Linnaean herbarium and occasionally also fragments of critical plants. In a letter dated 20 March 1789 Jussieu thanks Smith for his reception as a member of the newly created Linnean Society. "I hope that [the Society] will pardon me for not being wholly Linnaean: I deviate from that great man in his systematics, which seem to keep science away from its true goal, but I hold in high esteem his nomenclature, his genera, his species; and I believe that he has rendered a real service to botany in this respect, although he often omits from his genera the essential characters derived from the insertions."

Bernard died in 1777, his last years made gloomy by the failing of his sight.

Antoine–Laurent succeeded him as *sous–démonstrateur aux Écoles de Botanique du Jardin Royal* on 18 June 1778. Meanwhile he continued to deputize for Lemonnier until 1785, when the latter was replaced as professor of botany by René–Louiche Desfontaines (1750–1833). Desfontaines, two years younger than Antoine–Laurent and not engaged in numerous time–consuming outside activities, like Lemonnier, could give his full energy to the professorship. This enabled Antoine–Laurent to start writing the *Genera Plantarum*; the book appeared in the first days of August 1789.

The tumultuous events of 1789 hardly shook Antoine–Laurent. He seems to have had a great gift for keeping aloof from the happenings around him, and this is no doubt the reason why he lived through those eventful years without suffering any personal injury or loss of property.

Until the revolution the *Jardin du Roi* consisted of a botanic garden and a natural history cabinet. This cabinet contained a variety of collections and odd *curiosa*, of which the Tournefort and Vaillant herbaria were the most important botanical items. There was neither a general herbarium nor a library: it is important to take these circumstances into account in connection with Jussieu's work on his *Genera*. This work was done almost exclusively with the books in his own library, though he may occasionally have used books from the *Bibliothèque nationale* or from other private libraries.

One of the most important assets of the Jussieu library was its wealth of authentic manuscripts, letters and other botanical documents. The Jussieus had all been members of the *Académie des sciences* from an early age, and as such they had been in close contact with many correspondents. Under the *ancien régime* each academician had one or more personal correspondents from whom he received communications, letters, collections, etc. These materials did not go to the Academy but remained the property of the individual members, who could thereby accumulate interesting collections, provided they chose their correspondents well. The Jussieu family obtained in this way, as well as by purchase, collections of dried plants and of manuscripts and books which were unrivalled in France at the time, and which can best be compared with the collections of Sir Joseph Banks. There were other important botanical libraries at the time, such as that of L'Héritier de Brutelle, but the exceptional variety of manuscripts, letters and herbarium collections of the Jussieus made their house the main center of plant taxonomic research before the revolution. These collections were kept intact during the revolution, and added to in later years. In 1857, however, a few years after the death of the last of the botanical Jussieus, Adrien, they were dispersed.

With respect to herbarium material Jussieu's position was somewhat different, since he had access to the Tournefort and Vaillant herbaria, to the Commerson herbarium, and to some other smaller collections at the *Jardin du Roi*. His main support, however, came again from the Jussieu collections themselves, a very rich herbarium still kept separate today. For living plants Jussieu made use of public collections, mainly those in the *Jardin du Roi*, and, to a limited extent, those in private gardens and arboreta such as the Saint–Germain arboretum of Noailles and the Trianon garden. This last garden, however, had lost its importance in the years during which the *Genera plantarum* was prepared.

For an account of the long and successful career of Jussieu after 1789 until his death on 17 September 1836 I must refer to my earlier paper on this subject (1964).

JUSSIEU'S NATURAL SYSTEM

Antoine–Laurent de Jussieu's basic ideas on plant classification were first stated in the two memoirs of 1773 and 1774 and later in the Introduction to his *Genera plantarum*.

In his publication on the *Renoncules* of 1773 (1777) Jussieu discusses the principles of natural classification and refers to his three predecessors, Linnaeus, Adanson, and his uncle, with equal respect. Jussieu follows Adanson's terminology and speaks of the family of the *Ranunculi*. He cites the treatment by Adanson with approval and points out, for example, that Adanson had very appropriately compared the nectaries of *Helleborus* with the petals of *Ranunculus*. Adanson, in his report to the Academy on this article (*cf.* Hamy 1909, p. 62), praised it in general, but carefully pointed out the difference in the methods followed by Jussieu and by himself. In this paper Jussieu clearly states the principle of subordination of characters. Adanson applied this principle in practice and *a posteriori* but was more concerned with what he called the *génie* of each family, the particular combination of characters which led him to circumscribe the families. In his paper of 1774, the *Exposition sur un nouvel ordre de plantes* (publ. 1778), Jussieu developed his ideas fully to account for the new arrangement of the plants in the *Jardin du Roi*. Adanson is mentioned only incidentally, and his system is condemned in a general phrase in which Jussieu states that his uncle's Trianon system was more natural than the methods which had hitherto (1774) been published. This *Exposition* provides us with the key to Jussieu's opinions on the higher taxa (divisions, classes, families) of the plant kingdom.

In 1773 the Paris botanic garden was enlarged and had to be replanted and rearranged. The old arrangement was still that of Tournefort. Jussieu, who was charged with the rearrangement, did not want to plant the garden in accordance with the artificial Linnaean system, even though his esteem for it as a practical device was high; as a pupil of Bernard, he wanted to follow "the natural order."

"The plants ... seem ... to form with each other a continuous chain, of which the two extremes are the smallest herb and the largest tree. By means of a very smooth gradation one goes from one to the other, in the process assigning a place near each other to those of which the affinity is marked by a greater number of mutual relations. This order, which is that of nature, does not interest only the natural philosophers, but is of a more practical usefulness. Rational analysis, confirmed by experience, shows that plants that agree in characters also have the same properties, so that once the natural order is given one could determine the properties by means of external marks."

The natural order, says Antoine–Laurent, is like the philosopher's stone. "The impossibility of bringing together or even of knowing all the plants that must constitute the general chain will always be an obstacle that cannot be overcome. There will be empty spaces, difficult to fill, but even though nature has dispersed the material necessary for the reconstruction of this order, it enables us at least to get an inkling of the principles on which it is founded. Among the number of characters provided by plants there are a few essential ones which are general and invariable, and which apparently must form the basis of the required order. They are not arbitrary but based on observation, and are to be found only by going from the particular to the general."

In order to understand what families are, Antoine–Laurent points out that nature facilitates the work of botanists by providing seven main families which are clear–cut and generally admitted: grasses, lilies, composites, umbellifers, labiates, crucifers and legumes. These families serve to reveal the criteria for the natural order. All criteria that would tend to disrupt the accepted natural families must be rejected; those by which none of these families would be divided are to be retained. A basic rule for this approach towards the natural system is, therefore, "a character that varies in particular cases cannot have a general value." By means of this general principle one can at once dismiss characters with no general value, or which are insufficiently invariable. We shall find alternate and opposite, simple and pinnate leaves in the Compositae, tuberous and filamentous roots among the lilies, and so on. What remain are the parts of the 'fructification,' especially the most 'essential' parts, which can provide the primary characters for the natural order. Even the calyx and the corolla are not invariable: it is only the parts directly concerned with the ability to reproduce that provide the primary characters. The pistil and the stamens are therefore essential parts since they take care of that highest achievement of nature: self–reproduction. Antoine–Laurent concludes from this that because these are the organs that perform this highest function of nature, they must of necessity provide the primary characters for the natural classification. He goes one step further: among the parts of the 'fructification' it is evidently the seed, 'formed at such great cost,' that is the essential part *par excellence*, providing the primary characters on which the divisions of the natural order must be based.

Jussieu, seeking a criterion for the scale of the particular to the general, accepts as such the relation with the reproductional capacity of the plant. This is not really an inductive approach, as he seems to have thought, but an *a priori* assumption; the reasoning does not differ essentially from the aprioristic scholastic attitude of many of his predecessors, and it ignores the much clearer, inductive and empirical approach by Adanson (1763). On the contrary, this aspect of Antoine–Laurent's concept of 'natural' is Aristotelian, as was that of Cesalpino and Linnaeus, indicating the 'essence' of things, the qualities by which they (i.e. the plants) have come into being, have been born (*nata*). To find such a concept of nature in the mind of this French botanist at the end of the eighteenth century is perhaps not so surprising, since Jussieu's training and interest had been strictly botanical, and he had never shown much concern for the great spiritual movements of his time. This aprioristic archaism, however, is noticeable only in the higher ranks of Jussieu's system, i.e. his classes and divisions (see p. lxxj), and it is this part of his work that has not stood the test of time. On the family level Jussieu, like his predecessors, used a different philosophical reasoning in combination with his botanical intuition, and the results are still to be found in our present systems. Our classification on the family level is still mainly based on the principle of overall affinity first practised but not explained by Linnaeus in his *Classes* of 1738 and his *Fragmenta methodi naturalis* of 1751, and first consciously advocated by Adanson in 1763. Jussieu shows an interesting methodological dualism. For the higher ranks he applies rigidly the principle of subordination of characters derived from a scholastic background of *essentialia*, thus making his system artificial; his main practical effort, however, resulted in an excellent description of natural families and genera based on an intuitive assessment of overall affinity along traditional lines. This methodological inversion is amply discussed by Daudin (1926). Before analysing it further, two other 'old' notions among Jussieu's guiding ideas should be mentioned.

Jussieu's concept of the plant kingdom includes the acceptance of the *scala naturae*, the 'Great Chain of Being' (*cf.* Lovejoy 1936), which is the idea— mentioned above on several occasions— of a single series of living beings going from low to high. This static philosophical concept reflects the order of creation in a logical sense, without a time component. The *scala naturae* and its successor, the natural series, were in no way forerunners of evolutionary concepts, though sometimes the term 'tree of life' was used for them. We found this aspect also in Adanson's writings; he too was still of the opinion that the natural system (based on overall affinity) would ultimately show a linear arrangement from simple to involved. Jussieu was also aware (Intr. p. xxxv) of Linnaeus' comparison of the plant kingdom with a geographical map (*Philosophia botanica* no. 77), a more advanced, although equally static, notion of the interrelationship (just like Donati's famous "net" of 1750); but in his later writings he leaves the question open (*cf.* Daudin p. 207) or shows a certain preference for the single 'chain.' On balance he mostly advocates the principle of the natural series, the continuous chain of formal mutual relations between organisms from 'simple' to 'composite,' objectively extant in nature, not subject to change. Jussieu

Fig. 71. Letter by Antoine-Laurent de Jussieu to Baron de Chabrol, December 22, 1813. The Baron de Chabrol to whom this letter is addressed was Gilbert Joseph Gaspard, comte de Chabrol de Volvic (1773–1843) who was a member of the scientific commission for Egypt, one of the co-editors of the series of publications on the results of the expedition, author of Sur les moeurs et les usages des Egyptiens modernes, and prefect of the Département de la Seine from 1812–1830. Jussieu here accepts his second appointment as 'president' of the ninth arrondissement of Paris. [*Conservatoire botanique de Genève*]. *Reduced.*

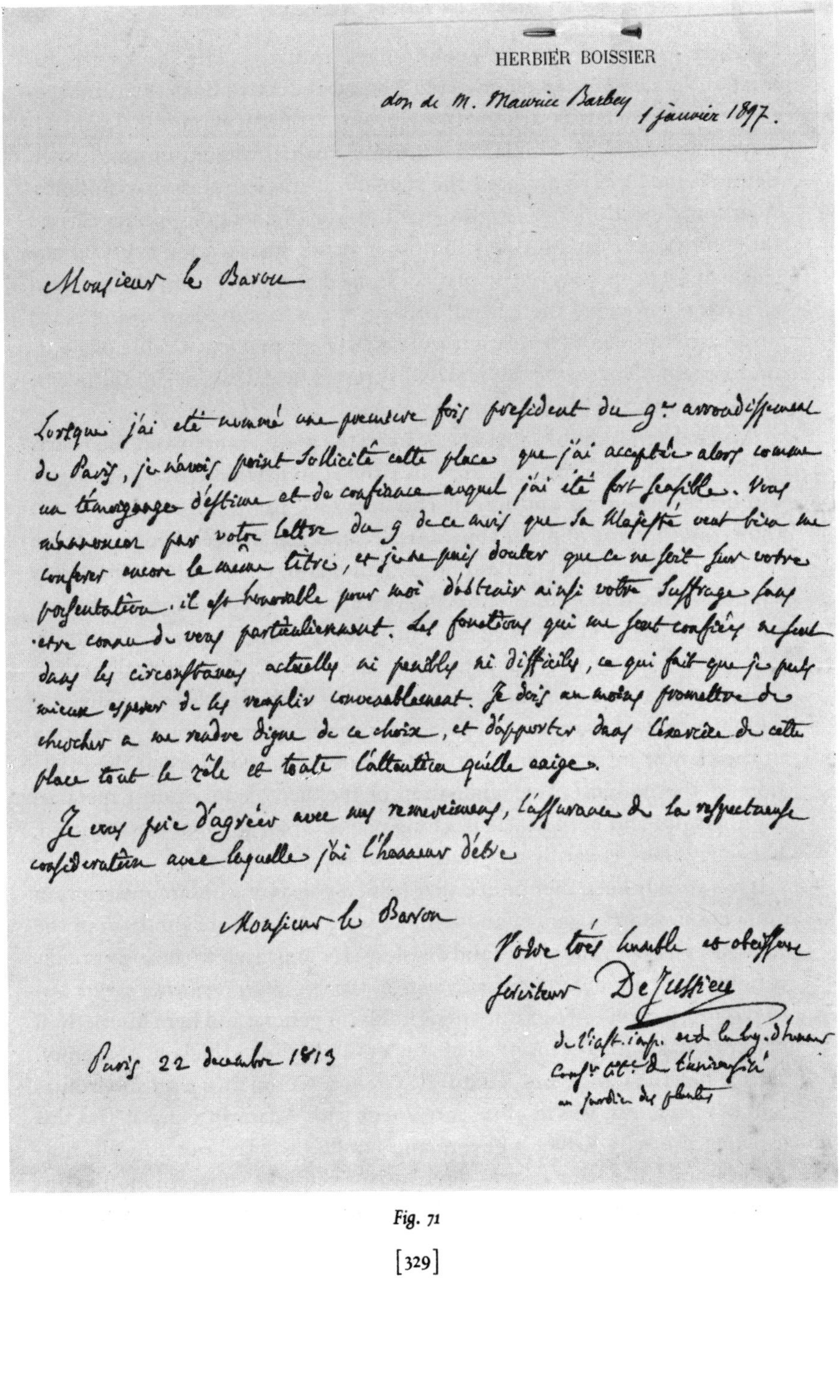

Monsieur le Baron

Lorsque j'ai été nommé une première fois président du 9.e arrondissement de Paris, je n'avais point sollicité cette place que j'ai acceptée alors comme un témoignage d'estime et de confiance auquel j'ai été fort sensible. Vous m'annoncez par votre lettre du 9 de ce mois que Sa Majesté veut bien me conserver encore le même titre, et je ne puis douter que ce ne soit sur votre présentation. il est honorable pour moi d'obtenir ainsi votre suffrage sans être connu de vous particulièrement. Les fonctions qui me sont confiées ne sont dans les circonstances actuelles ni pénibles ni difficiles, ce qui fait que je puis mieux espérer de les remplir convenablement. Je dois au moins promettre de chercher à me rendre digne de ce choix, et d'apporter dans l'exercice de cette place tout le zèle et toute l'attention qu'elle exige.

Je vous prie d'agréer avec mes remercîmens, l'assurance de la respectueuse considération avec laquelle j'ai l'honneur d'être

Monsieur le Baron

Votre très humble et obéissant
serviteur De Jussieu
de l'ast. imp. et de la lg. d'honneur
cons.r gén.l de l'université
au jardin des plantes

Paris 22 décembre 1813

Fig. 71

[329]

nowhere shows signs of pre-evolutionistic thinking. The species are distinct and stable entities characterized by reproductive links ('natural species'); the higher taxa are, in comparison, artificial or nominal, not always objectively discernible: they form a qualitative continuum. Jussieu never seems to have doubted the stability of species; obviously Buffon's, Adanson's and Lamarck's arguments in favor of changing species carried little conviction for him. On the other hand, Jussieu's remark that the (medicinal) properties of the plants can be determined from the external characters, provided the natural order is known, is modern, being based on an assumption of correlation and on the high predictive value of a natural system. This view, also clearly expressed by Adanson, should not be confused with the old belief in 'signatures.'

Jussieu defends the old analogy between the plant embryo and the hearts of higher animals (1773, p. 221, Intr. xlv), the acotyledones corresponding to the hearts of worms and insects (no auricles), the monocotyledones to those of fishes and reptiles (one auricle) and the dicotyledones to those of birds and mammals (two auricles). This analogy is brought forward in support of the importance of having the number of cotyledons as the primary character, and shows again a surprisingly 'unenlightened' attitude.

It is not necessary to give a detailed discussion of Jussieu's natural method of higher taxa. The main division is according to the cotyledons, a division dating back to Cesalpino. The secondary and tertiary divisions, resulting in the classes, are according to the structure of the corolla and the insertion of the stamens. The subdivision of the dicotyledones into apetalae, monopetalae and polypetalae has long played a part in plant classification, but today there is hardly any trace left of Jussieu's classes.

It has already been mentioned that Jussieu's ideas on the circumscription and classification of genera and families were much more subtle than the rigid rules used for the classes and divisions. His approach to the lower ranks is fundamentally different: *consociandae sunt species maiori caracterum numero conformes* (1789, p. xxxvi). The same thesis holds for genera, and here his method definitely takes into account all characters and follows the laws of affinity. This is not the concept of a natural system based on an *a priori* subordination of characters. It is in close agreement with Adanson's views, and this explains also why Jussieu's genera and families worked out so well, notwithstanding the later widely-discussed principle of subordination as opposed to that of equal weighting. Jussieu was an over-cautious man who scrupulously used the achievements of the past; he had no desire to revolutionize plant classification, and he stressed the provisional character of his own work. In his discussion of the principles underlying the classification of species into genera and genera into families (1789, pp. xxxvii seq.), he carefully explains how all characters have to be tested carefully by constant comparison. He comes to the conclusion that the characters, after careful consideration and observation, are of different 'weight' or value. This is an inductive way of working, not entirely unlike that of Adanson. In this work he is guided by the many genera accepted as natural by practically all botanists, a circumstance used by him as a touchstone for the value of characters, as explained above for the families. In essence this was a notion of correlation. His evaluation of characters was thus mainly based on observation and comparison, and not—as was the case with his evaluation of the 'really primary' characters used for the divisions and classes—on an aprioristic equalization of the natural and the essential. The divisions and classes are obtained by means of deduction, the families and genera by means of induction.

Jussieu's *Genera plantarum* (1789) is especially important because of the description and circumscription of the hundred families (*ordines naturales*) covering the entire plant kingdom.

Jussieu's complete system, the fifteen classes with the hundred families, was first published (with only some very minor differences) by Lamarck in his *Discours preliminaire* to the first volume of the *Encyclopédie méthodique* (1783). The descriptions of the families and many of the genera from A–Gor will also be found in the first two volumes of Lamarck's work. Lamarck does full justice to Jussieu's spiritual property and states that he follows this method because "cet ordre nous paroît offrir la distribution la plus naturelle des végétaux qu'on ait encore imagninée ..." Lamarck's treatment of the genera was fully independent of that of Jussieu, except that he assigned them to the latter's families.

As far as the cryptogams are concerned, Jussieu's system contains little that is noteworthy. The time had not yet come for the cryptogams, and for an assessment of Jussieu's true merits we must turn to the angiosperms; neither the microscopic techniques necessary for the cryptogams nor the knowledge of the great variety of fossil records necessary for the assessment of the ferns and gymnosperms were available in 1789.

No better proof could be given of the importance of the *Genera plantarum* for the classification of the angiosperms than the choice of the book as the starting–point for the list of conserved family names in the *International Code of Botanical Nomenclature*. Seventy–six of the hundred family names used in the *Genera plantarum* are now conserved and attributed to A.-L. de Jussieu. This does not mean, however, that there were no earlier attempts. I have discussed previously (1963, 1964) the families of angiosperms of Adanson (1763) compared with those described by Linnaeus (1751, 1764), Bernard de Jussieu (1759, publ. 1789) and Antoine–Laurent de Jussieu (in the *Genera Plantarum*). Jussieu uses 11 family names of Linnaeus, 46 of Bernard de Jussieu and 6 of Adanson; 34 family names were used by him for the first time.

The *Genera plantarum*, even though still thoroughly old–fashioned in some less important aspects, was eminently successful because of the soundly inductive approach of Jussieu to the classification of species and genera. The grouping of his genera into families was so successful that many of his family concepts have remained in use until today. With the *Genera plantarum* the 'natural system' had gained a firm foothold in systematic botany, firm also because it accepted the main tenets of the Linnaean generic and nomenclatural reform. Biological systematics, however, posing the question of why and how the affinities came about, fared less well with Jussieu: it would do much better in the hands of his contemporary Lamarck.

LAMARCK

Lamarck's life and work exemplify perhaps most clearly the great change in thinking which occurred in the life sciences towards the end of the eighteenth century and which resulted in the establishment of biology as a discipline of its own. The dominance of the essentially static, hermeneutic, timeless thinking based on the principle of plenitude (a creation of self–contained perfection) came to an end and was replaced by dynamic and creative thinking, basically positivist, which allowed for concepts such as development and diversification in time.

Lamarck's life–span (1744–1829) is almost the same as that of Antoine–Laurent de Jussieu. The difference in development, however, is considerable. Jussieu reached his peak with the publication of his *Genera plantarum*. His later publications were essentially variations upon the themes elaborated

[332]

by him between 1770 and 1789. Jussieu's empiricism made him develop a natural system for the flowering plants which would be at the basis of all subsequent systems of that group of plants; however, he did not attempt in any way to explain diversity in terms of historical relationship. Lamarck's ideas, in his botanical period, developed more or less on a parallel with those of Jussieu. After 1789, however, his ideas continued to evolve, especially in connection with his work in zoology and geology. They culminated in the first full–fledged theory of descent and in the first interpretation of the natural affinities of living beings on the basis of phylogenetic relationship.

Little of this spectacular and fundamental turn of mind, however, is predicted by Lamarck's early botanical work. A brief review of Lamarckian botany, however, is in order, if only because he closes our era with the publication of the most detailed 'species plantarum' one could ask for at the time, the first botanical volumes of the *Encyclopédie méthodique*. A more general review of Lamarck's ideas, often of cosmic scope, is the subject of a different paper (Stafleu 1971a).

Lamarck's life is so well described by his numerous biographers that I repeat here only the list of the five main periods as given by Tschulok (1937):

1. 1744–1761, childhood at home and education at the Jesuit college of Amiens.

2. 1761–1768, army career,

3. 1768–1778, bank employee in Paris until the publication of the *Flore françoise*,

4. 1778–1793, botanist at the *Jardin des Plantes*

5. 1793–1829, professor of zoology at the *Museum d'Histoire naturelle*.

In his early botanical work Lamarck follows the lines of thought developed by Buffon, Bernard de Jussieu and Adanson. However, in addition to his elaboration of a natural system expressing the totality of biosystematic knowledge, he developed a simple analytical system facilitating identification. This 'analytical method' is explained at great length in the theoretical introduction to the *Flore françoise* (1778) and is essentially an elaborate, usually dichotomous key of the kind which is now a routine element of our floras. Lamarck states that the natural system cannot provide a means for easy and rapid identification and naming of plants; it merely portrays the

[333]

marche de la nature. For identification a pragmatic and artificial analysis is needed. The main purpose of the *Flore françoise* is to provide such a means of identification, one which is therefore fully comparable in aim to Linnaeus's sexual system, with the difference that Lamarck did not presume his analytical key to be anything else but just that.

Lamarck frequently uses the term *marche de la nature.* Before 1793 he used this purely in the context of a timeless creation, and as an expression of his conviction that any attempt to depict diversity by means of dividing lines, classes, families, or genera is nothing but an avowal of weakness by the human mind. All these concepts are human: the immense variability and variation in nature is caught only very incompletely by such procedures. Lamarck draws the line with species, because these can be regarded as identifiable reproductive communities.

Soon after he had completed the *Flore françoise* and made a European tour accompanying Buffon's son, Lamarck was invited to prepare the botanical part of Panckoucke's great *Encyclopédie méthodique.*

Panckoucke's *Encyclopédie* was a worthy successor to the *Grande Encyclopédie* of Diderot and d'Alembert. Between 1781 and 1832 not less than 166 quarto volumes were published (of which 40 were atlas volumes with illustrations, maps and indexes) dealing with separate disciplines. The arrangement of the subject matter within the volumes, however, was mostly alphabetical.

Lamarck wrote the text for the first two volumes and part of the third of the series *Botanique;* the work was completed by Poiret between 1792 and 1817. In addition to the main text, a richly illustrated synoptic review of the genera and species was published separately under the title *Tableau encyclopédique des trois règnes de la nature, Botanique,* to which Lamarck contributed not less than 900 plates. This synoptic treatment follows the Linnaean system (at the request of the publisher!) and presents genera and species in the classical Linnaean manner, with 'essential' characters (brief) and 'natural' characters (elaborate). The accompanying plates (*Illustration des genres*) constituted for a long time the most elaborate botanical iconography.

The main text has, in alphabetical order, descriptions (in French) of both taxa and concepts. With respect to the taxa, popularization went so far as to make all key words French: in order to find the treatment of the genus *Plumeria,* for instance, one has to look under 'Franchipanier.' The descriptive detail is amazing: for each species full synonymy and literature references are given, as well as ample descriptive morphology and information on geographical distribution. The genera are all attributed to families and the family circumscriptions and treatments closely follow those of Jussieu. In fact, by 1782, when the first botanical volume of the *Encyclopédie* was published, Jussieu's *Genera plantarum* was still seven years away. Lamarck published Jussieu's system, with due acknowledgment, long before Antoine–Laurent did this himself; the treatments of the families in the first two volumes (A–Gor) have precedence over those in the *Genera plantarum*.

The first volume starts off with a *Discours préliminaire*, a historical review of plant systematics which bears a strong resemblance to that given by Adanson in his *Familles des plantes* (1763). Lamarck pays Adanson one handsome compliment: "Néanmoins M. Adanson ... qui s'est livré depuis long-temps avec une ardeur incroyable à l'étude non seulement de toutes les parties de la Botanique, mais même de toutes les branches de l'Histoire naturelle ... aura toujours la gloire d'avoir publié le premier des familles des Plantes déterminées dans le dessein de faire connoître les vrais rapports des végétaux entr'eux."

The theoretical articles published by Lamarck in the first two volumes provide a good picture of his methodological thinking in his pre–evolutionary days. Since I have dealt with these articles in some detail elsewhere, I discuss here only Lamarck's attitude towards Linnaeus and his writings. Lamarck has a positive attitude with respect to Linnaean nomenclature, but differs with him on almost all theoretical issues.

In the article 'Genres' Lamarck attributes the current concept of generic circumscription to Tournefort. He admits that Linnaeus did much to increase our knowledge of genera, but he criticises, correctly, the fact that so many Linnaean generic diagnoses appear to be based on a single species of the group. Lamarck recognised obviously the rôle of essentialist thinking in this centering of generic diagnoses on single species (the type concept, now purely pragmatic, was born from essentialism) and stresses the importance of describing the diversity within a genus.

He does not share Linnaeus's conviction that the genera are 'natural' and objectively existing in nature. Linnaeus "a prononcé l'anathême contre ceux qui assureroient que les genres ne sont point dans la nature." It was much simpler for him [Linnaeus] to support his opinion by the so–called axioms and extremely laconic maxims with which he filled his *Philosophia botanica* and *Critica botanica* than by solid proof, which alone could convince those not impressed by mere authority.

Linnaeus and others, says Lamarck, maintained that nature makes no jumps, "ce qui signifie, si je ne me trompe, que la série de ses productions doit être nuancée dans toute son étendue." This alone makes it impossible to find well established, concrete lines of separation in nature between groups such as genera. Linnaeus's dogma of the natural and objective character of genera provided him with an excuse for the arbitrary nature of his generic circumscriptions. The 'natural character' was invoked to authorize the adoption of many unsuitable assemblages of species.

Linnaeus stated that the genus constitutes the character not the character the genus (*Phil. bot.* no. 169). Lamarck rejects this: the genera are small parts of a great series, characterised by form relationships, and a product of 'art' rather than 'nature.' There are no "Brigades, regiments, battalions, and squadrons" in nature (a reference to the *Philosophia botanica*); such divisions are pragmatic. Nature shows a gradual, almost continuous increase in organization, but no hierarchy. The *scala naturae* is not a scale with steps; it is a slope paved with species.

The Enlightenment was anti-authoritarian. Exponents of this thinking, such as Buffon and Lamarck, denied the objective existence of a power hierarchy, whether in society or in nature. Rationalising this, they opted for the far end of the concept of plenitude: continuity. Such a shift was necessary before they could take the second step: morphological continuity in the world of living beings reflects continuity in time. This step, however, was not taken by Lamarck until well after 1789.

Epilogue

The success of Linnaeus's methods and ideas in systematic botany was founded on their eminent practicality. When he entered the field, Linnaeus was confronted with a chaotic situation caused by a great diversity of often incompatible nomenclatural and classification practices which all failed to meet the demands of a discipline faced with a rapidly increasing flow of information. Linnaeus looked upon himself with some justification as the one who recognized the intrinsic order of nature, which had been obscured only by the faulty practices and unclear concepts of many of his predecessors.

Linnaeus's methods were based on philosophical principles and logical a priori assumptions which gradually lost their relevance to the natural sciences during the eighteenth century. Even so, the direct results of his work were salutary: descriptions were standardized, ranks fixed, names given according to precise rules and a classification proposed which permitted rapid and efficient storage and retrieval of taxonomic information. No wonder that much of what Linnaeus proposed stood the test of time. The designation of species by binary names which have the character of code designations is only one element out of many which show the profound practicality underlying Linnaeus's activities and publications.

The question whether or not Linnaeus advanced systematic biology can only be answered in a positive way: his contribution to systematics was the greatest by any single author. To start an information system and coding device which is still fully accepted after more than two centuries is a feat which finds no counterpart in any of the other sciences. Even the coming of the electronic age has not necessitated any fundamental change in the essentially Linnaean methods of naming taxa. Our computers work as easily with the system of binary nomenclature as the basis of their 'thesaurus' for systematic biology as they would have done with more modern systems possibly more mathematical, but devoid of the extremely valuable mnemonic qualities of Linnaean nomenclature.

Linnaeus's merits were of course numerous. It is not necessary to elaborate upon them now. His ideas caught on rapidly and spread throughout Europe with astonishing speed and success. Within a few years after the publication of the *Species plantarum*, authors who failed to adopt the Linnaean binary nomenclature and generic reform created for themselves an enormous handicap. Many of their writings were doomed to oblivion because of their lack of communication with the new Linnaean language spoken by the other authors.

Linnaeus's ideas were put forward within the framework of what was already in his time rapidly becoming an antiquated philosophy. During the course of the period accepted for this essay this essentialist thinking was gradually replaced by the more modern nominalist and empiricist approaches; many of the most faithful Linnaeans did not share this essentialism with the master. Linnaeus himself was such a good naturalist that he often broke through his own aprioristic barriers in favour of describing or analysing nature in accordance with what he called 'observation.' He knew quite well that the 'principles of truth' had to emerge through such unbiassed observation.

Linnaeus shared with most of his contemporaries a surprising lack of appreciation of the time element in understanding life. It was in this respect perhaps that his teachings were most vulnerable, because they did not provide an opening towards biology. His essentially static concept of the universe as a created entity, illustrating the wisdom of the Creator, had no room for the dynamic views of romanticism. Towards the end of the era the essentialist incubus was disappearing: better information on fossil plants and animals, on hybridization, mutation and variation, on plant–habitat relationships, on overall affinity, had swept away the world–picture of timeless essentials in favour of an appreciation of diversity on an empirical basis, stimulating further inductive research and paving the way for hypothetico–deductive science on a positivist basis, admitting the development of such concepts as phylogeny and evolution. The step from an unbiassed study of diversity in space to that of diversity in time was the logical consequence of this development.

Epilogue

All these new ideas and events, however, needed a medium in the way of descriptive procedure, standardized terminology and nomenclature, and simple devices for handling systematic information in general. It was Linnaeus who provided this medium. To recognize the fact that this Linnaean legacy still serves us successfully today is perhaps the greatest compliment which we can pay to that universal naturalist, arch–systematist, excellent observer and systematic genius, Carl Linnaeus.

References *

ACHARIUS, E. 1776 – see Linnaeus, C. 1776.

ADANSON, M. 1757 – *Histoire naturelle du Sénégal. Coquillages*. Paris.

ADANSON, M. 1763 – *Familles des plantes*. Paris, 2 vols. *Facsimile* reprint Lehre 1966, with an introduction by Frans A. Stafleu.

AGASSIZ, L. 1962 – *Essay on classification*. Cambridge, Mass. (reprint of original edition of 1857).

AITON, W. 1789 – *Hortus kewensis*. London, 3 vols.

AMOREUX, M. 1822 – Notice historique sur Antoine Gouan. *Mémoires de la Société Linnéenne de Paris* 1: 656–731. 1822.

ANDREAS, C. H. 1971 – Tiberius Lambergen, een tijdgenoot van David de Gorter. *Gorteria* 5(7–10): 119–123.

AUBLET, J. B. C. F. 1775 – *Histoire des plantes de la Guiane françoise*. Paris, 4 vols.

BARR, K. 1923 – *Linnés Nemesis Divina*. Stockholm.

BAUHIN, C. 1623 – *Pinax theatri botanici*. Basel.

BEAGLEHOLE, J. C. 1955 – *James Cook, The Voyage of the Endeavour*. Cambridge.

BEAGLEHOLE, J. C. 1962 – *The "Endeavour" Journal of Joseph Banks*. Sydney.

BEER, G. R. DE 1953 – Haller's Historia stirpium. *Annals of Science* 9(1): 1–46.

BERG, Å. 1965 – Laudatur et alget. *Svenska Linné–Sällskapets Årsskrift* 47: 1–4.

BERGIUS, P. J. 1750 – see Linnaeus, C. 1750.

BERGIUS P. J. 1767 – *Descriptiones plantarum ex Capite Bonae Spei*. Stockholm [SO 649d].

BERR, H. (ed.) 1952 – *L'Encyclopédie et le progrès des sciences et des techniques*. Paris.

BIWALD, G. L. 1764 [–1769] – *Selectae ex Amaenitatibus Academicis Caroli Linnaei Dissertationes*. Graz [for details see Soulsby 1324–1328 and Widder 1967].

* The abbreviation SO refers to the numbers in Soulsby (1933).

[341]

References

BLOT, N. S. 1747 – *An ut naturali cuique plantarum classi idem vegetationis character sic eadem medica facultas?* Thèse, Caen, 26 janvier 1747.

BLUNT, W. 1971 – *The compleat Naturalist; a life of Carl Linnaeus.* (in press) (not seen).

BODENHEIMER, F. S. and A. H. UGGLA 1953 – The "album itineris" of Frederic Hasselquist. *Svenska Linné–Sällskapets Årsskrift* 35: 18–30.

BOERMAN, A. J. 1953 – *Carolus Linnaeus als middelaar tussen Nederland en Zweden.* Utrecht.

BOERMAN, A. J. 1953a – Carolus Linnaeus, a psychological study. *Taxon* 2: 145–156. 1953.

BOERMAN, A. J. 1957 – Linnaeus becomes candidatus medicinae at Harderwijk. A neglected Linnaean document. *Svenska Linné–Sällskapets Årsskrift* 39–40: 33–47.

BOISSEAU, F. G. 1821 – Louis Gérard, in *Dictionnaire des Sciences médicales, Biographie*, vol. 4.

BOURDIER, F. 1952 – Buffon d'après ses portaits, in R. Heim et al., *Buffon*. Paris 1952, pp. 167–180.

BREMEKAMP, C. E. B. 1950 – Linné's verklaring van de rangorde der systematische groepen. *Verslag afd. Natuurkunde, Koninklijke Nederlandse Akademie van Wetenschappen* 59(9): 116–117.

BREMEKAMP, C. E. B. 1953 – A re-examination of Cesalpino's classification. *Acta botanica neerlandica* 1(4): 580–593.

BREMEKAMP, C. E. B. 1953a – Linné's views on the hierarchy of the taxonomic groups. *Acta botanica neerlandica* 2(2): 242–253.

BREMEKAMP, C. E. B. 1953b – Linné's significance for the development of phytography. *Taxon* 2: 47–54.

BREYNE, J. 1739 – *Prodromus fasciculi rariorum plantarum ... Icones.* Danzig.

BROWNE, P. 1756 – *The civil and natural history of Jamaica in three parts.* London.

BRYK, F. 1919 – *Linnaeus im Auslande.* Stockholm.

BRYK, F. 1953 – Linné und die Species plantarum. *Taxon* 2: 63–73.

BRYK, F. 1954 – Promiskuität der Gattungen als artbildender Faktor. *Taxon* 3: 165–173.

BUCK R. C. and D. L. HULL 1966 – The logical structure of the Linnaean hierarchy. *Systematic Zoology* 15: 97–111.

BUFFON, G. L. LECLERQ, Comte de, 1749–1788 – *Histoire naturelle, générale et particulière, avec la description du Cabinet du Roi.* Paris 1749–1767, 15 vols; *Histoire naturelle des Oiseaux.* Paris 1770–1783, 9 vols; *Histoire naturelle. Suppléments.* Paris 1774–1789,

7 vols. Microfiche edition, Inter Documentation Company, Zug, no. 5436.

BULLIARD, J. B. F. 1776–1783 – *Flora parisiensis*. Paris, 6 vols.

BULLIARD J. B. F. 1780 [–1793] – *Herbier de la France*. Paris, 13 vols.

BURMAN, J. 1736–1748 – *Taalrijk register der Plaat– ofte Figuur–Beschrijvingen der Bloem-dragende gewassen*. Amsterdam, 4 vols. [Dutch translation of J. W. Wein-mann, *Phytanthoza iconographia*, 1734–1745].

BURMAN, J. 1737 – *Thesaurus zeylanicus*. Amsterdam.

BURMAN, J. 1738–1739 – *Rariorum africanarum plantarum ad vivum delineatarum iconibus ac descriptionibus illustratarum decas prima* [*–decima*]. Amsterdam.

BURMAN, J. 1755 – *Index universalis in sex tomos et auctuarium herbarii Amboinensis Cl. Georgii Everhardi Rumphii*. Appended to G. E. Rumphius, *Auctuarium*, 1755.

BURMAN, J. 1757 – *Wachendorfia*. Amsterdam; also published in *Nova Acta Phys. Med. Acad. Caes. Leop.–Carol. Nat. Cur.* 2: 192–198. 1761.

BURMAN, J. 1769 – *Flora malabarici sive index in omnes tomos Horti malabarici*. Amsterdam.

BURMAN, J. 1769a – *Index alter in omnes tomos Herbarii Amboinensis*. Leiden/Amsterdam.

BURMAN, N. L. 1759 – *Specimen botanicum de Geraniis*. Leiden.

BURMAN, N. L. 1768 – *Flora indica*. Amsterdam/Leiden.

BURMAN, N. L. 1773 – Heliophila descripta. *Nova Acta Regiae Societatis Upsaliensis* 1: 94–96.

BURMAN, N. L. 1770 – Florula corsicae aucta ex scriptis Dn Jaussin. *Nova Acta Phys. Med. Acad. Caes. Leop.–Carol. Nat. Cur.* 4 (App): 205–254.

BURMAN BECKER, J. G. [s.d.] – *Notices historiques et généalogiques sur la famille Burman*. København.

BURTT, B. L. 1966 – Adanson and modern taxonomy. *Notes from the Royal Botanic Garden Edinburgh* 26: 427–431.

CAIN, A. J. 1958 – Logic and memory in Linnaeus's system of taxonomy. *Proceedings of The Linnaean Society of London* 169: 144–163.

CAIN, A. J. 1959 – Deductive and inductive methods in post–linnaean taxonomy. *Proceedings of The Linnean Society of London* 170(2): 185–217.

CALLOT, E. 1965 – *La philosophie de la vie au XVIIIme siècle*. Paris.

CAMERON, H. C. 1952 – *Sir Joseph Banks*. London.

CANDOLLE, A. P. de 1862 – *Mémoires et souvenirs*. Genève.

CARRUTHERS, W. 1906 – On the original portaits of Linnaeus. *Proceedings of The Linnean Society of London*. 118th session: 59–69.

CASSIRER, E. 1951 – *The philosophy of the Enlightenment.* Translated by Fritz C. A. Koelln and James P. Pettegrove. Princeton.

CAVANILLES, A. J. 1785–1790 – *Monadelphiae classis dissertationes decem.* Paris.

CAVANILLES, A. J. 1791–1801 – *Icones et descriptiones plantarum, quae aut sponte in Hispania crescunt, aut in hortis hospitantur.* Madrid, 6 vols. *Facsimile* edition Lehre 1965.

CESALPINO, A. 1583 – *De plantis libri XVI.* Florence.

CHARPENTIER, J. et M. 1967 – *L'encyclopédie, avec une chronologie de l'Encyclopédie, une étude générale de l'oeuvre, une analyse méthodique des articles choisis, avec des notes.* Paris.

CHENON, L. J. 1751 – see Linnaeus, C. 1751.

CLOS, D. 1888 – Louis Gérard, un des précurseurs de la méthode naturelle. *Mémoires de l'Académie des Sciences, Inscriptions et Belles-Lettres de Toulouse* sér. 8. 10: 342–370. 1888.

COLLINGWOOD, R. G. 1945 – *The idea of nature.* New York, repr. New York 1960.

CRANTZ, H. J. N. VON 1762–1767 – *Stirpes austriacae.* Wien/Leipzig, 3 vols.

CRANTZ, H. J. N. VON 1766 – *Institutiones rei herbariae juxta nutum naturae digestae ex habitu.* Wien, 2 vols.

CRANTZ, H. J. N. VON 1769 – *Classis cruciformium emendata.* Leipzig.

CURTIS, W. 1777 – *Linnaeus's system of botany so far as relates to his classes and orders of plants.* London.

CURTIS, W. [1775–] 1777–1798 – *Flora londinensis.* London, 2 vols.

CURTIS, W. 1787–x – *The botanical magazine.* London, 177 vols. (being ctd.)

CURTIS, W. H. 1941 – *William Curtis 1746–1799.* Winchester.

CUVIER, G. 1807 – Éloge historique de Michel Adanson. *Mémoires de la Classe des Sciences ... de l'Institut national de France* 7(1): 159–188.

DAHLGREN, K. V. O. 1951 – Philosophia botanica, ett 200-Årsminne. *Svenska Linné-Sällskapets Årsskrift* 33–34: 1–30.

DANDY, J. E. 1961 – Homonyms in the Prodromi of Thunberg and Burman. *Bothalia* 7(3): 427–428.

DANDY, J. E. 1967 – *Index of generic names of vascular plants 1753–1774.* Utrecht (Regnum vegetabile vol. 51.)

DANDY, J. E. and F. R. FOSBERG, 1954 – The type of *Amaryllis belladonna* L. *Taxon* 3: 231–232.

DARLINGTON, W. 1849 – *Memorials of John Bartram and Humphry Marshall.* Philadelphia. *Facsimile* reprint 1967, New York and London, with an introduction by J. Ewan.

DARWIN, E. 1789–1791 – *The botanic garden.* Part 1, *The economy of vegetation.* London

1791, part 2. *The loves of plants*. London 1789.

DAUDIN, H. [1926] – *De Linné à Jussieu. Méthodes de la classification et idée de série en botanique et en zoologie (1740–1790)*. Paris.

DAUDIN, H. 1926a – *Cuvier et Lamarck. Les classes zoologiques et l'idée de série animale*. Paris.

DAWSON, W. 1958 – *The Banks letters*. London.

DE BEER, G. R. 1949 – The correspondence between Linnaeus and Johann Gesner, *Proceedings of the Linnean Society of London* 161st session (1948–1949): 225–241.

DIDEROT, D. & J. D'ALEMBERT 1750–1780 – *Encyclopédie, ou dictionnaire raisonné des sciences, des arts et métiers, par une société de gens de lettres*. Paris, 36 volumes. Microfiche edition, Inter Documentation Company, Zug, no. 5437.

DILLEN, J. J. 1732 – *Hortus elthamensis*, London, 2 vols.

DONATI, V. 1750 – *Della storia naturale marina dell'Adriatico. Saggio*. Venezia.

DÖRFLER, I. 1907 – *Botaniker-Porträts*. Lieferung III und IV. C. v. Linné und seine botanischen Zeitgenossen. Wien.

DRYANDER, J. 1798–1800 – *Catalogus bibliothecae historico-naturalis Josephi Banks*. London. *Facsimile* edition New York/London/Amsterdam 1966.

DUCHESNE, A. N. 1766 – *Histoire naturelle des fraisiers*. Paris.

DUCROS, L. 1900 – *Les encyclopédistes*. Paris.

DUGHI, R. 1963 – L'iconographie d'Adanson, in R. Heim et al., *Michel Adanson*. Paris.

DU RIETZ, R. 1966 – Tryckningen av Species plantarum 1753, *Svenska Linné-Sälskapets Årsskrift* 48: 60–87.

EHRHART, F. 1791 – Erklärung der vornehmsten Kunstwörter, welche in Wachendorf's Pflanzensystem vorkommen. *Beiträge zur Naturkunde* 6: 1–13.

ELMGREN, G. 1795 – see Linnaeus, C. 1759.

ENGEL, H. 1957 – Carolus Linnaeus in Holland, in Linnaeus commemorated 1707—Mar 23rd—1957, *Communication no. 103 from the National Museum for the History of Science*. Leiden.

ENGEL–LEDEBOER, M. S. J. and H. ENGEL 1964 – *Carolus Linnaeus Systema naturae 1775, Facsimile of the first edition. With an introduction and a first English translation of the "Observationes."* Nieuwkoop.

EWAN, J. 1967 – see Darlington, W. 1849.

EWAN, J. 1967 – see Marshall, H. 1785.

EWAN, J. 1969 – *A short history of botany in the United States*. New York/London.

EWAN, J. 1970 – Plant collectors in America: backgrounds for Linnaeus, *in*

P. Smit and R. J. Ch. V. ter Laage, *Essays in biohistory* (Regnum vegetabile vol. 71), pp. 18–54.

FÉE, A. L. A. 1832 – *Vie de Linné*. Paris.

FLORSCHÜTZ, P. A. 1960 – *Introduction to Hedwig's "Species muscorum,"* in *facsimile* edition of Hedwig, *Species muscorum* Weinheim 1960.

FORSSKÅL, P. 1775 – *Flora aegyptiaco-arabica*. København. [published by C. Niebuhr].

FORSTER, J. R. et G. FORSTER 1776 – *Characteres generum plantarum, quas in itinere ad insulas maris australis collegerunt, descripserunt, delinearunt annis MDCCLXXII–MDCCLXXV* [auctores]. London.

FRANZÉN, O. 1964 – Hur Linnébilden formades (1778–1850). *Svenska Linné–Sällskapets Årsskrift* 46: 5–41.

FREDBÄRJ, T. 1963 – Johannes Moraeus, Linnaei svärfader. *Svenska Linné–Sällskapets Årsskrift* 45: 103–127.

FREDBÄRJ, T. 1965 – Ett nyfunnet manuskript till Fundamenta botanica. *Svenska Linné-Sällskapets Årsskrift* 47: 5–15.

FRIES, R. E. 1931 – P. J. Bergius, ett tvåhundra-årsminne, *Acta horti bergiani* 11(1): 1–11. tt. 1–2.

FRIES, R. E. 1943 – Daniel Solander, *Levnadsteckningar över Kungl. Svenska Vetenskapsakademiens Ledamöter* 7(1): 59–81 (no. 114).

FRIES, R. E. 1951 – De Linneanska "apostlarnas" resor. *Svenska Linné-Sällskapets Årsskrift* 33–34: 31–40.

FRIES, T. M. 1903 – *Linné, lefnadsteckning*, Stockholm, 2 vols.

FRIES, T. M. 1909 – *Bref och Skrifvelser af och till Carl von Linné*. Afd. 1. del III. Stockholm.

FUCHS, H. P. 1962–1963 – Nicolaas Meerburgh und die drei von ihm verfassten botanischen Tafelwerke. *Acta botanica neerlandica* 11: 69–89 (1962), 12: 12–16 (1963).

GAERTNER, J. 1788–1791 [–1792] – *De fructibus et seminibus plantarum*. Stuttgart/Tübingen, 2 vols.

GAGE, A. T. 1938 – *A history of The Linnean Society of London*. London.

GARSIDE, S. 1942 – Baron Jacquin and the Schönbrunn Gardens. *Journal South African Botany* 8: 201–224.

GÉRARD, L. 1761 – *Flora gallo-provincialis*. Paris.

GERSHOY, L. 1944 – *From despotism to revolution, 1763–1789*. New York.

GESNER, J. 1759–1773 – *Phytographia sacra generalis* [*et specialis*]. Zürich, parts 1–7 and 1–3.

GESNER, J. 1795–1826 – *Tabulae phytographicae analysin generum plantarum exhibentes*

Zürich, 2 vols., folio. Con commentatione edidit Christian Salomon Schinz.

GIDON, F. 1934 – Linné, Jussieu ou Adanson? (A propos d'un texte de 1747.) *Mémoires de l'Académie Nationale des Sciences, Arts et Belles-Lettres de Caen.* Nouvelle série 7: 287–309.

GILBERT, E. J. 1952 – Un esprit-une oeuvre. Bulliard, Jean Baptiste François, dit Pierre (1753–1793). *Bulletin trimestriel de la Société mycologique de France* 68(1): 5–131.

GILIBERT, J. E. 1782 – *Flora lithuanica inchoata.* Grodno/Wilna, 2 vols.

GILIBERT, J. E. 1785–1787 – *Caroli Linnaei botanicorum principis Systema plantarum Europae.* Vienne, 7 vols.

GILIBERT, J. E. 1792 – *Excercitia phytologica.* Lyon.

GILIBERT, J. E. 1798 – *Histoire des plantes d'Europe.* Lyon, 2 vols.

GILMOUR, J. S. L. 1940 – Taxonomy and philosophy, in J. S. Huxley, *The new systematics.* London.

GILMOUR, J. S. L. 1955 – Linnaeus's 'Species plantarum'; the man and the book. *Proceedings of The Linnean Society of London* 165(2): 156–157.

GINANNI, G. 1755 – *Opere posthume* (tomo 1). Venezia.

GISEKE, P. D. 1792 – *Praelectiones in ordines naturales plantarum.* Hamburg.

GLEDITSCH, J. G. 1749 – Système des plantes sur la situation et la liaison des étamines. *Histoire de l'Acacémie Royale des Sciences et Belles Lettres* [Berlin] 1749: 3–136.

GLEDITSCH, J. G. 1753 – *Methodus fungorum.* Berlin.

GLEDITSCH, J. G. 1764 – *Systema plantarum a staminum situ.* Berlin 1764.

GLEDITSCH, J. G. 1780 – *Caroli Linnaei ... Philosophia botanica ...* Edito secunda. Berlin 1780 [SO 445].

GMELIN, S. G. 1768 – *Historia fucorum.* St. Petersburg.

GOERKE, H. 1966 – *Carl von Linné. Arzt, Naturforscher, Systematiker 1707–1778.* Stuttgart.

GOERKE, H. 1967 – Linné und Johann Andreas Murray. *Svenska Linné-Sällskapets Årsskrift* 49: 65–73.

GOURIE, N. 1953 – *The prince of botanists: Carl Linnaeus.* London.

GORTER, D. DE 1745 – *Flora gelro-zutphanica, exhibens plantas per ducatum Gelriae et comitatum Zutphaniae crescentes.* Harderwijk.

GORTER, D. DE 1761 – *Flora ingrica, ex schedis Stephani Kraschennikow botanices et historiae naturalis professoris quondam Petropolitani confecta et propriis observationibus aucta.* St. Petersburg.

GORTER, D. DE 1767 – *Flora belgica, exhibens plantas per Foederatum Belgium crescentes.* Utrecht.

GORTER, D. DE 1781 – *Flora VII Provinciarum Belgii foederati indigena.* Haarlem.

GORTER, D. DE 1782 – *Leer der plantkunde.* Amsterdam.

GOUAN, A. 1762 – *Hortus regius monspeliensis.* Lyon.

GOUAN, A. 1765 – *Flora monspeliaca.* Lyon.

GOUAN, A. 1773 – *Illustrationes et observationes botanicae.* Zürich.

GRÅBERG, J. M. 1762 – see Linnaeus, C. 1762.

GREENE, E. L. 1912 – *Carolus Linnaeus.* Philadelphia.

GRONOVIUS, J. F. 1715 – *Disputatio inauguralis Camphorae historiam exhibens.* Leiden.

GRONOVIUS, J. F. 1739–1743 – *Flora virginica.* Leiden. *Facsimile* reprint Jamaica Plain 1946; ed. 2, Leiden 1762, *facsimile* reprint Jamaica Plain 1946.

GRONOVIUS, J. F. 1755 – *Flora orientalis.* Leiden.

GROSCLAUDE, P. 1951 – *Un audacieux message: L'Encyclopédie.* Paris.

GRUFBERG, I. O. 1759 – see Linnaeus, C. 1759.

GUÉDES, M. 1968 – L'édition originale de la Philosophia botanica de Linné (1751). *Journal of the Society for the Bibliography of Natural History* 4(7): 385–389.

HAARTMAN, J. J. 1751 – see Linnaeus, C. 1751.

HAGBERG, K. 1939 – *Carl Linnaeus.* Stockholm; new ed. 1957; English translation London 1952.

HALL, H. C. VAN 1830 – *Epistolae ineditae Caroli Linnaei.* Groningen.

HALLER, A. VON 1742 – *Enumeratio methodica stirpium Helvetiae indigenarum.* Göttingen.

HALLER, A. VON 1753 – *Enumeratio plantarum horti regii et agri gottingensis.* Göttingen.

HALLER, A. VON 1768 – *Historia stirpium indigenarum Helvetiae inchoata.* 3 vols. Bern.

HALLER, A. VON 1771–1772 – *Bibliotheca botanica.* Zürich.

HAMY, E. T. 1909 – *Les débuts de Lamarck.* Paris.

HASSELQUIST, F. 1757 – *Iter palaestinum.* Stockholm [SO 3577].

HEDWIG, J. 1782 – *Fundamentum historiae naturalis muscorum frondosorum.* Leipzig, 2 vols.

HEDWIG, J. 1784 – *Theoria generationis et fructificationis plantarum cryptogamicarum.* St. Petersburg.

HEDWIG, J. 1801 – *Species muscorum frondosorum.* Leipzig. *Facsimile* edition with an introduction by P. A. Florschütz, Weinheim 1960.

HEIM, R. et al 1952 – *Bvffon.* Paris.

HELLER, J. L. 1945 – Classical mythology in the Systema naturae of Linnaeus. *Transactions of the American Philological Association* 76: 333–357.

HELLER, J. L. 1959 – Index auctorum et librorum a Linnaeo (Species plantarum, 1753) citatorum, in C. Linnaeus, *Species plantarum* a facsimile of the first edition, volume 2, London [The Ray Society].

HELLER, J. L. 1964 – The early history of binomial nomenclature. *Huntia* 1: 33–70.

HELLER, J. L. 1968 – Linnaeus's Hortus cliffortianus. *Taxon* 17: 663–719.

HELLER, J. L. 1970 – Linnaeus's Bibliotheca botanica. *Taxon* 19: 363–411.

HÉRISSANT, L. A. P. 1771 – *Bibliothèque physique de la France*. Paris.

HESSELGREN, N. L. 1749 – see Linnaeus, C. 1749.

HILL, J. 1751 – *A general natural history ... vol. 2. A history of plants*. London.

HILL, J. 1756 [–1757] – *The British herbal*. London.

HILL, J. 1757 – *Eden: or, a compleat body of gardening*. London.

HILL, J. 1757a – *The sleep of plants*. London.

HILL, J. 1759–1775 – *The vegetable system*. London. 26 vols.

HILL, J. 1760 – *Flora britannica*. London.

HILL, J. 1768 – *Hortus kewensis*. London.

HIORTH, J. 1752 – see Linnaeus, C. 1752.

HIRSCHING, F. C. G. 1794–1815 – *Historisch–litterarisches Handbuch berühmter und denkwürdiger Personen welche in dem achtzehnten Jahrhundert gelebt haben*. Leipzig, 17 vols.

HOFSTEN, N. VON 1958 – Linnaeus's conception of Nature. *K. Vetenskaps–societeten in Upsala, Årsbok* 1957 (Uppsala 1958).

HOFSTEN, N. VON 1962–1963 – A system of "double entries" in the zoological classification of Linnaeus. *Zoologiska Bidrag. från Uppsala* 35: 603–631; also published, in Swedish, in *Svenska Linné–Sällskapets Årsskrift* 50: 1–12. 1968.

HOLBACH, PAUL HENRI DIETRICH, BARON D' 1770 – *Système de la nature, ou les lois du monde physique et du monde moral*. London [i.e. Amsterdam].

HORT, A. 1938 – *The "Critica botanica" of Linnaeus*. London.

HOUTTUYN, M. 1773–1783 – *Natuurlijke historie of uitvoerige beschrijving der dieren, planten en mineraalen, volgens het samenstel van den Heer Linnaeus. ...* Tweede deel, [Planten], eerste-veertiende stuk. Leiden.

HUDSON, W. 1762 – *Flora anglica*. London.

HULL, D. L. 1965 – The effect of essentialism on taxonomy. Two thousand years of stasis (1). *The British Journal for the Philosophy of Science* 15–16 (60–6.)

HULL, D. L. 1969 – The natural system and the species problem, in *Systematic biology*, Washington D.C.

HYLANDER, N. 1945 – Linné, Duchesne och smultronen. *Svenska Linné–Sällskapets Årsskrift* 28: 17–40.

JACKSON, B. D. 1881 – *Guide to the literature of botany*. London 1881. *Facsimile* reprint

New York/London 1964.

JACKSON, B. D. 1911 – Linnaeus, *Encyclopaedia britannica* 16: 732–733.

JACKSON, B. D. 1923 – *Linnaeus (afterwards Carl von Linné): the story of his life, adapted from the Swedish of Theodor Magnus Fries.* London.

JACQUIN, N. J. 1760 – *Enumeratio systematica plantarum, quas in insulis Caribaeis vicinaque Americes continente detexit novas, aut jam cognitas emendavit.* Leiden. Reprint Nürnberg 1762; *facsimile* reprint of 1760 edition, Zug 1967.

JACQUIN, N. J. 1762 – *Enumeratio stirpium plerarumque, quae sponte crescunt in agro vindobonensi, montibusque confinibus.* Wien.

JACQUIN, N. J. 1763 – *Selectarum stirpium americanarum historia.* Wien 1763. *Facsimile* reprint New York 1971.

JACQUIN N. J. 1781–1793 [–1795] – *Icones plantarum rariorum.* Wien, 3 vols.

JACQUIN, N. J. 1785 – *Anleitung zur Pflanzenkenntnis nach Linné's Methode.* Wien [SO 696–698].

JACQUIN, N. J. 1797–1804 – *Plantarum rariorum horti caesarei schoenbrunnensis descriptiones et icones.* Wien, 4 vols.

JACQUIN, N. J. 1806 – *Stapeliarum in hortis vindobonensibus cultarum descriptionibus.* Wien.

JANSEN, A. 1885 – *Jean-Jacques Rousseau als Botaniker.* Berlin.

JESSEN, K. F. W. 1864 – *Botanik der Gegenwart und Vorzeit in culturhistorischer Entwicklung.* Leipzig. *Facsimile* reprint Waltham, Mass. 1948.

JUEL, H. O. 1921 – A revision of Kalm's herbarium in Upsala. *Svenska Linné-Sällskapets Årsskrift* 4: 16–23.

JUNG, J. 1679 – *Isagoge phytoscopica.* Hamburg.

JUSSIEU, ADR. DE 1855 – Caroli a Linné ad Bernardum de Jussieu ineditae, et mutuae Bernardi ad Linnaeum epistolae. *Memoirs of the American Academy of Arts and Sciences* ser. 2. 5: 179–234.

JUSSIEU, ANT. DE 1728 – De la nécessité d'établir dans la méthode nouvelle des plantes, une classe particulière pour les Fungus, à laquelle doivent se rapporter, non seulement les Champignons, les Agarics, mais encore les Lichen. *Mémoires de l'Académie Royale des Sciences* 1728: 377–383.

JUSSIEU, A. L. DE 1773 [1777] – Examen de la famille des Renoncules. *Mémoires de mathématique et de physique de l'Académie Royale des Sciences* 1773: 214–240; see also *Histoire de l'Académie Royale des Sciences* 1773: 34–38.

JUSSIEU, A. L. DE 1774 [1778] – Exposition d'un nouvel ordre de plantes adopté dans les démonstrations du jardin royal. *Mémoires de Mathématique et de Physique de l'Académie Royale des Sciences* 1774: 175–197; see also *Histoire de l'Académie Royale des Sciences* 1774: 27–30.

JUSSIEU, A. L. DE 1789 – *Genera plantarum*. Paris. *Facsimile* reprint Weinheim 1964, with an introduction by Frans A. Stafleu.

KALM, P. 1753–1761 – *En resa till Norra America*. Stockholm, 3 vols. [SO 2586 b–j].

KÖLREUTER, J. G. 1761 – *Vorläufige Nachricht von einigen das Geschlecht der Pflanzen betreffenden Versuchen und Beobachtungen*. Leipzig.

KÖLREUTER, J. G. 1763–1766 – *Fortsetzung der vorläufigen Nachricht von einigen das Geschlecht der Pflanzen betreffenden Versuchen und Beobachtungen*. [Erste] 1763, Zweyte 1764, Dritte 1766, all Leipzig.

KRAMER, W. H. 1756 – *Elenchus vegetabilium et animalium per Austriam inferiorem observatorum*. Wien.

KROK, Th. O. B. N. 1925 – *Bibliotheca botanica suecana*. Uppsala.

KRONFELD, E. M. 1905 – Jacquin. *Österreichische Rundschau* 3: 237–251.

LAM, H. J. 1957 – Carolus Linnaeus (1707–1778). *Nieuwe Rotterdamse Courant* 18 mei 1957.

LAMARCK, J. B. A. P. M. DE 1778 – *Flore françoise ou description succincte de toutes les plantes qui croissent naturellement en France*. Paris, 3 vols.

LAMARCK, J. B. A. P. M. DE 1783–1798 – *Encyclopédie méthodique. Botanique*. Paris [vols. 1–4 are by Lamarck entirely or in part].

LAMARCK, J. B. A. P. M. DE 1788 – Mémoire sur les classes les plus convenables à établir parmi les végétaux. *Histoire de l'Académie Royale des Sciences* [*Paris*] 1785: 437–453.

LAMARCK, J. B. A. P. M. DE 1791–1799 – *Tableau encyclopédique et méthodique des trois règnes de la nature*. Paris [volumes 1–5(1)]. Alternative title: *Illustration des genres*.

LAMARCK, J. B. A. P. M. DE 1801 – *Hydrogéologie*. Paris.

LAMARCK, J. B. A. P. M. DE 1809 – *Philosophie zoologique*. Paris. *Facsimile* reprint Weinheim 1960.

LANJOUW, J. et H. UITTIEN 1940 – Un nouvel herbier de Fusée Aublet découvert en France. *Recueil des Travaux botaniques néerlandais* 37: 133–170.

LARSON, J. L. 1967 – Linnaeus and the natural method. *Isis* 58(3): 304–320.

LASÈGUE, A. 1845 – *Musée botanique de M. Benjamin Delessert*. Paris. *Facsimile* reprint Lehre 1970.

LEHMANN, H. 1971 – Classification and explanation in biology. *Taxon* 20: 257–268.

LESTIBOUDOIS, F. J. 1781 – *Botanographie belgique*. Lille.

L'HÉRITIER DE BRUTELLE, C. L. 1784–1785 – *Stirpes novae aut minus cognitae*. Paris.

L'HÉRITIER DE BRUTELLE, C. L. 1788 – *Sertum anglicum*. Paris. *Facsimile* reprint with introductions by W. Blunt, J. S. L. Gilmour and F. A. Stafleu. Pittsburgh 1963.

LIDÉN, J. H. 1778 – *Catalogus disputationum, in academiis et gymnasiis Sveciae* [1] [Disputationes Upsalienses] Uppsala.

LIGHTFOOT, J. 1777 – *Flora scotica.* London, 2 vols.

LINDEBOOM, G. A. 1968 – *Herman Boerhaave. The man and his work.* London.

LINDMAN, C. A. M. 1908–1910 – A Linnaean herbarium in the Natural History Museum in Stockholm. *Arkiv för Botanik* 7(3) 1908, 9(6) 1910.

LINDROTH, S. 1966 – Two centuries of Linnaean studies, *in* T. R. Buckman [ed.], *Bibliography and natural history.* Lawrence, Kansas, pp. 27–45.

LINNAEUS C. * 1733 – Iter ad fodinas & officinas metallicas Westmanniae & Dalekarliae, published 1889 by E. Ährling in *Carl von Linnés Ungdomsskrifter.* Stockholm [SO 27, 183a].

LINNAEUS, C. 1735 – *Systema naturae.* Leiden.

ed. 1, Amsterdam 1735, SO 39.
ed. 2, Stockholm 1740, SO 46,
ed. 3, Halle 1740, SO 47,
ed. 4, Paris 1744, SO 48,
ed. 5, Halle 1747, SO 50,
ed. 6, Stockholm 1748, SO 51,
ed. 7, Leipzig 1748, SO 52,
ed. 8, Stockholm 1753, SO 53–56,
ed. 9, Leiden 1756, SO 57.
ed. 10, Stockholm 1758–1759, 2 vols., SO 58,
ed. 11, Leipzig 1762 [probably non–existent],
ed. 12, Stockholm 1766–1768, 3 vols., SO 62.
Facsimile reprints: ed. 1, Berlin 1881, Stockholm 1907, Uppsala 1960, Nieuwkoop 1964; ed. 10, vol. 2, Weinheim 1964.

LINNAEUS, C. 1736 – *Fundamenta botanica.* Amsterdam [SO 253–274]. *Facsimile* reprints: Weinheim 1961, München 1968.

LINNAEUS, C. 1736a – *Bibliotheca botanica.* Amsterdam; other editions Halle 1747 and Amsterdam 1751 [SO 250–252]. *Facsimile* reprint München 1968.

LINNAEUS, C. 1736 – *Methodus juxta quam physiologus accurate & feliciter concinnare potest historiam cujuscunque naturalis subjecti, sequentibus hisce paragraphis comprehensa.*

* For all further bibliographical details, especially on full titles, editions and commentaries, see Soulsby 1933. The "SO" numbers following the titles refer to this main bibliography of the works of Linnaeus.

[352]

Leiden (one folio page, see fig. 3; SO 40, usually appended to copies of the 1735 edition of the *Systema naturae*).

LINNAEUS, C. 1736 – *Musa cliffortiana*. Leiden [SO 250–252].

LINNAEUS, C. 1737 – *Critica botanica*. Leiden [SO 276–278].

LINNAEUS, C. 1737a – *Genera plantarum*. Leiden; ed. 2, Leiden 1742; ed. 3, Paris 1743; ed. 4, Halle 1752; ed. 5, Stockholm 1754; ed. 6, Wien 1767 [SO 284–327]. *Facsimile* reprint of ed. 5, Weinheim 1960.

LINNAEUS, C. 1737b – *Flora lapponica*. Amsterdam [SO 279–283].

LINNAEUS, C. 1737c – *Hortus cliffortianus*. Amsterdam [SO 328–330]. *Facsimile* reprint Lehre 1968.

LINNAEUS, C. 1737d – *Methodus sexualis sistens genera plantarum secundum mares et feminas in classes et ordines redacta*. Leiden 1737 [appended to 1737a] [SO 285].

LINNAEUS, C. 1738 – *Classes plantarum*. Leiden [SO 332–338].

LINNAEUS, C. 1744 – *Dissertatio botanica de Peloria*. Uppsala [D. Rudberg], also published in *Amoenitates academicae* 1: 280–298. 1749 [SO 1395–1400].

LINNAEUS, C. *Flora svecica*. Stockholm; ed. 2, Stockholm; 1755, [SO 407–411].

LINNAEUS, C. 1745a – *Öländska och Gothländska Resa*. Stockholm/Uppsala [SO 202–208].

LINNAEUS, C. 1746 – *Sponsalia plantarum*. Stockholm [J. G. Wahlbom], also published in *Amoenitates academicae* 1: 61–109. 1749 [SO 1447–1460].

LINNAEUS, C. 1747 – *Flora zeylanica*. Stockholm [SO 420–423].

LINNAEUS, C. 1749 – *Pan svecicus*. Uppsala [N. L. Hesselgren], also in *Amoenitates academicae* 2: 225–262. 1751 [SO 1565–1584].

LINNAEUS, C. 1749a – *Gemmae arborum*. Uppsala [author and defendant: P. Loefling]; also in *Amoenitates academicae* 2: 182–224. 1751 [SO 1556–1562].

LINNAEUS, C. 1749–1769 – *Amoenitates academicae*. Stockholm, 7 vols. [SO 1272–1331].

LINNAEUS, C. 1750 – *Semina muscorum* [P. J. Bergius], also in *Amoenitates academicae* 2: 284–306. 1751 [SO 1596–1602].

LINNAEUS, C. 1751 – *Philosophia botanica*. Stockholm, Amsterdam. *Facsimile* reprint Lehre 1966.

LINNAEUS, C. 1751a – *Dissertatio botanica, qua nova plantarum genera ...* [L. J. Chenon], also in *Amoenitates academicae* 3: 1–27, 1756 [SO 1628–1631].

LINNAEUS, C. 1751b – *Plantae hybridae*. Uppsala [J. J. Haartman], also in *Amoenitates academicae* 3: 28–62. 1756 [SO 1632–1637].

LINNAEUS, C. 1752 – *Plantae esculentae patriae*. Uppsala [J. Hiorth], also in *Amoenitates academicae* 3: 74–99. 1756 [SO 1648–1656].

[353]

References

LINNAEUS, C. 1752a – *Specimen academicum, quo Euphorbia ejusque historia naturalis et medica exhibetur*. Uppsala [J. Wiman], also in *Amoenitates academicae* 3: 100–131. 1756 [SO 1658–1662].

LINNAEUS, C. 1753 – *Species plantarum*. Stockholm 2 vols.; ed. 2. Stockholm 1762–1763, 2 vols. *Facsimile* reprint of ed. 1, London 1957–1959 [SO 480–529].

LINNAEUS, C. 1754 – *Flora anglica*. Uppsala [J. O. Grufberg], reprinted *Journal of Botany* 47 (1909) suppl.

LINNAEUS, C. 1754 – *Herbarium amboinense*. Uppsala [O. Stickman], also in *Amoenitates academicae* 4: 112–142. 1759 [SO 1813–1816].

LINNAEUS, C. 1756 – *Flora palaestina*. Uppsala [B. J. Strand], also in *Amoenitates academicae* 4: 443–467. 1759 [SO 1886–1890].

LINNAEUS, C. 1756a – *Elementa botanica*. Edidit Dan. Solander. Uppsala [SO 540].

LINNAEUS, C. 1759 – *Plantarum jamaicensium pugillus*. Uppsala [G. Elmgren], also in *Amoenitates academicae* 5: 389–413. 1760 [SO 2058–2061].

LINNAEUS, C. 1759a – *Flora jamaicensis*. Uppsala [C. G. Sandmark], also in *Amoenitates academicae* 5: 371–388. 1760 [SO 2087–2090].

LINNAEUS, C. 1760 – *Theses medicae*. Uppsala [J. C. D. Schreber], also published in *Amoenitates academicae* 6: 40–43. 1763 [SO 2111–2114].

LINNAEUS, C. 1762 – *Fundamentum fructificationis*, Uppsala [J. M. Gråberg], also published in *Amoenitates academicae* 6: 279–304. [SO 2214–2218].

LINNAEUS, C. 1767–1771 – *Mantissa plantarum*. Stockholm, 2 parts [SO 62, 116, 311–314]. *Facsimile* reprint Weinheim 1961.

LINNAEUS, C. 1776 – *Planta aphyteia*. Uppsala [E. Acharius], also published in *Amoenitates academicae* 8: 310–317. 1785 [SO 2457–2458].

LINNAEUS, C. 1823 – *Egenhändiga anteckningar af Carl Linnaeus om sig sjelf*. Uppsala (German translation Berlin 1826).

LINNAEUS, C. *Nemesis divina*, see Barr, K.

LINNELL, T. 1953 – *Några ord om Linnés Peloria och dess locus classicus*. *Svenska Linné–Sällskapets Årsskrift* 35: 62–70.

LOEFLING, P. 1749 – see Linnaeus, C. 1749.

LOEFLING, P. 1758 – *Iter hispanicum*. Stockholm.

LOTSY, J. P. 1907 – *Carolus Linnaeus, één en ander over zijne beteekenis, vooral ten opzichte van het soortsbegrip*. Haarlem.

LOUGH, J. 1968 – *Essays on the Encyclopédie of Diderot and d'Alembert*. London.

LOVEJOY, A. 1936 – *The great chain of Being*. Cambridge, Mass. [reprint Harper Torchbook, New York 1960].

LÖWEGREN, Y. 1952 – *Naturaliekabinett . . . under 1700–talet*. Lychnos–Bibl. 13. Lund.

References

Ludwig, C. G. 1737 – *Definitiones generum plantarum*. Leipzig 1737; ed. 2, Leipzig 1747; ed. 3, edited and published by G. R. Boehmer, Leipzig 1760.

Ludwig, C. G. 1739 – *Observationes in methodum plantarum sexualem Celeb. Linnaei*. Leipzig.

Ludwig, C. G. 1739a – *De sexu plantarum*. Leipzig.

Ludwig, C. G. 1742 – *Institutiones historico–physicae regni vegetabilis*. Leipzig 1752; ed. 2, Leipzig 1757.

Ludwig, C. G. 1760–1764 – *Ectypa vegetabilium*. Halle.

Lütjeharms, W. J. 1936 – *Zur Geschichte der Mykologie, Das VXIII. Jahrhundert*. Gouda.

Magnol, P. 1689 – *Prodromus historiae generalis plantarum in quo familiae plantarum per tabulas disponuntur*. Montpellier.

Maiden, J. H. 1909 – *Sir Joseph Banks*. Sydney/London.

Marchant, J. 1719 – Observations sur la nature des plantes. *Mémoires de l'Académie Royale des Sciences* 1719: 59–66. pl. 6 et 7.; see also *Histoire de l'Académie Royale des Sciences* 1719: 57–58.

Marshall, M. 1785 – *Arbustum americanum*. Philadelphia. *Facsimile* reprint New York and London 1967, with an introduction by J. Ewan.

Martin, K. 1962 – *French liberal thought in the eighteenth century*. London.

Martyn, T. 1763 – *Plantae cantabrigienses*. London.

Mayr, E. 1963 – *Animal species and evolution*. Cambridge, Massuchetts.

Mayr, E. 1968 – Theory of biological classification. *Nature* 220: 545–548.

Mayr, E. 1969 – *Principles of systematic zoology*. New York.

Mayr, E. 1969a – Discussion footnotes on the philosophy of biology. *Philosophy of Science* 36(2): 197–202.

Medikus, F. K. 1783 – *Botanische Beobachtungen des Jahres 1782*. Mannheim.

Medikus, F. K. 1786 – *Theodora speciosa*. Mannheim.

Medikus, F. K. 1787 – *Ueber einige künstliche Geschlechter aus der Malvenfamilie*. Mannheim.

Medikus, F. K. 1789–1791 – *Philosophische Botanik*. Mannheim, 2 Hefte.

Meese, D. 1760 – *Flora frisica of lijst der planten welke in de provincie Friesland in het wilde gevonden worden*. Franeker.

Mentzel, C. 1682 – *Index nominum plantarum universalis*. Berlin.

Merrill, E. D. 1921 – A review of the new species of plants proposed by N. L. Burman in his Flora indica. *Philippine Journal of Science* 19(3): 329–388.

Merrill, E. D. 1938 – A critical consideration of Houttuyn's new genera and new species of plants, 1773–1783. *Journal of the Arnold Arboretum* 19: 291–375.

[355]

MERRILL, E. D. 1939 – Additional notes on Houttuyn's binomials. *Journal of the Arnold Arboretum* 20: 264–268.

MERRILL, E. D. 1954 – The botany of Cook's Voyages. *Chronica botanica* 14 (5/6): i–iv, 161–384. tt. 80–90.

MILLER, P. 1731 – *The gardeners dictionary.* London; ed. 7 [1756–] 1759, London, 2 vols.; ed. 8, 1768, London.

MILLER, P. 1754 – *The gardeners dictionary. Abridged from the last folio edition.* Ed. 4. London. *Facsimile* reprint Lehre 1969, with an introduction by W. T. Stearn.

MILNER, J. D. 1906 – *Catalogue of portraits of botanists ... The Royal Botanic Gardens.* London.

MOED, F. 1966 – Carl von Linné und die Konstanz der Arten. *Zeitschrift für Geschichte der Naturwissenschaften, Technik und Medizin* 1(4): 1–3.

MOENCH, C. 1777 – *Enumeratio plantarum indigenarum Hassiae.*

MOENCH, C. 1794 – *Methodus plantas horti botanici et agri marburgensis, a staminum situ.* Marburg.

MOODY, J. W. T. 1964 – Erasmus Darwin, M. D., F. R. S., a biographical ... note. *Journal of the Society for the Bibliography of natural History* 4: 210–213.

MORNET, D. 1911 – *Les sciences de la nature en France au XVIIIe siècle.* Paris.

MOUTON-FONTENILLE DE LA CLOTTE, M. Y. P. 1798 – *Tableau des systèmes de botanique.* Lyon [other ed. 1801].

MURRAY, J. A. 1774 – *Systema vegetabilium.* Ed. 13. Goettingen /Gotha [SO 573].

MURRAY, J. A. 1784 – *Systema vegetabilium.* Ed. 14. Goettingen [SO 583].

MURRAY, J. A. 1798 – *Systema vegetabilium.* Ed. 15. Paris [SO 608].

NATHORST, A. G. 1908 – Carl von Linné as a geologist. *Annual Report Smithsonian Institution* 1908: 711–743.

NECKER, N. J. DE 1768 – *Deliciae gallo-belgicae.* Strasbourg, 2 vols.

NECKER, N. J. DE 1790 – *Elementa botanica.* Neuwied, 3 vols.

NEILREICH, A. 1855 – Geschichte der Botanik in Nieder–Oesterreich. *Verhandlungen des zoologisch–botanischen Vereins in Wien* 5: 23–76.

NICOLAS, J. P. 1963 – Adanson, the man. In G. H. M. Lawrence [ed.] *Adanson* 1: 1–122. Pittsburgh.

NISSEN, C. 1966 – *Die botanische Buchillustration, ihre Geschichte und Bibliographie,* ed. 2. Stuttgart (3 parts in one volume).

NORDENSTAM, B. 1961 – Notes on some Linnaean dissertations. *Botaniska Notiser* 114(3): 276–280.

NORDSTRÖM, J. 1955 – Linné och Gronovius. *Svenska Linné-Sällskapets Årsskrift* 37–38: 7–22.

OLIVER, F. W. [editor] 1913 – *Makers of British botany. A collection of biographies by living botanists.* Cambridge.

OOSTSTROOM, S. J. VAN 1941 – Het herbarium van David de Gorter. *Nederlandsch kruidkundig Archief* 51: 252–274.

OOSTSTROOM, S. J. VAN & TH. J. REICHGELT 1958 – Het herbarium van Rainville en de Gorters Flora VII Provinciarum. *Acta botanica neerlandica* 7: 605–613.

OSBECK, P. 1757 – *Dagbok öfwer en ostindisk resa.* Stockholm.

OSBORN, H. F. 1929 – *From the Greeks to Darwin.* ed. 2. New York/London.

PENNELL, F. W. 1930 – Genotypes of the Scrophulariaceae in the first edition of the 'Species plantarum.' *Proceedings of the Academy of Natural Sciences at Philadelphia* 82: 9–26.

PLUCHE, N. A. 1732–X – *Le spectacle de la Nature, ou entretiens sur les particularités de l'histoire naturelle.* Paris, 9 vols. (botany in part 2, tome 2).

PLUMIER, C. 1755–1760 – *Plantarum americanarum fasciculus primus (–decimus).* Amsterdam/Leiden [curav. J. Burman].

POPPER, K. R. 1950 – *The open society and its enemies.* Vol. 1, The spell of Plato. London.

PULLE, A. A. 1938 – *Compendium van de terminologie, nomenclatuur en systematiek der zaadplanten.* Utrecht; ed. 2, 1950; ed.3, 1952.

PULTENEY, R. 1781 – A general view of the writings of Linnaeus. London [SO 33a].

QUESNÉ, F. A. 1788 – *Philosophie botanique de Charles Linné.* Paris/Rouen.

RAMSBOTTOM, J. 1938 – Linnaeus and the species concept. *Proceedings of The Linnean Society of London* 150: 192–219.

RAMSBOTTOM, J. 1955 – Linnaeus's nomenclature. *Proceedings of The Linnean Society of London* 165(2): 164–166.

RAMSBOTTOM, J. 1959 – Caroli Linnaei Pan Svecicus. *Transactions of the Botanical Society of Edinburgh* 38: 151–167.

RAUSCHENBERG, R. A. 1967 – Daniel Carl Solander, the naturalist on the Endeavour Voyage. *Isis* 58: 367–374.

RAUSCHENBERG, R. A. 1968 – Daniel Carl Solander, naturalist on the Endeavour. *Transactions of the American Philosophical Society,* new series, 58(8): 1–66.

RAY, J. 1682 – *Methodus plantarum nova.* London. *Fascimile* reprint Weinheim 1962.

RAY, J. 1724 – *Synopsis methodica stirpium Britannicarum* ... Ed. 3 [by J. J. Dillen]. London.

REYNOLDS GREEN, J. 1904 – *A history of botany in the United Kingdom from the earliest times to the end of the 19th Century.* London/ Toronto/New York.

RICKETT, H. W. 1955 – Notes on the Linnaean dissertations. *Lloydia* 18: 49–60.

RIVINUS, A. Q. 1690 – *Introductio generalis in rem herbariam.* Leipzig.

ROGER, J. 1963 – *Les sciences de la vie dans la pensée française du XVIIIme siècle.* Paris.

ROSE, H. 1775 – *The elements of botany.* London.

ROTTBØLL, C. F. 1772 – *Descriptiones plantarum rariorum.* København.

ROUSSEAU, P. 1945 – *Histoire de la science.* Paris.

ROYEN, A. VAN 1740 – *Florae leydensis prodromus.* Leiden.

RUDBERG, D. 1744 – see Linnaeus, C. 1744.

RUDOLPH, R. C. 1965 – Illustrations from Weinmann's Phytanthoza inconographia. *Huntia* 2: 1–28.

RUMPHIUS, G. E. 1741–1755 – *Herbarium amboinense.* Amsterdam/Den Haag/ Utrecht, 7 vols.

RUMPHIUS, G. E. 1755 – *Het auctuarium ofte vermeerdering op het Amboinsch Kruydboek.* Amsterdam [ed. J. Burman].

RUPPIUS, H. B. 1718 – *Flora jenensis* Frankfurt/Leipzig (n.v.); ed. 2, id. 1726; ed. 3, edited and published by A. von Haller, Jena 1745.

RYDÉN, S. 1961 – Johan Alströmer och Daniel Solander, twå Linné lärjungar i London 1777–1778. *Svenska Linné–Sällskapets Årsskrift* 42: 53–71.

RYDÉN, S. 1965 – *Pehr Löfling. En linnélärjunge i Spanien och Venezuela 1751–1756.* Stockholm.

SACHS, J. 1875 – *Geschichte der Botanik.* München; French translation, *Histoire de la botanique du xvi siècle à 1860.* Paris 1892; *facsimile* reprint of 1875 original New York/Hildesheim 1966.

SANDMARK, C. G. 1759 – see Linnaeus, C. 1759.

SAUVAGES, F. BOISSIER DE LA CROIX DE 1743 – *Projet d'une méthode sur les feuilles des plantes.* Montpellier.

SAUVAGES, F. BOISSIER DE LA CROIX DE 1751 – *Methodus foliorum.* Den Haag.

SAUVAGES, F. BOISSIER DE LA CROIX DE 1763 – *Nosologia methodica* (n.v.).

SAVAGE, S. 1936 – Caspar Bauhin's Pinax and Burser's herbarium. *Proceedings of The Linnean Society of London* sess. 148: 16–26.

SCHAEFFER, J. C. 1759 – *Vorläufige Beobachtungen der Schwämme um Regensburg.* Regensburg.

SCHAEFFER, J. C. 1759 – *Isagoge in botanicam expeditorum.* Regensburg.

SCHAEFFER, J. C. 1760 – *Botanica expeditior.* Regensburg.

SCHIERBEEK, A. 1956 – Albrecht von Haller. *Biologisch Jaarboek Dodonaea* 23: 348–381.

SCHMID, G. 1937 – Linné im Urteil Johann Beckmanns, mit besonderer Beziehung auf F. C. Medikus. *Svenska Linné–Sällskapets Årsskrift* 20: 47–70.

SCHMIDT, K. P. 1952 – The "Methodus" of Linnaeus, 1736. *Journal of the Society for the Bibliography of Natural History* 2(9): 369–374.

SCHREBER, J. C. D. 1760 – see Linnaeus, C. 1760.

SCHREBER, J. C. D. 1772 – *Caroli a Linné ... Materia medica*, ed. alt. Leipzig/Erlangen [SO 971–972], also ed. 4, 1782 and ed. 5, 1787 [SO 973–975].

SCHREBER, J. C. D. 1785–1790 – *Caroli a Linné ... Amoenitates academicae.* Erlangen, 10 vols.

SCHREBER, J. C. D. 1789–1791 – *Caroli a Linné ... Genera Plantarum*, ed. 8, Frankfurt [SO 322].

SCHREIBERS, C. N. J. et S. ENDLICHER 1841 – *Caroli Linnaei epistolae ad Nicolaum Josephum Jacquin ex autographis edidit ...* Wien.

SCOPOLI, J. A. 1754 – *Methodus plantarum enumerandis stirpibus ab eo hucusque repertis destinata.* Wien.

SCOPOLI, J. A. 1760 – *Flora carniolica.* Wien; ed 2., Wien 1771–1772, 2 vols.

SCOPOLI, J. A. 1763 – *Introductio ad diagnosim et usum fossilium.*

SCOPOLI, J. A. 1777 – *Introductio ad historiam naturalem sistens genera lapidum, plantarum, animalium hactenus detecta characteribus essentialibus donata.* Wien.

SCOPOLI, J. A. 1786–1788 – *Deliciae florae et faunae insubricae.* Pavia, 3 vols.

SÉGUIER, J. F. 1740 – *Bibliotheca botanica.* Den Haag.

SÉGUIER, J. F. 1745 – *Plantae veronenses.* Verona, 2 vols.

SELLING, O. H. 1963 – Daniel Solander's Naturaliekabinett och dess öden. *Svenska Linné-Sällskapet's Årsskrift* 45: 128–137.

SMITH, B. 1960 – *European vision and the South Pacific 1768–1850.* Oxford.

SMITH, E. 1911 – *The life of Sir Joseph Banks.* London, New York.

SMITH, J. E. 1821 – *A selection of the correspondence of Linnaeus.* London, 2 vols.

SMITH, LADY 1832 – *Memoir and correspondence of the late Sir James Edward Smith* London, 2 vols.

SOLANDER, D. 1756 – see Linnaeus, C. 1756.

SOULSBY, B. H. 1933 – *A catalogue of the works of Linnaeus (and publications more immediately relating thereto) preserved in the libraries of the British Museum (Bloomsbury) and the British Museum (Natural History) (South Kensington).* London.

SPRAGUE, T. A. 1935 – Linnaeus as a nomenclaturist. *Taxon* 2: 40–46.

SPRAGUE, T. A. 1955 – The plan of the Species plantarum. *Proceedings of The Linnean Society of London* 165(2): 151–156.

SPRENGEL, K. 1817–1818 – *Geschichte der Botanik.* Leipzig, 2 vols.

STAFLEU, F. A. 1963 – Adanson and the Familles des plantes. In G. H. M. Lawrence [ed.] *Adanson* 1: 123–264. Pittsburgh.

STAFLEU, F. A. 1963a – L'Héritier de Brutelle; the man and his work, in L'Héritier, *Sertum anglicum, facsimile* reprint Pittsburgh.

STAFLEU, F. A. – *Introduction to Jussieu's Genera plantarum*. Weinheim. Also in *facsimile* reprint of A. L. Jussieu, *Genera plantarum*. Weinheim 1964 (Historiae naturalis classica 35).

STAFLEU, F. A. 1967 – Introduction to Jacquin's 'Caribbean Enumeratio,' in N. J. Jacquin, *Enumeratio systematica plantarum, facsimile* reprint Zug.

STAFLEU, F. A. 1967a – *Taxonomic literature. A selective guide to botanical publications with dates, commentaries and types.* Utrecht.

STAFLEU, F. A. 1967b – Conrad Moench: a rebel against Linnaeus. *Taxon* 16: 46–48.

STAFLEU, F. A. and V. WESTHOFF 1968 – Flora der Schweiz. *Taxon* 17: 289–292.

STAFLEU, F. A. 1969 – Miller's 1754 Gardeners dictionary. *Taxon* 18: 713–715.

STAFLEU, F. A. 1969a – Joseph Gaertner and his Carpologia. *Acta botanica neerlandica* 18(1): 216–223.

STAFLEU, F. A. 1970 – Jacquin and his American plants, in N. J. Jacquin, *Selectarum stirpium americanarum historia. Facsimile* reprint New York. [publ. 1971].

STAFLEU, F. A. 1970a – *Benjamin Delessert and Antoine Lasègue.* Lehre. Also published in Lasègue, *Musée botanique de M. Benjamin Delessert, facsimile* reprint Lehre 1970, and in *Taxon* 19(6): 920–936 (slightly amended.)

STAFLEU, F. A. 1971 – N. J. Jacquin, zijn 'Enumeratio' en zijn 'Selectarum stirpium.' *Gorteria* 5(7–10): 208–213.

STAFLEU, F. A. 1971a – Lamarck: the birth of biology. *Taxon* 20: 397–442.

STEARN, W. T. 1955 – Linnaeus's 'Species plantarum' and the language of botany. *Proceedings of The Linnean Society of London* 165(2): 158–164.

STEARN, W. T. 1957 – *An introduction to the Species plantarum and cognate botanical works of Carl Linnaeus.* London. Also published in Carl Linnaeus, *Species plantarum, a facsimile* of the first edition 1753. London 1957–1959, 2 vols. [The Ray Society].

STEARN, W. T. 1958 – Botanical exploration to the time of Linnaeus. *Proceedings of The Linnean Society of London* 169 (1956–1957) (3): 173–196.

STEARN, W. T. 1959 – Four supplementary Linnaean publications. In C. Linnaeus, *Species plantarum* vol. 2, London [The Ray Society *facsimile* edition] London pp. 73–102.

STEARN, W. T. 1959a – The background of Linnaeus's contributions to the nomenclature and methods of systematic biology. *Systematic zoology* 8: 4–22.

STEARN, W. T. 1960 – Notes on Linnaeus's 'Genera plantarum', in Carl Linnaeus, *Genera plantarum fifth edition 1754. Facsimile* reprint Weinheim 1960 (Historiae naturalis classica 3).

STEARN, W. T. 1961 – Botanical gardens and botanical literature in the eighteenth century In *Catalogue of botanical books in the collection of Rachel McMasters Miller Hunt* vol. 2(1). Pittsburgh, pp. xli–cxl.

STEARN, W. T. 1961a – Introductory notes on Linneaus's 'Mantissa plantarum. In C. Linnaeus, *Mantissa plantarum, facsimile* reprint Weinheim 1961 (Historiae naturalis classica 7).

STEARN, W. T. 1961b – The influence of Leyden on botany in the seventeenth and eighteenth centuries (Early Leyden Botany). Leiden. *Leidsche voordrachten* 37: 7–42.

STEARN, W. T. 1962 – The influence of Leyden on botany in the seventeenth and eighteenth centuries. *British Journal for the History of Science* 1(2²): 137–158.

STEARN, W. T. 1966 – *Botanical Latin. History, Grammar, Syntax, Terminology and Vocabulary.* London/Edinburgh/New York.

STEARN, W. T. 1966a – The use of bibliography in natural history, *in* T. R. Buckman, *Bibliography and Natural History.* Lawrence, Kansas, pp. 1–26.

STEARN, W. T. 1966b – *Early Marburg Botany.* Koenigstein-Taunus. Also published in C. Moench, *Methodus, facsimile* reprint Koenigstein-Taunus.

STEARN, W. T. 1967 – Hill's The British herbal 1756–1757. *Taxon* 16: 494–498.

STEARN, W. T. 1969 – A Royal Society appointment with Venus in 1769: The voyage of Cook and Banks in the Endeavour in 1768–1771 and its botanical results. *Notes and Records of The Royal Society of London* 24: 64–90.

STEARN, W. T. 1969a – The abridgement of Miller's Gardeners dictionary, in J. Miller, *The gardeners dictionary, abridged,* 4, 1754, *facsimile* reprint Lehre 1969.

STEARN, W. T. 1969b – *Introduction* [to: *facsimile* reprint of William Curtis, *A short history of the Brown–tail moth* (1782) Plaistow.]

STEARN, W. T. 1970 – Boerhaave as a botanist, in G. A. Lindeboom, *Boerhaave and his time.* Leiden, pp. 114–122.

STEELE, A. R. 1964 – *Flowers for the King. The expedition of Ruiz and Pavon and the Flora of Peru.* Durham, North Carolina.

STEVENSON, A., J. E. DANDY and W. T. STEARN 1961 – A bibliographic study of William Curtis' *Flora londinensis* 1777–98 [1775–], reprinted from volume II of the *Catalogue of botanical books in the collection of Rachel McMasters Miller Hunt.* Pittsburgh, pp. 389–412.

STÖVER, D. H. 1792 – *Leben des Ritters Carl von Linné.* Hamburg.

STRAND, B. J. 1756 – see Linnaeus, C. 1756.

SVENSON, H. K. 1945 – On the descriptive method of Linnaeus. *Rhodora* 47: 273–302, 363–388.

SVENSON, H. K. 1953 – Linnaeus and the species problem. *Taxon* 2: 55–58.

SWEM, E. G. 1949 – *Brothers of the Spade.* Worcester, Massachusetts.

SYDOW, C. O. VON 1963 – Den unge Linnés författarskap. *Svenska Linné–Sällskapets Årsskrift* 45: 3–19.

SYDOW, C. O. VON 1965 – Bibliografi över 1961, 1962 och 1963 års Linné litteratur med tillägg till förul utgivna förteckningar. *Svenska Linné–Sällskapets Årsskrift* 47: 70–78.

THUNBERG, C. P. 1767 – *Dissertationem physiologicam de Venis resorbentibus.* Uppsala [under C. Linnaeus].

THUNBERG, C. P. 1781–1801 – *Nova genera plantarum,* Uppsala, 16 parts.

THUNBERG, C. P. 1784 – *Flora japonica.* Leipzig 1784. Facsimile reprint Tokyo 1933.

THUNBERG, C. P. 1791–1821 – *Museum naturalium academiae Upsaliensis.* Uppsala [for details see Krok 1925, p. 709].

THUNBERG, C. P. 1794–1800 – *Prodromus plantarum capensium.* Uppsala, 2 parts.

THUNBERG, C. P. 1807–1820 – *Flora capensis.* Uppsala/København, 2 vols.

TOURNEFORT, J. P. DE 1700 – *Institutiones rei Herbariae, editio altera.* Paris 3 vols.

TULLBERG, T. 1907 – *Linnéporträtt.* Stockholm.

TURRILL, W. B. 1959 – *The Royal Botanic Gardens, Kew, past and present.* London.

UGGLA, A. H. 1937 – Linné och Burmannerna. *Svenska Linné–Sällskapets Årsskrift* 20: 128–144.

UGGLA, A. H. 1939 – G. D. Ehret's växt plansch över sexual systemet. *Svenska Linné–Sällskapets Årsskrift* 22: 108–113.

UGGLA, A. H. 1945 – Jonas Dryander. *Proceedings of The Linnean Society of London.* 156: 99–102.

UGGLA, A. H. 1953 – Frederic Hasselquist ett tvåhundraårsminne. *Svenska Linné–Sällskapets Årsskrift* 35: 5–17.

UGGLA, A. H. 1953a – The preparation of the Species plantarum. *Taxon* 2: 60–62.

UGGLA, A. H. 1954–1955 – Daniel Solander och Linné. *Svenska Linné–Sällskapets Årsskrift* 37–38: 23–64.

UGGLA, A. H. 1957 – *Linnaeus.* Stockholm [in Dutch.]

References

UGGLA, A. H. 1960 – Linné och bananen. *Svenska Linné–Sällskapets Årsskrift* 42: 79–88.

UGGLA, A. H. 1968 – Om Linnés Nemesis divina. *Svenska Linné–Sällskapets Årsskrift* 50: 13–19.

URBAN, I. 1902 – Notae biographicae peregrinatorum Indiae occidentalis botanicorum. *Symbolae antillanae* 3: 14–158. *Facsimile* reprint Amsterdam 1964.

VÁCZY, C. 1971 – Les origines et les principes du développement de la nomenclature binaire en botanique. *Taxon* 20: 573–590.

VAILLANT, S. 1718 – *Sermo de structura florum.* Leiden.

VILLARS, D. 1786–1789 – *Histoire des plantes de Dauphiné.* 3. vols. Grenoble.

VOSS, W. 1882 – Johannes Antonius Scopoli, *Verhandlungen der Zoologisch-botanischen Gesellschaft in Wien* 31 (Abh.): 17–66.

WACHENDORFF, E. J. VAN 1747 – *Horti ultrajectini index.* Utrecht.

WAHLBOM, J. G. 1746 – see Linnaeus, C. 1746.

WEIN, K. 1931 – F. Ehrhart und J. A. Murray, zwei Typen der Botaniker der Aufklärungszeit. *Svenska Linné–Sällskapets Årsskrift* 14: 72–84.

WEINMANN, J. W. [1734–] 1737–1745 – *Phytanthoza iconographia.* Regensburg., 4 vols.

WIDDER, F. J. 1967 – Die Grazer Ausgaben von Linnés Amoenitates academicae. *Botanische Jahrbücher* 86: 186–208.

WILLEY, B. 1940 – *The eighteenth-century background. Studies on the idea of nature in the thought of the period.* London. [here quoted from the Peregrine books edition, Harmondsworth 1962].

WIMAN, J. 1752 – see Linnaeus, C. 1752.

WITHERING, W. 1776 – *A botanical arrangement of all the vegetables naturally growing in Great Britain.* London, 2 vols.; ed. 2, London 1787 [–1792], 3 vols.; ed. 3, London 1796, 4 vols.

WOODRUFF, L. L. 1926 – The versatile Sir John Hill. *The American Naturalist* 60: 417–442.

ZANDER, R. 1952 – *Geschichte des Gärtnertums.* Stuttgart.

ZOLLER, H. 1958 – Albrecht von Haller's Pflanzensammlungen in Göttingen, sein botanisches Werk und sein Verhältnis zu Carl von Linné. *Nachrichten der Akademie der Wissenschaften in Göttingen. II. Mathematisch–Physikalische Klasse.* 1958 (10): 217–251.

Index

The references are to the page numbers; those printed in *italics* refer to illustrations, those followed by an explanation mark to the main treatment of the relevant subject. The abbreviation L. refers to Linnaeus; P.B. to the *Philosophia botanica*.

Index

Gruinales 272
Guettard, J. E. 87, 275
Guiana, French 280, 282–286, 318
Gymnospermae 69, 173 (E. Wachendorff)

Haak, C. 163
Haak, Th., 159–185
Haarlem 11, 12
Habitat, P. B. 78
Habitus, P. B. 67, 70–71
Hadrian 40, 40n
Haller, A. von 38 (monographer, P.B.); 45 (erudition in his natural method); 87 (diagnostic phrase-names); *167* (letter from J. Burman); 180 (visit to Leiden); 194 (and G. A. Scopoli); *244* (portrait); 245–250! life and works, relation to L., floristic research, biosystematic approach, reasons for oblivion); 271 (contacts with J. E. Gilibert); 272 (among *auctores reformatoris); 314* (letter from M. Adanson); 320 (Adanson in isolation, like Haller, through non-acceptance of L.'s reforms)
Hamburg 8
Hammarby 19
Harderwijk 7, 10–11, 176
Hartecamp, de 11–16, 13, 114, 171
Hartog, J. 165, 169
Hasselquist, F. 144, 149!
Hebe 323
Hebenstreit, J. E. 242
Hedwig, J. 253, 254–255!
Helen, of Troy, wife of Menelaus 12, 100
Helenium 100
Heliophila 170
Helleborus 325
Helsingborg 8
Helxine 96
HERBA 106n
Herbaria 38 (historical development); 89 (species to be known on basis of herbarium material); 112–114, 288 (Linnaean); 232–236 (J. Banks); 233 (G. Clifford); 233–236 (British and French); 235 J. E. Smith; 235, 324, 325 (J. P. de Tournefort, S. Vaillant); 298 (J. J. Rousseau); 323 (J. Dombey, Ph. Commerson)

Heredity, L. on 56
Héritier de Brutelle, C. L. L', *see* L'Héritier de Brutelle
Hermann, P. 9 (gives impetus to Leiden garden); 42 ('fructist'); 165 (Ceylon collections and J. Burman, *Thesaurus zeylanicus*); 169 (collections used for N. L. Burman, *Flora indica*); 194 (and G. A. Scopoli); 233 (herbarium)
Herminium 95
Hero worship of L. 3
Heterodox taxonomists, P. B. 41
Hibisci 66
Hierarchy 61 (categories of classes); 134–139! (origin); 197 (G. A. Scopoli)
Hill, J. 197 (Scopoli's *Anomalae* called *Hillii*); 207–210! (life and works, relation to L., strong leaning towards natural system); 211 (uses binomials in 1761); 217 (at beginning of Banksian era); 231 (special adviser to Lord Bute on Kew)
Hippocrates 37
Histoire naturelle, see Natural History
Historical element in biology, Buffon 306–309
Holbach, P. H. T., baron d' 211, 213, 282, 296
Holl, W. 244
Holland 8–16 (L. in); 157–183 (Linnaeans)
Holosteum 98
Holy alliance, science and religion 213, 216
Hönigmann, "Libanos" 40
Hope, J. 201
Hortensia 323
Horticulture, British 201, 205–207, 217
Hortulanorum princeps (J. Miller) 205
Hortus cliffortianus, L. 11–12 (genesis of book); *13* (title-page); 16 (publication delayed); 87 (reform of specific names, translation part of preface); 91 (distaste of varieties expressed in preface); 104, 161 (binary literature references); 114 (herbarium); 116 (ranks with *Classes* and *Species*); 162 (Gronovius uses data from H. C.); 166 (idem J. Burman); 171 (idem E. Wachendorff); 199 (J. J. Dillen's *Hortus elthamensis* prototype for H. C.); 203 (drawings by J. D. Ehret); 261 (praise by F. K. Medikus)
Hortus uplandicus, L. 6

[374]

Maiden, J. H. 219

Maillet, C. F. 207

Malesherbes, C. G. Lamoignon de 271 (L. Gérard's *Flora gallo-provincialis* dedicated to him); 275 (attended Bernard de Jussieu's courses); 280–281! (amateur botanist, position, protector of botanists, *philosophes* and encyclopedists); 282 (contact with F. Aublet); 286 (and C. L. L'Héritier); 317 (and M. Adanson)

Malpighi, M. 43

Malus 69

Malvaceae 131, 261, 318, 322

Malvales 131, 173

Malvineae 131

Mantissa plantarum, L. 139, 170

Maoris 229

Map of the world 46, 133, 328

Marchant, J. 63, 134

Marche de la nature 334

Maria Theresia, of Austria 180, 184, 194

Marie-Antoinette, of France 278

Marshall, H. 202!

Marsilea 99

Martyn, J. 217

Martyn, T. 110, 201, 203

Marum 214

Masson, F. 232

Master, knows species 84

Materia medica, L. 145

Mattioli (Matthioli), P. 281

Maurepas, J. F. Phélypeaux, comte de 279

Mauritius (Ile de France) 223, 282

Medikus, F. K. (Medicus) 252 (his influence on C. Moench); 256 (violent anti-Linnaean); 260–265! (life and work, serious criticism of L., convinced nominalist); 263 (title-page *Philosophische Botanik*)

Medulla 48, 49, 51, 134–137

Meerburgh, N. 173, 183

Meese, D. 174

Melissa 216

Melo-Pepo 95

Memory 57–58, 74, 82

Mentzel, C. 43

Mentzelia 131

Menzies, A. 232

Mercure de France 297

Mercurialis 63, 134

Metamorphosis 95

Metaphysical hybridization 136–137

Meteorology 193

Methodi naturalis praeludium, A. van Royen 158, 159, 160, 161

Methodici, P. B. 36, 39, 41, 60

Method(us), Linnaean sense 12, 15, 45, 58

Methodus calycina 116–118

Methodus juxta quam physiologus ..., L. 12, 15

Methodus naturalis, L. 46 (a tribute to the principle of plenitude); 76 (less genera listed than in sexual system); 125–133! (the *Fragmenta methodi naturalis* discussed); 272 (L. Gérard's system inspired by L.); 277 (comparison with Bernard de Jussieu's *Ordines*); 328 (present family structure Angiosperms still based on it); see further under *Fragmenta methodi naturales* and for other natural systems under the respective author's names.

Michaux, A. 280

Micheli, P. A. 123, 250

Micheli (taxon) 197

Microscopium 122

Microscopy 255

Middle Rhine botany 256–265!

Miller, P. 16, 43 (gardener, P. B.); 109 (uses binary names in his Gardeners Dictionary, ed. 8; 199 (and L.'s visit to England); 205–207! (life and work, his *Dictionary*, British horticulture); 206 (portrait); 208 (handwriting); 217 (stands at beginning of Banksian era); 219 (and J. Banks); 233 (his herbarium acquired by J. Banks)

Miscellaneae 136

Mission des académiciens du Pérou 279

Mithridates 36n

Mnemonic qualities of Linnaean nomenclature 338

Moench, C. 252–253!

Monocotyledones 69, 330

Monographers, P. B. 38

Monopetalae 330

Monorchis 95

Monstrosities 319

Montesquieu 296

Montpellier botany 267–273!

Moraea, Sara Lisa 8, 16

Moraeus, J. 8

Index

COLOPHON

The design of this book is by Wil van Antwerpen.
The photos of the illustrations have been made by P. D. van der Poel.
The text of this book is set in Monotype Spectrum.
Except for the jacket, which was executed by Drukkerij Van Rossum, Utrecht,
the book was printed by Koninklijke Drukkerij Van de Garde, Zaltbommel.
It has been bound by C. H. F. Wöhrmann & Zonen, Zutphen.